The Independent Hostel Guide 2017

England
Wales
Scotland

D0522510

Edited by
Sam Dalley and Alice Lockett

 Independent Hostels UK

ISBN 978-0-9565058-6-6

Independent Hostel Guide 2017: England, Wales and Scotland
26th Edition, Editors: Sam Dalley and Alice Lockett

British Library Cataloguing in Publication Data. A catalogue record for this book is available at the British Library ISBN 978-0-9565058-6-6

Published by: Independent Hostels UK, Speedwell House, Upperwood, Matlock Bath, Derbyshire, DE4 3PE.

Tel: +44 (0) 1629 580427.   © Independent Hostels UK, 2017
Printed by: Deltor www.deltoruk.com
Cover Photos by Jonathan Hollands www.flickr.com/jonhollands

Front Cover Photograph: Yorkshire Dales (pg 200). **Back Cover Photographs:** Eroica Britannia Festival www.eroicabritannia.co.uk, Hardraw Old School Bunkhouse (pg 200), Piggery Poke kitchen (pg 339) **Internal Photographs:** Photos on pages 1,2,3,4,5 Yorkshire Dales. Photos on page 6,7 Porthmadog near Snowdon Lodge (pg382). Photo on page 537 Hardraw Old School Bunkhouse (pg 200). Photo on page 540 Palace Farm Hostel (pg 76). Photos on page 403 credited to Tony Jones. Photo on page 503 credited to Brain Sutherland. Photo on page 512 credited to Ike Gibson. Photo on page 367 credited to Martin Thirkettle. Photo on page 288 credited to Mike Emmett. Other pages contain photos provided by the bunkhouses and hostels.

Distributed in the UK by: Cordee Books and Maps,
                                      3a De Montfort Street, Leicester,
                                      LE1 7HD. Tel: (0116) 2543579

ISBN 978-0-9565058-6-6

9 780956 505866 >

CONTENTS

INDEPENDENT HOSTELS UK

Independent Hostels UK is a network of 350+ bunkhouses, hostels and group accommodation centres. These provide a unique form of accommodation ideal for groups, individuals and families who enjoy good company, travel and the outdoors.

KEY

Dormitories	
Private rooms	
Family rooms	
Blankets or duvets provided	
Sheets required	
Sleeping bags required	
Hostel fully heated	
Some areas heated	
Drying room available	
Showers available	
Cooking facilities available	
Shop at hostel	
Meals provided at hostel (with notice)	
Breakfast only at hostel (with notice)	
Meals available locally	
Clothes washing facilities available	
Facilities for less-able people	
Computer with internet facilities	
WiFi available	
Within 1,3,5 miles of NCN as the crow flies	
Bike shed	
Affiliated to Hostelling International	
Simple accommodation. Clean, friendly and basic	
Best Price Guarantee	

KEY

 Accommodation for groups only

 Dog friendly

 VisitScotland Quality Assured

 VisitWales Quality Assured

 VisitEngland Quality Assured

 Bronze, Silver, Gold Green Tourism Business Award

pp **per person**

GR **Ordnance Survey grid reference**

BEST PRICE GUARANTEE `BEST PRICE`

The hostels and bunkhouses displaying the Best Price symbol promise that you will get their accommodation at the lowest price if you contact them direct. Contact them by phone, email, via our website or the accommodation's own website and you can rest assured that you will get the best rates available.

Why do we offer a Best Price Guarantee? Many websites take a commission of up to 20 % from your money before they pass it on to the accommodation. This increases the price you pay and the accommodation has less money to spend on your stay.

Independent Hostel networks across the world have united to offer their members the opportunity to offer a Best Price Guarantee if you book direct. To see the hostels outside the UK who are offering the Best Price Guarantee have a look at:-

www.bestprice-hostels.com

WHAT ARE
INDEPENDENT HOSTELS ?

Independent hostels have shared areas, self-catering kitchens and bedrooms with bunks. They are great for group get-togethers and for outdoor enthusiasts. Bunkhouses, camping barns, backpackers' hostels and outdoor centres are all types of independent hostels.

HOSTELS

▲ Self-catering facilities
▲ Stay for just one night
▲ Private bedrooms, en suite rooms and dorms
▲ Wild locations for outdoor activities
▲ City centre locations for independent travellers
▲ Families, individuals and groups are welcome
▲ Hostels can be booked sole-use for get-togethers
▲ No membership required
▲ Independent Hostels are all privately owned.
▲ Only 5% are also in the YHA or SYHA.

HOLIDAY IDEAS
FROM OUR BLOG

Have a look at the holiday ideas on the following pages.

To find the perfect place for your holiday send an enquiry from our website. Use the **Send Enquiry** button to select preferred locations and facilities then write a message to all the hostels and bunkhouses ideal for your stay.

www.independenthostels.uk

Follow our social media for news and special offers.

GREAT PLACES FOR

FAMILY GATHERINGS

By Alice Lockett

We like holidaying with other families. The kids get to spend time together and parents can enjoy a drink and a home cooked meal without the "whose going to drive home" conundrum! Independent Hostels are the perfect solution. We stayed at Hardraw Old School Bunkhouse in Wensleydale, Yorkshire (pg 200). The bunkhouse is perfect for groups of families as it has four dorms with 3-8 beds, providing each family with their own room. There is a lovely large communal room with wood-burner, table tennis table, piano and a huge table perfect for eating together and playing board games! In addition the bunkhouse owners, Helen and Andy, provide outdoor expeditions and taster sessions in caving and ghyl scrambling which keep the kids entertained and was a great new experience. Find out more at www.independenthostels.co.uk/blog

DOG FRIENDLY

Torran Bay Hostel

Rattray Head Hostel

HOSTELLING

By Gail Piper

A search for 'Dog Friendly' accommodation on our website will bring up a map of 122 hostels, bunkhouses and camping barns who will welcome your dog as well as you! Gail Piper visited Torran Bay Hostel(pg 433) near Lochgilphead at the top of the Mull of Kintyre penninsula and here is what she had to say "We had a most enjoyable 3 night stay at Torran Bay on the West Coast of Scotland. The hostel is just 3 years old with comfortable and spacious en suite guest rooms, and it was very dog friendly. While my partner fished, Bruce the dog and I enjoyed strolling around the loch edge, relaxing and enjoying the view. Find out more about Gail's Dog Friendly stay on www.independenthostels.co.uk/blog

Corris Hostel

Denton House

COAST TO COAST

By Sam Dalley

The Coast to Coast routes are very popular but accommodation is limited in the small villages along the way. Many walkers and cyclists resort to carrying heavy camping gear. Independent hostels are a great alternative, providing company in the evenings, self-catering kitchens, drying rooms and a huge resource of information from staff and fellow travellers. There are lots of cycling and walking routes from coast to coast, the most famous are Wainwright's Walk from St Bee's Head in the Lake District to Robin Hood Bay on the Yorkshire Coast and the Sea to Sea (C2C) coast to coast cycle route from Whitehaven, Egremount or Workington in the Lake District to Tynemouth or Sunderland on the Durham coast.

Find out more at www.independenthostels.co.uk/blog

EXPLORING

BRISTOL

By Brian Schæfer Dreyer

Having visited Bristol several times on day trips, I was excited to finally get to stay around for a few days and explore, as I checked in to the Rock 'n' Bowl hostel (pg 56). Its entrance is found just around the corner from the street art adorned Nelson Street, and conveniently located between all the big contrasts of Bristol's diverse neighbourhoods. Whether you're into high street shopping, old markets, street art and urban vibes, culture along the harbour, or posh neighbourhoods and big attractions – Bristol has got it all, and most of it within walking distance of the Rock 'n' Bowl hostel.

Find out more at www.independenthostels.co.uk/blog

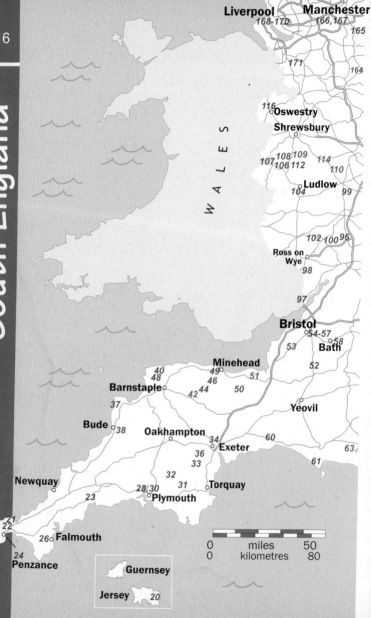

South England

Liverpool
168-170

Manchester
166, 167
165

171

164

116 Oswestry

Shrewsbury

107 *108* *109* *114*
106 *112* *110*

Ludlow
104 *99*

102 *100* *96*

Ross on
Wye
98

97

W A L E S

Bristol
54-57
53 *58*
Bath
52

Minehead
40 *49* *51*
48 *46*
Barnstaple *42* *44* *50*

Yeovil

37

Bude *38*
Oakhampton
34 *60*
Exeter
36 *63*
33 *61*
32
Newquay *28 30* *31* Torquay
23 Plymouth

21
22
26 Falmouth

0 ____ miles ____ 50
0 ____ kilometres ____ 80

24
Penzance

Guernsey

Jersey *20*

South England

KEY

45 - **Hostel page number**

45 - **Page number of group only accommodation**

Sheffield
156
149 154160 152 142
162 150 144
158
148 146 134 140
136 132 128
137 163
138 130
Derby

Lincoln
126

Skegness

Nottingham
118

120,121, 122
119

King's Lynn

124

Norwich

Leicester

Peterborough

Birmingham
117

Coventry

Northampton

Cambridge

94 Ipswich
92

Luton

Colchester

81

Oxford
74

London
82 - 91

Reading

80
76 78
Canterbury
Dover

72 Guildford

Salisbury

69
68

70 71

Hastings

66

Portsmouth

Brighton

64
62

Bournemouth

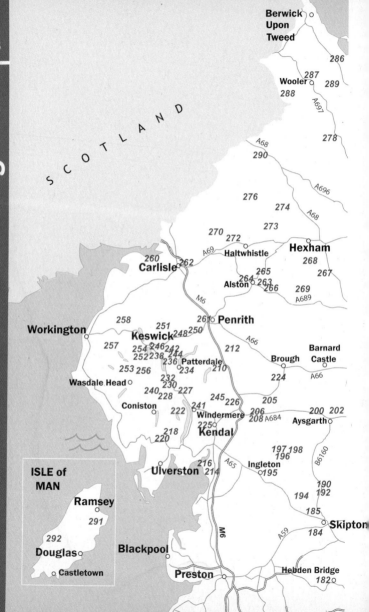

North England

SCOTLAND

Berwick
Upon
Tweed

286

287
Wooler   289
288

278

A68
290

A697

276   274
273
A696

270   272
A69   Haltwhistle   Hexham   A68
260   262   265   268
Carlisle   264 263   267
Alston   266   269
258   M6   A689

261   Penrith
251   250
Keswick 248   212   A66   Barnard
257   254 246 242   Brough   Castle
252 238 244   236   Patterdale
253 256   234   210   224   A66
232   230 227
Wasdale Head   240   245 226   205
228   241   206   200 202
Coniston   222   Windermere   208 A684
225   Aysgarth
218   Kendal
220
197 198
196   B6160
194   192
190
185   Skipton
184

ISLE of
MAN
Ramsey
291
292
Douglas
Castletown

A66
216   A65   Ingleton
Ulverston   214   195

A59
Blackpool   M6
Hebden Bridge
Preston   182

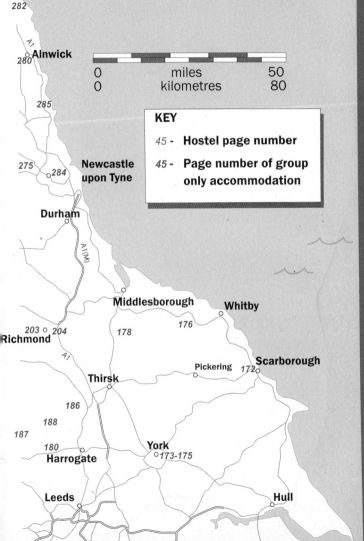

KEY

45 - Hostel page number

45 - Page number of group only accommodation

North England

JERSEY ACCOMMODATION
AND ACTIVITY CENTRE
ENGLAND

A 5 minutes' walk from the pretty fishing port of Gorey in St Martin (restaurants, bars and a regular bus to St Helier), the JAAC has a wide range of rooms including private en suites and dorms with shared showers. Facilities include 60 seat dining room, sauna, 2 large lounges, laundry, drying room, cycle storage and extensive outside space. Ball and board games are available as well as a TV and DVD player. Ideal for families and large groups who can often be in the same area of the hostel. Single sex dorms available. Breakfast included, packed lunches and a 2 course evening meals available. Camping with electric hook-up, running water and a shower and toilet block available. On-site activities include climbing wall and zip wire for under 12s, archery, bush craft and an all ages obstacle course. Off-site: a wide range of outdoor pursuits or "Escape from a Castle" by completing a range of physical and problem solving tasks. Beds, food, transport & activity packages available. Walkers and cyclists welcome.

DETAILS

- **Open** - Feb-Dec. Reception 08:30 -20:00
- **Number of beds** - 110 (Bunk 1x10 6x8 1x6 4x4) (En suite 1x6 2x4 2x3 4x2 2x1)
- **Booking** - First night deposit required. Full payment if less than 10 days before arrival. 20% deposit for group bookings. Groups of 20+ get in touch for rates.
- **Price per night** - Breakfast inc. Bunks £27-£32pp. Singles and en suite bunk £29-£34pp. Twin en suites £58-£68. Family 3, 4 & 6 en suites and groups please enquire.
- **Public Transport** - No1 bus from Liberty Station, St Hellier to Gorey Pier (8 min uphill walk to JAAC) or No13 bus to Ramsons Garden centre, (5 min walk to hostel).
- **Directions** - Follow directions to The East and then Gorey. From Gorey Pier continue up the hill past the church take the next right, JAAC is 200m on your right.

CONTACT: Anna Stammers
Tel: 01534 498636
info@jerseyhostel.co.uk www.jerseyhostel.co.uk
La Rue de La Pouclee et Des Quatre Chemins, Faldouet, St Martins, Jersey, Channel Islands JE3 6DU

COHORT
HOSTEL

Cohort is a newly renovated hostel housed in an old Wesleyan chapel and schoolrooms in the centre of St Ives. It has spectacular original features and comfortable, contemporary rooms with custom built pod beds. Facilities include free superfast WiFi, an in-house bar, lounge, private courtyard, dining room, movie/TV room with Netflix and a fully equipped kitchen with a small supermarket open 7 days a week next door. Sleeping accommodation is in private rooms and shared dorms. Storage for (surf) boards, bikes & bags is available. Helpful staff will be delighted to share with you all the delights that South West Cornwall and St Ives have to offer. Situated just 5 minutes from train/bus stations and lots of parking nearby. Less than a minute's walk to over 50 cafés, bars and galleries and seconds from St Ives' 5 spectacular beaches and the coastal path.

DETAILS

- **Open** - February - December, 8am - 10pm
- **Number of beds** - 61: 1x8, 7x6, 1x4, 2x twin, 1x twin/triple
- **Booking** - Book via website. Groups should email or phone.
- **Price per night** - Beds from £20
- **Public Transport** - From Penzance train get off at St Erth, take branch line to St Ives, also National Express Bus from London and Newquay. Nearest airports: Newquay (45 minutes) or Exeter (1.45 hours).
- **Directions** - From A30 take A3074 (St Ives), follow the road for about 2 miles into St Ives. At St Ives Harbour Hotel turn right into the main town and follow the road until it turns sharply to the right and goes downhill. At Nat West bank turn left. Cohort is past Co-op on Right. NO PARKING use local car parks.

CONTACT: Reception
Tel: 01736 791664
hello@stayatcohort.co.uk www.stayatcohort.co.uk
The Stennack, St Ives, Cornwall, TR26 1FF

LOWER PENDERLEATH
ST IVES FARM HOSTEL
ENGLAND

Just three miles from St Ives' beaches and 5 miles from Penzance, Lower Penderleath Farm Hostel near St Ives provides self-catering accommodation in four twin rooms, one room with an alpine dormitory for 12 (large room with mattresses) and a family maisonette. All rooms are private and lockable, three rooms have twin beds and the fourth has a bunk bed. No bedding is provided. The hostel has a fully equipped kitchen. A dining room adjoins the kitchen and there are plenty of showers and toilets. Heating is by oil filled towel radiators and drying racks are provided. The self contained family maisonette has a small kitchen and private shower and toilet. The water on site is natural mineral water sold as bottled mineral water in 1989 and now visitors can cook, drink and shower in it. A picturesque footpath leads to the village of Cripples Ease just ten minutes' walk away where there is a pub that serves meals. The village of Halsetown, with its own pub, is also in walking distance.

DETAILS
- **Open** - Easter-Oct incl.Open all day. Arrive between 9.00am-8pm depart by 10 am.
- **Number of beds** - 24: 4x2, dorm platform of 12, 1x4 self contained maisonette
- **Booking** - Please PHONE before arriving. Office hours 8.30am to 8pm) Minimum 2 night stay
- **Price per night** - £19pp, £38 twin room. £100 maisonette. Children full price, bring your own cot. 1 person per bed. Bring your sleeping bag and pillow.
- **Public Transport** - Local buses pass the road end three quarters of a mile from the hostel. Service runs four times a day between St Ives and Penzance.
- **Directions** - Pass Penderleath camping park on left and 300m further on right hand side you will find Lower Penderleath Farm and Hostel.

CONTACT: Russell Rogers
Tel: 07723 014567
rusrogers60@gmail.com www.stivescampingandhostel.com
Lower Penderleath Farm, Towednack, St.Ives, Cornwall, TR26 3AF

Welcome to this quirky, Camino inspired hostel just a short leafy lane from the Eden Project. Facilities at this comfortably converted stable yard include free WiFi, mixed bunk rooms and a communal lounge. Self-caterers are always welcome in the courtyard kitchen. A simple DIY toasty breakfast is available, alternatively cooked food is available on request.

The hostel is in Garker Hamlet inland of St Austell bay, 2 miles from the Northwest Coast Path at Carlyon Bay and less than two miles off the ancient Saints Way pilgrimage trail. National Cycle routes 2 and 3 converge close to the gate less than 60 miles from Lands End. St. Austell and Par mainline railway stations are both nearby providing easy access to Newquay, Truro and onwards to Penzance and Falmouth.

Edens Yard can accommodate cars by prior arrangement.

DETAILS

- **Open** - April to mid October (inclusive). Arrive between 4pm and 10pm.
- **Number of beds** - 1x6, 1x8
- **Booking** - Book by phone or enquire by email.
- **Price per night** - £15
- **Public Transport** - Trains to St Austel or Par. Take bus from St Austal to Eden Project and short walk to hostel. Pickup from train station available for £5.
- **Directions** - Cars only by prior arrangement please phone for directions

CONTACT: Neal or Julia
Tel: 01726 814907
info@edensyard.uk www.edensyard.uk
17 Tregrehan Mills, St. Austell, Cornwall, PL25 3TL

PENZANCE
BACKPACKERS

Penzance, with its mild climate, its wonderful location looking across to spectacular St Michael's Mount, with all the coach and rail services terminating here, is the ideal base for exploring the far SW of England and the Scilly Isles.

Whether you are looking for sandy beaches and sheltered coves, the storm lashed cliffs of Land's End, sub-tropical gardens, internationally acclaimed artists, the remains of ancient cultures, or simply somewhere to relax and take time out, Penzance Backpackers is for you. Situated in a lovely tree-lined road close to the sea front, with the town centre, bus station and railway station only a short walk away. Accommodation is mostly in small bunk-bedded rooms with bed linen. Fully equipped self-catering kitchen, hot showers, comfortable lounge, lots of local information and a warm welcome all included.

DETAILS

- **Open** - All year, 10.00-12.00, 17.00-22.00
- **Number of beds** - 30: 2 double, 1x 4 (double + 2 bunks), 3x6, 1x7.
- **Booking** - We require a deposit equivalent to the first night of your stay.
- **Price per night** - From £17 per person. £38 for 2 people in private room.
- **Public Transport** - Penzance has a train station and National Express service. 15 mins' walk from train/bus station or catch buses 1, 1a, 5a or 6a from Tourist Information/bus/train station. Ask for top of Alexandra Road.
- **Directions** - From Tourist Information/bus/train station either follow quay and promenade to mini-roundabout, turn right up Alexandra Rd, we are a short way up on the left; or follow main road through town centre until second mini-roundabout, turn left down Alexandra Rd; we are on right.

CONTACT: Mathew
Tel: 01736 363836
info@pzbackpack.com www.pzbackpack.com
The Blue Dolphin, Alexandra Road, Penzance, TR18 4LZ

FALMOUTH LODGE
BACKPACKERS

Falmouth's beautiful natural harbour provides a picturesque background to the main street of charming shops, restaurants, cafés and pubs. Voted the 2nd best coastal town, Falmouth is renowned for its sandy beaches, Pendennis Castle, exotic gardens, Arts Centre and the Princess Pavilion. Go sightseeing on ferries to St Mawes, Truro, Flushing and the Helford Passage. On a rainy day visit the National Maritime Museum and the Ships and Castle leisure pool. Take advantage of watersports, fishing trips, sailing, diving, with tuition and equipment hire. Judi has moved back from Grenada in the West Indies to be your host at Falmouth Lodge. Judi welcomes guests to enjoy all Cornwall has to offer and has added her own character and flavour to the hostel. Relaxed, friendly and clean, Falmouth Lodge Backpackers is just two minutes' walk from the Blue Flag beach of Gyllyngvase and the South West Coast Path and eight minutes' walk into town and the harbour. Free WiFi and internet facilities. Free parking. No curfew. Complimentary tea, coffee and breakfast. Well-equipped kitchen and cosy lounge with TV/DVD and games.

DETAILS

- **Open** - All year. 9am-12 noon and 5-10pm. Reception open from 5pm.
- **Number of beds** - 28: 2x2/3, 3x4/5, 1x6/7,1xdbl/family ensuite (some sea views).
- **Booking** - Telephone or email in advance. Walk-ins also welcomed.
- **Price per night** - From £19 per person
- **Public Transport** - Train - change at Truro for Falmouth town station 250 mtrs. National Express to Falmouth. By air - London Stansted/Gatwick to Newquay
- **Directions** - On A39 look for Gyllyngvase Rd on right, then left to Gyllyngvase Ter.

CONTACT: Judi
Tel: 01326 319996, mobile 07525 722808
judi@falmouthlodge.co.uk www.falmouthbackpackers.co.uk
9 Gyllyngvase Terrace, Falmouth, Cornwall, TR11 4DL

STAYKATION HOTEL
FOR BACKPACKERS

Whether you're a backpacker or a budget traveller you will enjoy Staykation Hotel for Backpackers in Plymouth. This friendly hostel offers a warm welcome to all its guests. The excellent city centre location is just a 10 minute walk from the train and bus stations and within easy walking distance to the ferry port. Located near some of the top bars, clubs, restaurants and theatres with friendly staff on site and available 24/7. Security is taken seriously with 24hr CCTV.

Facilities include a small but perfectly formed self-catering kitchen with fridge freezer, utensils and microwave, a common room, free linen, towels & WiFi. The dorm beds each have their own power light, lockers and tea and coffee facilities. All bedding is provided and the beds are made up ready to sleep in. There is an outside smoking area. Credit cards are accepted and all taxes are included in the overnight fee. Families welcome with children over 10 years of age. No pets.

DETAILS

- **Open** - All Year. Check in from 2pm, check out 10am.
- **Number of beds** - 10: 1x4, 1x6
- **Booking** - Book via email or telephone. A valid passport or picture ID is required for all guests.
- **Price per night** - £20pp (includes all taxes)
- **Public Transport** - Train / bus stations.10 minutes walk, Ferry port 5 min' walk.
- **Directions** - Walking from train station: cross over Saltash road and walk towards the town centre, at the roundabout turn right and follow Western Approaches until you get to Toys R Us. Bare right onto Union Street follow this until you come to the hostel.

CONTACT: Carole Reynolds
Tel: 01752 269333 Mob:07455971473
carolereynolds99@hotmail.co.uk
94 Union Street, Plymouth, PL1 3EZ

PLYMOUTH
BACKPACKERS HOTEL

Located 5 minutes' walk from Plymouth city centre and within easy walking distance of the train and bus stations and ferry port, Plymouth Backpackers Hotel is the perfect base for a visit to Plymouth.

The Hotel is just five minutes from the city centre with a plethora of shops, cinemas and the Plymouth Pavilions. It is also within walking distance of Plymouth Hoe, the famous park overlooking Plymouth's stunning natural harbour.   With the ferry port just 5 minutes' walk away, why not stop over on your way to Europe?

This family run hostel has accommodation in single, twin, family or single sex dorms of up to 5 people. Communal areas include a kitchen, lounges and outdoor areas. All rooms have a kettle and some are en suite. Parking is available.

DETAILS

- **Open** - All Year, all day
- **Number of beds** - 11 rooms
- **Booking** - Book via website
- **Price per night** - From £15pp (dorm), £18pp single or double room.
- **Public Transport** - Train & bus stations 10 minutes' walk, Ferry port 5 minutes.
- **Directions** - From train station walk cross over Saltash road and walk towards the town centre, at the roundabout turn right and follow Western Approaches until you get to Toys R Us. Bare right onto Union Street follow this until you come to the hostel.

CONTACT: Lee Walters
Tel: 01752 213 033 mob:07910 857 841
plymouthbackpackershotel@gmail.com www.plymouthbackpackershotel.co.uk
102 Union Street Plymouth, PL1 3HL

Harford Bunkhouse & Camping offers comfortable budget accommodation on the edge of South Dartmoor. An ideal choice if you are planning to start the Two Moors Way walk from south to north.

Run alongside a working Dartmoor farm, the bunkhouse offers dormitory style accommodation with bunk beds in each of the rooms. A kitchen, large seating area, toilets and showers are all within the bunkhouse.

The campsite is divided between two of the farm's meadows. Campers can use the toilets and showers located within the bunkhouse buildings. Facilities include a wash-up area, drying room, laundry facilities and disabled access. There are also two camping pods and a cabin in the meadows. These sleep up to 6 people each and have the same facilities as camping. Small campfires and BBQs are allowed at the farm's discretion. Children and dogs welcome.

DETAILS

- **Open** - All year. Open all hours.
- **Number of beds** - 40-50 beds
- **Booking** - Phone or email.
- **Price per night** - From £15pp. Camping pods and cabin £50 each. Camping £7.50pp.
- **Public Transport** - Train or Bus to Ivy Bridge (30 mins' walk)
- **Directions** - From Ivybridge take Harford Road. Bunkhouse is 1.5 miles from Ivybridge in The Dartmoor National Park.

CONTACT: Julie Cole
Tel: 01752 691883 or 07968566218
julie.cole6@btinternet.com www.harfordbunkhouse.com
West Combeshead, Harford, Ivybridge, Devon, PL21 0JG

FOX TOR
CAFÉ AND BUNKHOUSE

Princetown in Dartmoor is an ideal base for anyone wishing to spend time on Dartmoor whether it is to walk, climb, cycle, kayak or just relax and enjoy the spectacular scenery. Fox Tor Café Bunkhouse is situated near the centre of the village and offers self-catering accommodation for up to 12, in 3 rooms of 4. It has central heating and a kitchen equipped with microwave, fridge, kettle, toaster and sink. There are separate male and female showers and toilets with under-floor heating. Bunkhouse guests have the option to use the drying room / store room (big enough for bicycles) and can book packed lunches and breakfasts for an early start. The café has wood burning stoves and hosts seasonal events and activities such as Christmas wreath making. Guided walks and off-road mountain biking are available and we hire out mountain bikes. Free WiFi is available. Contact Abbi or Dave for more details

DETAILS

- **Open** - All year. All day. Arrive from 4.30pm, leave by 10.30am.
- **Number of beds** - 12: 3 x 4
- **Booking** - Advisable with 50% deposit.
- **Price per night** - From £11.00 pp. £33.00 for 1 person in a private room. £36.50 for 2 in a private room. £40.00 for 3 in a private room. £44.00 for 4 in a private room.
- **Public Transport** - Trains at Exeter and Plymouth. Devon Bus 98 Tavistock-Princetown. Devon Bus 82 Exeter-Plymouth. First 272 Gunnislake-Newton Abbot.
- **Directions** - GR 591 735. Just off the mini roundabout in the centre of Princetown on the Two Bridges road (B3212). 20 mins' drive from Tavistock, 15 mins Yelverton, 35 mins Ashburton.

CONTACT: Abbi or Dave
Tel: 01822 890238
enquiries@foxtorcafe.com www.foxtorcafe.co.uk
Two Bridges Road, Princetown, Dartmoor, Devon, PL20 6QS

Sparrowhawk is a small, friendly eco-hostel in the centre of Moretonhampstead, popular with cyclists, hikers, bikers, artists and photographers, located within the breathtaking Dartmoor National Park. Moretonhampstead is 14 miles west of Exeter and can be reached by direct bus. Accommodation is in a beautifully converted, fully equipped stable, with solar-heated showers and a secure bike shed. High open moorland is close by for great hiking, cycling and off-road mountain biking, while the rocky tors rising up on the hilltops offer climbers a challenge. Wild swims in the rivers amongst woodlands or out on the moor are a must for the adventurous traveller. Magnificent stone circles, dwellings and burial sites of ancient civilizations together with wild ponies, buzzards, flora and fauna are all here to be explored. Moretonhampstead has shops, cafés, art gallery/studios and pubs serving good food/ beer. CTC/ Cicerone LeJoG and Dartmoor Way cycle routes are on the doorstep.

DETAILS

■ **Open** - All year
■ **Number of beds** - 18: 1 x 14 plus double / family room
■ **Booking** - Book ahead if possible by phone or email.
■ **Price per night** - Adults £19. Under 14 £10. Double/family room £40/ £10 per child.
■ **Public Transport** - Direct from Exeter Bus 359, indirect 178. From Okehampton or Newton Abbot Bus 173 or 179. Enquires Tel 0870 6082608.
■ **Directions** - From Exeter, take the B3212 signposted on the one-way system at Exe Bridges. From Plymouth head towards Yelverton and then B3212. The hostel is on Ford Street (A382) 100 metres from tourist office.

CONTACT: Alison
Tel: 01647 440318 - 07870 513570
ali@sparrowhawkbackpackers.co.uk www.sparrowhawkbackpackers.co.uk
45 Ford Street, Moretonhampstead, Dartmoor, Devon, TQ13 8LN

EXETER GLOBE
BACKPACKERS

A city centre hostel within easy walk of the beautiful old port, cathedral, shopping district and a wonderful mix of pubs, clubs, live music, restaurants and café scene. Great for the young and "young at heart" who enjoy a vibrant city centre. Twenty minutes' drive to Exmouth with its 2 mile sandy beach for all sail sports and start of the Jurassic Coastline, and the same to Dartmoor National Park for walking, climbing, cycling and horse riding. Exeter is an excellent place to find work and is just 2½ hours by train to London. In addition to male, female and mixed dorms there are private rooms and three large double rooms with additional bunks, sitting area, tea/coffee making facilities, hair dryer and towels. The new 5 star wet rooms are going down a treat! Free WiFi. Not suitable for hen and stag groups, DSS, unaccompanied under 18s and families. ID required.

DETAILS

■ **Open** - All year (phone for Xmas). Check in / Check out; Mon-Fri: 8.30 to 12noon and 3.30pm to 11pm. Sat,Sun: 8.30am-11pm. Earlier check out by arrangement only.,
■ **Number of beds** - 46-52: 1x10, 3x8, 1x6, 3x2/4 (dbl/twin plus bunk bed)
■ **Booking** - To secure booking please phone ahead.
■ **Price per night** - Dorms from £17.50pp or £75pp per week. Private rooms from £45 for two people, £75 for four people. 50p for card payments. £5 key deposit.
■ **Public Transport** - National Express, local bus companies and rail networks. 24 hour parking ticket available from hostel which is cheaper then local car parks.
■ **Directions** - Bus station: over main road, take first turning on left "Southernhay East". Stay on LHS walk until you reach the Southgate Hotel. Hostel is diagonally opposite. From Central Station: take Queen St to High St, turn right then, at 1st lights turn left on to South St. Continue to large junction at bottom of hill. Cross at lights.

CONTACT: Duty Manager
Tel: 01392 215521
info@exeterbackpackers.co.uk www.exeterbackpackers.co.uk
71 Holloway Street, Exeter, EX2 4JD

BLYTHESWOOD
HOSTEL

Blytheswood is set in secluded, native woodland on the eastern edge of the National Park. Originally a WW1 hut, the cabin has been a hostel since the 1930s. Friendly and peaceful, with a homely living room, wood burner, self-catering kitchen, picnic tables, barbecue and fire pit. Walk straight from the door through the woods to Heltor and Blackingstone Rock, or along the river to Fingle Bridge and Castle Drogo. Cross the stepping stones to Dunsford village or visit nearby Moretonhampstead and Chagford for supplies, cream teas, crafts and pubs. We're an ideal base from which to explore open moorland, the cathedral city of Exeter, and the beaches of South Devon. We're on the Land's End to John O'Groats cycling route and Steps Bridge is an access point to the River Teign. Favoured by walkers, cyclists and birdwatchers, the surrounding National Trust woodland and nature reserve are rich in wild flowers, butterflies and birds, and home to badgers, deer and otters. Staying in the woods provides the perfect opportunity for guests to find their own pace of life.

DETAILS

- **Open** - All year.
- **Number of beds** - 20: 1x6, 1x4 (family), 1x2 (cabin) and 2x4 (cabins).
- **Booking** - Booking advisable. Deposit required for group bookings.
- **Price per night** - £16 per adult. Children under 16 £10. Whole hostel £240pn for two nights or more. £280 for one night.
- **Public Transport** - Trains & coaches Exeter. 359 bus from Exeter to Steps Bridge.
- **Directions** - 8 miles from Exeter on the B3212 towards Moretonhampstead, one mile outside Dunsford. Park at Steps Bridge carpark and walk up our drive opposite.

CONTACT: Lewis and Sarah
Tel: 01647 252435
lewissleeman@gmail.com   www.blytheswood.co.uk
Steps Bridge, Dunsford, Devon, EX6 7EQ

ELMSCOTT
HOSTEL
ENGLAND

Elmscott, a former Victorian school, offers a next-to-nature retreat, surrounded by unspoilt coastline with sea views of Lundy Island. Great for walking, cycling, surfing and bird watching, there are amazing rock formations and quiet lanes to explore. The famous fishing village of Clovelly is a few miles away with its cobbled streets and pretty harbour. Elmscott is a few minutes' walk from the South West Coast Path which passes spectacular coves and river mouths. The accommodation is in one unit of 20 beds and another of 12 with mixed dorms, single sex dorms and private rooms. Access is available from 5pm in the afternoon to 10am in the morning (unless by prior arrangement). In winter accommodation is only available for groups. There is a new spacious large kitchen and dining area which is a great addition to the school room and the original well equipped kitchen in the school house. Games room and shop.

DETAILS

- **Open** - Bookings taken all year please email for availability.
- **Number of beds** - 32 (35 in winter): 1 unit of 20: 2x6, 2x4; 1 unit of 12: 1x6, 1x4, 1x2. Extra 3 bed room available for sole use bookings in winter.
- **Booking** - In summer book direct with the hostel by phone or email. In winter book via the YHA website or for last minute bookings call the owners.
- **Price per night** - Adult £20 to £22, under 16s £15.50 to £17. Enquire for special prices for groups or longer stays.
- **Public Transport** - Nearest trains Barnstaple (25 miles). Buses from Barnstaple to Hartland (4 miles from hostel). Phone hostel for taxi service.
- **Directions** - The hostel is in the small hamlet of Elmscott 4 miles from the village of Hartland. Grid Ref 231 217.

CONTACT: John, Thirza and Kate
Tel: Hostel 01237 441367/ Owners 01237 441276/ Kate 01237 441637
john.goa@virgin.net www.elmscott.org.uk
Elmscott, Hartland, Bideford, Devon, EX39 6ES

A relaxed place with a variety of bedrooms and large garden.

Close to town, beaches and South West Coastal Path.

No stag groups please. An ideal base to see the South West's attractions: The Eden Project, Tintagel Castle, The Tamar Lakes, Dartmoor and Bodmin Moor. There are competition standard surfing beaches nearby. Families with children aged over 5 welcome. Meet old friends or make new ones, on the deck, in the lounge or around the dining room table after cooking up a storm in the fully fitted kitchen. You can make your stay whatever you want it to be.

DETAILS

- **Open** - All year except Christmas week, 8.30am to 1pm and 4.30pm to 10.30pm.
- **Number of beds** - 39: 2x6, 4x4, 1x3, 1x2, 3xdbl
- **Booking** - Advisable, credit card secures booking. Photo ID at check in. (Groups 6 or more by prior booking) No stag groups. At least one adult (18+) per booking.
- **Price per night** - From £18pp dorm rooms (single night supplement)
- **Public Transport** - To Bude: From Exeter via Okehampton buses X9, 599. From Newquay X10 (changing at Okehampton). From Bideford 85. All buses First Bus Company. There are train and bus links from London to Exeter.
- **Directions** - From A39, head into Bude down Stratton Rd past Morrisons on your right, follow the road down past Esso garage. Take the second road on the right, Killerton Road (before the Bencollen Pub). Continue up to the top of the road and Northshorebude is on the corner on your left. Turn into Redwood Grove and parking is the first on the left.

CONTACT: Sean or Janine
Tel: 01288 354256
sean@northshorebude.com www.northshorebude.com
57 Killerton Road, Bude, Cornwall, EX23 8EW

OCEAN
BACKPACKERS

Ocean Backpackers is situated close to Ilfracombe's picturesque harbour. This cool, clean and friendly hostel offers excellent facilities for walkers, cyclists, surfers, divers as well as families, schools and activity groups. Facilities include a self-catering kitchen, dining area, communal lounge with free internet/WiFi, large storage basement, patio area and free car park. Nestled in an area of Outstanding Natural Beauty, Ilfracombe has many shops, galleries, pubs and restaurants.The harbour became home to Damien Hirst's statue "Verity" in 2012 and is fastly becoming an "arts destination". Ilfracombe is the start of the Route 27 Coast-to-Coast ride to Plymouth and the South West Coast Path provides wonderful walks with stunning scenery that take your breath away! It is just a short drive to the sandy surf beaches of Woolacombe, Croyde and Saunton and the spectacular Exmoor National Park. We welcome groups of all sizes that enjoy the buzz of a Backpackers and have a love of the great outdoors! Weekly discounts are available and the whole hostel can be hired for exclusive use.

DETAILS

- **Open** - Mar-Nov. Reception 9-12pm and 4pm-10pm No curfew.
- **Number of beds** - 55:- 1x8, 5x6, 1 x single, 2 x double, 3 x double & bunk.
- **Booking** - Booking advised but not essential.
- **Price per night** - Dorm beds £13.00-£19.00. Double rooms £42-£48 per room.
- **Public Transport** - Direct coaches from London Victoria/Heathrow/Plymouth/Exeter. By train take the Tarka line to Barnstaple then bus to Ilfracombe.
- **Directions** - Ocean Backpackers is by the harbour opposite the bus station. For more detailed directions go to the website and click on directions.

CONTACT: Chris and Abby
Tel: 01271 867835 Mob: 07866 667716
info@oceanbackpackers.co.uk www.oceanbackpackers.co.uk
29 St James Place, Ilfracombe, Devon, EX34 9BJ

ROCK AND RAPID
BUNKHOUSE

An ideal place to come for an adventurous or relaxing break. The Rock and Rapid Adventure Centre is an AALA registered centre that offers activities such as climbing, coasteering, canoeing and surfing.

The bunkhouse can be rented out for sole use, for an activity package or a full programme, including food, can be put together for your group. The North Devon coastline is only 15 minutes away from the centre, and surfing lessons and other water sports are on offer. On-site there is an indoor climbing and bouldering wall where climbing lessons are available for the beginner or climbers can register and use the wall themselves. The bunkhouse lends itself to groups wanting good quality but cheap accommodation. Being in a rural setting there are no neighbours; therefore it is ideal for groups such as hen and stags, as well as family or school groups wanting a quiet escape.

DETAILS

- **Open** - All year, 24 Hours.
- **Number of beds** - 40: 2 x 18, 2 x 2
- **Booking** - Email or phone us for any more information and for a booking form.
- **Price per night** - £235 per night sole use.
- **Public Transport** - Railway station in either Tiverton or Barnstaple with buses or taxis easily available to South Molton.
- **Directions** - Rock and Rapid Bunkhouse is based at the Rock and Rapid Adventures Ltd centre in North Devon. Only 15 minutes from the North Devon coastline and minutes from the Exmoor National Park.

CONTACT: Jade Evans
Tel: 0333 600 6001
bunkhouse@rockandrapidadventures.co.uk www.rockandrapidadventures.co.uk
Hacche Mill, South Molton, EX36 3NA

BLINDWELL
BUNKHOUSE

Bunkhouse on a traditional Exmoor hill farm, with far reaching views of Devon and Dartmoor with high quality comfortable bunks and mattresses, including drying/ laundry room and secure cycle/equipment lockup. The bunkhouse has hot water and underfloor heating from biomass boiler, solar panels supplementing electricity all included. On Sustrans cycle route 3, off-road mountain bike trails nearby and many beautiful walking trails. Set at the top of a secluded valley with lots of wildlife including red deer, buzzards, Exmoor ponies. Many Exmoor beauty spots within easy reach. 16 beds in three rooms The Mole x 6 ,The Danesbrook x 4 and ground floor The Barle x 6 with disabled access. Shared toilets and showers with underfloor heating and disabled facilities. Outside toilet facilities. Traditional local pubs nearby.

DETAILS

- **Open** - All year,
- **Number of beds** - 16 1x6,1x6,1x4
- **Booking** - Booking via website or telephone 01598740246
- **Price per night** - £18pp excl bedding. Any week night whole bunkhouse £288, Weekend Fri/Sat £576, Christmas and New Year by arrangement. Bedding £5pp
- **Public Transport** - Nearest train station Umberleigh or Taunton. Nearest buses stop at South Molton or Dulverton. Local Taxis service South Molton
- **Directions** - From A361 at South Molton turn right and go through North Molton towards Withypool after 4miles at the top of the hill turn right towards Hawkridge, straight through 4 x way then take sharp back right immediately before cattle grid follow brown signs for Blindwell Bunkhouses half a mile on right hand side

CONTACT: Carol Delbridge
Tel: 01598 740246
delbridge.carol@googlemail.com www.blindwellbunkhouse.co.uk
Blindwell Farm, Twitchen, Sandyway, South Molton, EX36 3LT

EXFORD
HOSTEL

Set beside the pretty meandering river Exe in the moorland village of Exford, Exford Hostel is in the middle of the Exmoor National Park. The perfect base for mountain biking, horse riding, walking and lots of other outdoor activities and fantastic for school trips and field visits. This former Victorian hunting lodge, with private en suite rooms as well as dorms, is perfect for individuals, couples, families or larger groups. Catering is available for parties and schools requiring sole use. Facilities include a fully equipped self-catering kitchen, dining room, lounge, conference & classroom provision and ample parking. The tranquil wooded garden is surrounded by the river Exe and is perfect for camping (8 pitches) and viewing the stars in the Exmoor Dark Skies Reserve. Close to the South West Coastal Path, the Coleridge Way & the Doone Valley, Exford Hostel provides a unique taste of Exmoor for those on a quest for adventure, looking for a moorland break, celebrating with family & friends or simply enjoying life at a slower pace.

DETAILS

- **Open** - All year, all day.
- **Number of beds** - 49
- **Booking** - Via email or phone
- **Price per night** - From £19 per person.
- **Public Transport** - Nearest train & bus stations at Taunton. 1hr by taxi/minibus.
- **Directions** - A358 from Taunton toward Minehead for approx 3 miles, turn left onto the B3224. Keep on B3224 for approx 16 miles eventually signed Exford. Go through Exford, over the bridge and turn left, then immediately left into the hostel car park.

CONTACT: Reception
Tel: 01643 831229
info@exfordhostel.co.uk www.exfordhostel.co.uk/
Exford Hostel, Exe Mead, Exford, Somerset TA24 7PU

MULLACOTT FARM
CAMPING BARN

Set in 30 acres on the coastal preservation area of North Devon, the farm boasts sea views overlooking Woolacombe, Lundy Island, Lee Bay, Ilfracombe, and the Welsh coast on a clear day. The camping barn is a former stable block with all accommodation on ground level with raised sleeping areas. Each platform has mattresses at no extra charge, bring your own sleeping bag or bedding as well as warm clothing. There are air curtain heaters throughout the barn. Accommodation includes a dining area and well-fitted kitchen with electric full-size oven, hob, fridge-freezer, microwave, toaster, kettle, sinks with hot water from a water heater (all coin-operated) and basic cooking equipment and cutlery. A tumble dryer has also recently been added. Candles are NOT allowed, as they are a fire risk. A picnic and BBQ area are adjacent and a toilet block with ladies and gents toilets and electric shower (coin-operated) is a few steps away; as is a covered storage area for rucksacks, cycles, surfboards etc. Sorry no stag/hen parties. Mullacott Farm also provides B&B, camping and static caravan accommodation.

DETAILS

- **Open** - All year, all day.
- **Number of beds** - 20
- **Booking** - By phone or email
- **Price per night** - £10 per person per night. Sole use: by arrangement.
- **Public Transport** - Train to Barnstable, No 21/21a bus to Mullacott Cross (400m).
- **Directions** - A361 towards Ilfracombe. 300m from Mullacott Cross turn left into Mullacott Farm drive. Follow the signs, up to the farmhouse on the rhs.

CONTACT: Alison and Adrian Homa
Tel: 01271 866877
relax@mullacottfarm.co.uk www.mullacottfarm.co.uk
Ilfracombe, Devon, EX34 8NA

Base Lodge is ideally situated for exploring Exmoor, the Quantocks and the North Devon coast by mountain bike or foot. Excellent off and on road mountain biking for all levels. Guided mountain biking and secure lock up facilities. Exmoor affords excellent scenic moor and coastal views and the 600+ mile long South West Coastal Path starts here in Minehead. Other activities can be arranged including mountain biking, navigational training, climbing, surfing, pony-trekking and natural history walks and talks.

Base Lodge is clean, comfortable and friendly, providing a shared, fully equipped kitchen and dining room. Local pubs and restaurants are all within walking distance.

DETAILS

- **Open** - All year, all day access once booked (reception open from 3pm).
- **Number of beds** - 22: 2x2, 1x7, 1x6, 1x5
- **Booking** - Booking advisable, bookings taken by phone or email or take a chance and call in. Deposit required for groups or exclusive use.
- **Price per night** - Dorms £17.50, private single £7.50 supplement, twin/ double £40. Exclusive use of Base Lodge from £200. Family room discount.
- **Public Transport** - Coach station 5 min walk. Buses from Taunton, Exeter and Tiverton. Train station: Taunton (26 miles). Steam railway from Taunton to Minehead.
- **Directions** - With the sea behind you, drive/walk up The Parade until you reach Park Street, continue straight on until you reach a fork. Take the right fork into The Parks (Baptist Church on your right). Only limited parking is available.

CONTACT: Wendy or Graham
Tel: 01643 703520 or 0773 1651536
togooutdoors@hotmail.com www.togooutdoors.co.uk/BaseLodge/Base Lodge
Web-page.html
16 The Parks, Minehead, Somerset, TA24 8BS

CHITCOMBE FARM
CAMPING BARNS

A small family run farm in West Somerset, on the edge of Exmoor. Providing inexpensive basic accommodation, with an emphasis on a warm and dry place to stay after a day out in the locality. So if you're looking to have a day hiking on Exmoor, or training for the UK 70.3 IRONMAN, or just spending time in the countryside this could be the place for you. The Hay Barn, is a dormitory style open plan barn with bunks, two bathrooms with showers, a kitchen and seating area for up to 12 people, more by prior arrangement. It is centrally heated, with hot and cold running water at no extra charge. The Cart Shed is more of an open plan chalet with a kitchen, bathroom with shower, seating area and bunks for four people, if you require extra beds for this barn there is a sofa bed (double). Also centrally heated with hot and cold running water. You will need to bring everything as if you were camping, mattresses are provided but no pillows

DETAILS

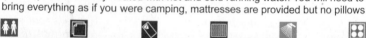

- **Open** - All year.
- **Number of beds** - 16: The Hay Barn 12, The Cart Shed 4. More by arrangement
- **Booking** - Book via website or phone
- **Price per night** - £20 per person. Sole occupancy: The Hay barn £200 per night, The Cart Shed £75 per night
- **Public Transport** - Train to Taunton, local buses to Wiveliscombe. pick up available from here for a small fee
- **Directions** - Don't use sat nav. From B3190 Raleigh's Cross to Bampton road at crossroads take turning for Huish Champflower and Wiveliscombe, Chitcombe is the second left about three hundred yards from cross roads. Chitcombe is down a steep bumpy lane, about half a mile.

CONTACT: Sam Kennen
Tel: 01398 371274
stkennen@hotmail.co.uk chitcombebarns.co.uk/
Chitcombe Farm, Huish Champflower, Taunton, Somerset, TA4 2EL

CAMPBELL ROOM
GROUP ACCOMMODATION ENGLAND

The Campbell Room offers self-catering group accommodation for youth organisations, schools and universities, training courses, groups of walkers, cyclists and others. Sheltered at the mouth of a rural valley on the edge of the Quantock Hills AONB, the building offers a main activity hall which can also sleep 18 on comfortable mattresses, 2 bedrooms each sleeping 3, a multi-use cabin, fully equipped kitchen, washrooms, showers, drying room, campfire area and space for 1 or 2 tents. Many walking, hiking and mountain biking routes pass close to the centre, a swimming pool is nearby and the forest is within 10 minutes' walk. Other attractions and activities in the area include horse riding, high ropes, water sports, beaches with rock pools and fossils, the coastal resort of Minehead, the West Somerset Railway, Wells Cathedral, Glastonbury Tor, Wookey Hole, Cheddar Gorge, Dunster Castle, Tropiquaria Animal and Adventure Park, Exmoor and the county town of Taunton.

DETAILS

- **Open** - All year, by arrangement. Check current availability on the website.
- **Number of beds** - 24 recommended (but see website). 2x3, 1x18 max, 1x8 max
- **Booking** - Essential one month in advance with deposit. Bridgwater YMCA, Friarn Avenue, Bridgwater, Somerset, TA6 3RF.
- **Price per night** - £4.50 pp (2 leaders free for groups over 12), min £54 per night.
- **Public Transport** - Buses Mon to Sat from Bridgwater. Details on website.
- **Directions** - 10 miles from the M5 (junction 23 or 24). Centre is at T junction west of Aley, 1.5 miles south of Nether Stowey (on the A39 Bridgwater to Minehead road). GR ST187381. TA5 1HB / TA5 1HN. Full directions on our website.

CONTACT: Thomasina Williams
Tel: 01278 726 000
info@campbellroom.org.uk   www.campbellroom.org.uk
Campbell Room Group Accommodation, Aley, Over Stowey, Somerset.

MENDIP
BUNKHOUSE

Larkshall (Mendip Bunkhouse) is the Cerberus Spelaeological Society's headquarters and offers excellent modern facilities. As well as for members it is available for use by guest individuals or groups wanting accommodation on Mendip. It makes an ideal base for caving as well as many other outdoor activities including walking, cycling, climbing etc. It is also a good base for anyone wanting to explore the Somerset countryside and within very easy reach are the famous tourist attractions of Wells, Wookey Hole, Cheddar Gorge and caves, and the city of Bath. The accommodation provides all the home comforts with a kitchen/dining room, large lounge, showers and changing facilities. For anyone so inclined the central corridor can be traversed using the climbing holds fitted along the wall. There are two guest communal bunkrooms sleeping 12 and 19 respectively, with ample space to sleep large groups in comfort. For those that prefer, it is possible to camp. There is a large car park.

DETAILS

- **Open** - All year, 24 hours. Key available by prior arrangement.
- **Number of beds** - 31 (1 x 12 + 1 x 19). Unlimited camping available.
- **Booking** - Advisable. Email preferred, deposit required. Availability on website.
- **Price per night** - £6 per person. Sole use of bunkrooms £60 and £95 per night. Minimum charge £12 per person per stay.
- **Public Transport** - There is a bus stop near the crossroads in Oakhill on the A367. Taxis are available in Shepton Mallet, Wells and Frome
- **Directions** - Larkshall is 4 miles north of Shepton Mallet and 15 miles south of Bath off the A367. At the crossroads in Oakhill take road to Stoke St Michael. Larkshall is about one mile from Oakhill on the right (ST 6505 4720).

CONTACT:
Tel: 0845 475 0954
hostelbookings@cerberusspeleo.org.uk www.cerberusspeleo.org.uk
Cerberus Spelaeological, Larkshall, Fosse Road, Oakhill, Somerset, BA3 5HY

Just 10 miles outside Bristol, Goblin Combe Lodge is set in 8 acres of its own grounds with stunning views across the Severn Estuary and beyond. Set in 130 acres of woodlands, rich in history and geology with 80 acres designated as a site of special scientific interest, it offers something for everyone. The timber framed building is clad in larch and has a biomass central heating system, rainwater harvesting and a sewage treatment plant. Groups of up to 38 can be accommodated in 10 bedrooms sleeping 2, 4 & 6 people. The cottage alongside the Lodge provides a lounge, dining and catering facilities and is the ideal place to relax and warm yourself after a long day of activities or to prepare for an exciting night walk where you might meet the resident owls. The 18ft yurt is a great place for a drumming workshop, a day of meditation or just a get-together.

Fire pits and a BBQ area are included in the price. Smaller groups may be accommodated, camping available for the overspill of larger groups - please contact for information.

DETAILS

■ **Open** - All year. Please contact for opening times.
■ **Number of beds** - 38
■ **Booking** - By phone/email. Booking address Plunder Street, Cleeve, BS49 4PQ.
■ **Price per night** - Ask for prices. No min stay. Reductions for charities and schools.
■ **Public Transport** - The bus X1 between Bristol & Weston Super Mare stops at the end of Cleeve Hill Road on the A370. Nearest train station - Yatton - 3 miles.
■ **Directions** - Detailed directions to the site will be given upon booking

CONTACT:
Tel: 01934 833723
goblin.combe@groundwork.org.uk www.goblincombe.org.uk
Goblin Combe Lodge, Cleeve Hill, North Somerset, BS40 5PP

Bristol's most central backpacker hostel.

- clean & comfy beds - mixed/single sex dorms - private rooms
- individual bathrooms & free hot showers - free linen
- large kitchen - free tea, coffee & hot chocolate

Late night basement bar - piano & guitar room - DVD lounge - free WiFi -
luggage storage room - laundrette.

Run by backpackers for backpackers - no curfew after check in.

DETAILS

■ **Open** - All year, reception hours 9am -11.30pm (no curfew).
■ **Number of beds** - 90: Bunk bed accommodation in private twin, private triple or 6, 8 and 10 bed dorms.
■ **Booking** - Most cards, phone or walk in.
■ **Price per night** - £18pp. Private rooms from £41. See website for discounts.
■ **Public Transport** - See below.
■ **Directions** - Located in 'Old City', the historic centre of Bristol. From Bristol Central Bus Station (Marlborough St) 7 minutes' walk. Follow pedestrian signs to 'Old City' then see map above. From Bristol Temple Meads train station 12 minutes' walk. Follow pedestrian signs to 'Old City' then see map above. Or take bus number 8 or 9 to the 'Centre Promenade'. Disembark at The Bristol Hippodrome. From Airport take the 'Shuttle' to the Central Bus Station. By road follow signs for Baldwin Street in the city centre.

CONTACT:
Tel: 0117 9257900
martin.p.jefferies@gmail.com www.bristolbackpackers.co.uk
17 St Stephen's Street, Bristol, BS1 1EQ

Moored in the heart of Bristol's historic harbour, in a peaceful location only a five minute stroll to the city centre. The Kyle Blue Hostel Boat has private and shared cabins with a spacious upper deck providing fabulous views of the harbour from its tranquil lounge and well equipped self-catering kitchen. The Dutch Barge has been completely renovated and opened in Autumn 2016. Great for independent travellers or small group of friends or family, the Kyle Blue offers sleeping in four single/small double cabins, three five bed cabins, a Stern Cabin with four beds and a Bow Cabin with seven beds. There are four private shower rooms with shower, sink and WC and two separate WC's, one on each deck. The spacious lounge offers plenty of comfortable seating in which to relax after a hard day's sightseeing as well as a seated dining area and patio doors so you can take in the harbour views from the sofa! The Kyle Blue is moored in a residential area so no noise will be tolerated after 11pm.

DETAILS

■ **Open** - All year, all day
■ **Number of beds** - 30: 4x1 (2), 3x5 1x4 1x7
■ **Booking** - Online or by phone. Groups of 6 or more by special arrangement only.
■ **Price per night** - from £20 per person
■ **Public Transport** - Train at Bristol Temple Meads 10 minute walk, closest bus stop is a 2 minute walk at Gaol Ferry Steps.
■ **Directions** - Sat Nav: BS1 6AW: On foot Prince Street Bridge or Wapping Road, follow the quayside walkway in front of the M-Shed Museum until you reach the Brunel Buttery Café - the Kyle Blue is moored in front of the café.

CONTACT:
Tel: 07855 368525
kylebluebristol@gmail.com kylebluebristol.co.uk
Kyle Blue Wapping Wharf Museum Street Bristol BS1 6GW

The Rock n Bowl Hostel is situated in the heart of Bristol inside a historic 1930s building spanning across two massive floors with The Lanes; a bowling alley, bar and club venue on the ground floor.

A variety of rooms from private doubles to 20 bed dorms (including female only) means there will be a bed at a price to suit your budget all inclusive of a breakfast in the morning. Working with The Lanes, Rock N Bowl deliver the best discounts for all hostel guests on drinks, bowling, karaoke, and on their Italian style pizzas.

Facilities include a well equipped large kitchen, lounge with Sky TV including Sky Sports and BT sports packages and free WiFi. Towels are available to hire and laundry facilities are available.

DETAILS

- **Open** - All year, 24 hour reception.
- **Number of beds** - 1×20, 3×12, 1×10, 3×10 weekly bed dorm, 2×8, 2×6, 3×4, 1×4 female, 1xdouble/twin/3bed, 1xdouble
- **Booking** - Book online via the website or through bookings@rocknbowlmotel.com
- **Price per night** - Dorms from £10pp. Private rooms from £39. Weekly rooms from £90.
- **Public Transport** - Bristol Temple Meads: 20 mins. Coach station: 5 mins walk.
- **Directions** - 5 minute walk from the coach station. 20 minute walk from Temple Meads train station

CONTACT: The Reception Team
Tel: 0117 325 1980
bookings@rocknbowlmotel.com www.thelanesbristol.co.uk/hostel/
22 Nelson Street, Bristol, BS1 2LE

BATH YMCA

Bath YMCA offers a warm welcome and the best value accommodation. From its central location all the sights of this World Heritage City are easily reached on foot. Bath is also an ideal base for the explorer. Staying longer brings Stonehenge, Wookey Hole caves, Cheddar Gorge, the southern reaches of the Cotswolds, and more exciting destinations all within reach. With a total of 210 beds, Bath YMCA has a great deal of experience in making guests feel comfortable. There is a fully air conditioned lounge area with TV. Laundry, lockers, pool and football table, fax and internet facilities are available. The Health and Wellbeing Centre provides up to date equipment and qualified staff who work hard to provide 'Fitness with Fun'. Couples, families, groups and backpackers are all welcome. All these facilities and the YMCA's traditional sense of community will make your stay a truly memorable one. Awarded 3 stars by VisitBritain.

DETAILS

- **Open** - All year, 24-hour reception.
- **Number of beds** - 210: Dorms: 1x10, 3x12, 1x15, 1x18. Rooms: 7 x quad, 6 x triple, 29 x twin, 5 x double, 9 x single
- **Booking** - Credit card guarantees.
- **Price per night** - From: Dorm £21pp. Single £32pp. Twin £28pp. Double £30pp. Triple £23pp. Quad £22pp. Includes light breakfast.
- **Public Transport** - Bath has a train station and is served by National Express.
- **Directions** - Located approximately ½ mile from rail and bus station. Broad Street is located near the Podium Shopping Centre off Walcott Street.

CONTACT: Reception
Tel: 01225 325900
stay@bathymca.co.uk www.bathymca.co.uk
International House, Broad Street Place, Bath, BA1 5LH

Are you ready for a great workout?

Try a class:
BodyPump
Circuits
Yoga
Indoor cycling
Pilates
Kettlebells
Stretch & Tone

Pick up a timetable or see when the next class is

YMCA

MONKTON WYLD
COURT

This Victorian-Gothic mansion is located in Dorset's Area of Outstanding Natural Beauty, with easy access to the Jurassic Coast at Lyme Regis, and the Wessex and Monarch Ways inland. B&B is £35 per bed and dorm style accommodation is available for £20 where guests can use the vegetarian self-catering kitchen to prepare their own meals. Catered vegetarian meals can be purchased with advanced booking. It is also possible to camp in the grounds.

Monkton Wyld Court is also a charity promoting ways of living sustainably. Volunteers live communally and heat and cook using wood. Fesh water comes from wells; the volunteers use compost loos and waste water passes through a reed bed filtration system. Fruit and vegetables are grown in the organic garden; and eggs come from free-range chickens. Three Jersey cows provide all the milk, yoghurt and cheese. Flush toilets and private rooms available for guests.

DETAILS

- **Open** - Year-round. Office opening hours: 9am-5pm.
- **Number of beds** - 42 beds in a variety of sized rooms
- **Booking** - Book via website, by email or by phone.
- **Price per night** - £20 - £35 per person per night.
- **Public Transport** - Train to Axminster. First Bus from station (direction Lyme Regis / Bridport) to Hunter's Lodge (10min) + 40 min walk along B-road and lanes.
- **Directions** - Off A35 between Bridport (East) and Axminster (West), about 4 miles north of Lyme Regis. Monkton Wyld is sign-posted from the A35; 1 mile up the lane you will see St Andrew's Church on your left, driveway is just beyond it on your right.

CONTACT: Office Team
Tel: 01297 560342
info@monktonwyldcourt.org www.monktonwyldcourt.co.uk
Elsdon's Lane, Charmouth, Bridport, Dorset, DT6 6DQ

Located in the heart of Weymouth, the gateway to the beautiful and exciting Jurassic coastline and the host of the 2012 Olympic Games, Bunkhouse Plus has a mixture of bunk rooms with the 'Plus' of double en suites rooms making it ideal for everyone's stay. Situated close to the town centre, the safe swimming waters of the beach and the old harbour which hosts fantastic festivals of the sea. You can go wind and kite surfing, fishing, sailing, diving or rock climbing. Whatever your hobby, your stay will be as exciting or peaceful as you wish.

Bunkhouse Plus is also available for exclusive use. Sleeps 23 people all year round. Facilities include large self-catering kitchen with everything you need, lounge with Freeview TV and DVD. Large dining area, equipment wash down and drying room, cycle storage. Bedding, linen and towels included. Bunkhouse Plus is not suitable for stag/hen or similar party groups.

DETAILS

■ **Open** - All year, arrivals 4 pm onwards.
■ **Number of beds** - 23: 3×4, 1×3, 2×2, 2x double en suites
■ **Booking** - Via website or email.
■ **Price per night** - Beds from £19.99 pppn. Exclusive use of building, sleeps 23 from £100 per night winter, £250 per night summer.
■ **Public Transport** - Trains, bus and coach from all areas.
■ **Directions** - 5 minute walk from train/bus station. Follow Ranelagh Road to Walpole Street on right. From sea front head north, at Queen Victoria statue turn left into William Street across crossroads then bear to the left into Walpole Street.

CONTACT: Bunkhouse Plus
Tel: 01305775228
bunkhouseplus@gmail.com www.bunkhouseplus.co.uk
Bunkhouse Plus, 47 Walpole Street, Weymouth, DT4 7HQ

MYTIME
OUTDOOR CENTRE

MyTIME Outdoor Centre, previously know as the David Donald Field Studies Centre or the Poole and the Dorset Adventure Centre, provides the perfect accommodation for large self-catering groups, including families, groups of friends, youth, school, special interest groups. The site is an important part of Purbeck history, being a converted 1940's radar station within an SSSI and close to Lulworth Cove, Durdle Door, Arne, Corfe Castle, Swanage and Poole Harbour. The Centre, with its rustic charm, enjoys central heating and double glazing. A new wood-burner makes the lounge area warm and cosy on colder nights. The 24 beds can be supplemented by camping. There is a well-equipped kitchen, a spacious community room with table football and table tennis, a drying room, picnic area, BBQ, camping area, lots of space to run around and plenty of parking. Ramps to the main building (on one level), and an adapted toilet provide access for wheelchair users. Perfect for environmental studies or just to enjoy the coast, walking, outdoor activities or relaxing.

DETAILS

■ **Open** - All year.
■ **Number of beds** - 40: 24 inside: 1x2, 1x4 en suite, 1x8, 1x10. 16 camping.
■ **Booking** - Phone, or send a message via the contact form, for availability.
■ **Price per night** - Whole centre from £330 (24 people). 16 more can camp (BYO tents) at £7pp. Bedding sets available at £5pp. Winter fuel supplement £10 (Oct–Mar)
■ **Public Transport** - Train to Wareham. Wilts & Dorset Buses to Worth Matravers.
■ **Directions** - In Worth Matravers bear right by duck pond. Road turns sharp right then left onto Renscombe Rd. The drive to the centre is 200m further on right.

CONTACT: MyTIME Outdoor Centre
Tel: 01202 710701
enquiries@mytimecharity.co.uk www.mytimecharity.co.uk/Outdoor_Centre.html
Off Renscombe Rd, Worth Matravers, Isle of Purbeck, Dorset. BH19 3LL

CAREY OUTDOOR
EDUCATION CENTRE
ENGLAND

Based in Wareham Forest, Dorset, Carey Outdoor Education Centre has been running for over 65 years. The centre has two bunkhouses each providing basic group accommodation for up to 12 people with en suite toilets and separate showers. There is a self-catering cabin with domestic kitchen facilities as well as wash down facilities and covered hanging space for drying equipment. All bunkhouse bookings come with exclusive use of the entire site. Carey Outdoor Centre is a perfect base for groups wanting to visit Swanage (20 mins' drive) for climbing, Poole Harbour for watersports, the Jurassic Coast (20 mins), Portland (45 mins), Arne Nature Reserve (10 mins) for birdwatching and wildlife as well as Wareham Forest, Purbeck Ridges and Puddletown (30 mins) all great for mountain biking. On-site instructors can help with arranging and leading activities from as little as £12 per person. Bell tent hire in the secluded Purbeck woodland is also available for up to 40 people .

DETAILS

- **Open** - All year.
- **Number of beds** - Bunkhouses 24: 2x12, Bell tents 40: 8x5
- **Booking** - By telephone or email
- **Price per night** - One bunkhouse - £150; two bunkhouses - £300. Bell tents £250 for up to 20 people then £10 per per extra person (under 3s free) All rates plus VAT (unless an instructor is also booked.)
- **Public Transport** - Trains at Wareham 1.5 mile walk
- **Directions** - From north on A531 on arriving in Wareham go right on first and second roundabouts then first left onto Carey Road. Follow until arriving at the centre on the left.

CONTACT: Paul
Tel: 01929 552265
careyoec@dorsetcc.gov.uk www.dorsetforyou.com/carey
Carey Rd, Wareham, Dorset, BH20 7PB

Swanage Auberge, the bunkhouse that cares, is a refuge for climbers, walkers and divers, situated at the eastern end of the Jurassic Coast with excellent walking, diving and rock climbing on the doorstep. The bunkhouse is in the centre of Swanage town, a stone's throw from the South West Coast Path and all local amenities - pubs, shops, restaurants etc. Swanage Auberge is family run and self-contained with central heating, fully equipped self-catering kitchen, drying and laundry facilities and a meals service if required. There are two bunk rooms, one with 4 standard bunks and the other with 6 alpine style places (3 and 3).There is also a 5 bed dorm in the adjoining house. Towel, plus pillows are provided and bedding is included. There are three showers, loos and washrooms and an area to hang and wash wet-suits. Once booked in, the Auberge is available 24 hours a day. Parking is available for 2 vehicles and is allocated on a first come, first served basis. There is free on-street parking close by. Price includes cereal breakfast and beverages. Packed lunches available.

DETAILS
- **Open** - All year (phone mobile if no reply). Access all day.
- **Number of beds** - 15: 1x6, 1x4,1x5
- **Booking** - By phone (mobile in day time), email or online. Deposit required.
- **Price per night** - £20pp (one night), £18 if staying more than one night. Includes bedding, cereal breakfast, tea or coffee. Group rates available. No credit cards.
- **Public Transport** - Trains to Bournemouth, Poole or Wareham, bus to Swanage
- **Directions** - Turn left off High Street (opposite Earth Lights Café) into Mount Pleasant Lane. First left into Hardy Close. Swanage Auberge is at the end on the left.

CONTACT: Pete or Pam
Tel: 01929 424368. Mobile:07711 117668
bookings@swanageauberge.co.uk www.swanageauberge.co.uk
45 High Street, Swanage, Dorset, BH19 2LX

AVON TYRRELL
ACTIVITY CENTRE

Set in 65 acres of private grounds, in the heart of the New Forest National Park, Avon Tyrrell Activity Centre offers an extensive range of outdoor adventure and learning activities for groups and individuals as well as various on site accommodation options.

The Grade I listed house provides full or part board catering for large groups. Dormitory style bedrooms sleep between 2-10 people. B&B for smaller groups and individuals is also available. On site are 6, 12 and 14 berth self-catering lodges, plus Ready2Camp areas with ready pitched tents, electric hookups and campfire. Camping is available between March and October. In this stunning location there is so much to do on-site including; fundays, family events, bike hire and tracks, Go Adventure Activities for day visitors and on-site guests. Step over the stile and you are in the heart of the New Forest where you can enjoy long walks, explore local villages and enjoy some of the many cycling trails. Everyone is welcome at Avon Tyrrell and all of the activities and facilities are fully accessible so everyone can enjoy their time here.

DETAILS

- **Open** - All year, (March–Oct camping). Offices 08:30-17:00
- **Number of beds** - 110: Main house. Plus 6,12 and 14 berth lodges and campsite.
- **Booking** - Booking essential.
- **Price per night** - Please visit the website for prices, special offers and late deals.
- **Public Transport** - Trains at Christchurch, New Milton & Brockenhurst (6,7&10 m)
- **Directions** - GR SU185003. Half way between Burley and Bransgore.

CONTACT: Guest Services
Tel: 01425 672347
info@ukyouth.org www.avontyrrell.org.uk
Bransgore, Hampshire, BH23 8EE

WETHERDOWN
LODGE AND CAMPSITE

An award winning example of eco-renovation and part of The Sustainability Centre which promotes environmental awareness and low impact living in the heart of the South Downs National Park. We're right on the South Downs Way National Trail and ideal for walkers, cyclists, business away-days and family get-togethers. The Lodge has a fully equipped self-catering kitchen, a communal area, comfortable bedrooms with linen & towels provided, and shared bathrooms/toilets. A 'help yourself' breakfast is included. The centre has large grounds with woodland trails and a café open every day. The campsite has tipis and yurts, secluded woodland pitches and solar showers, offering a peaceful real camping experience. Within 2 miles there are country pubs, local shops and take-aways/deliveries.

DETAILS

■ **Open** - Hostel and campsite open all year. Tipi & yurts closed from Nov to April
■ **Number of beds** - 38: 10 x 3, 4 x 2
■ **Booking** - Book online via our website. Groups book by telephone or email.
■ **Price per night** - Lodge: Single occupancy £35 adult, additional adults £22 each. Additional children £12.50 (2-17). Children under 2 £5. Inc linen and breakfast. Camping: £12/adult £7/child (reductions Nov-Mar). Lge Yurts: £77.50 for 2 adults inc 1 bag of fire wood; £12.50/child. Exclusive use of either the campsite or Lodge £840 per night.
■ **Public Transport** - Trains at Petersfield, 6 miles (£20-25 by taxi). 38 bus to Clanfield, 67 to East Meon, 41 bus to Clanfield from Portsmouth Harbour .
■ **Directions** - GR 676 189. From A3 take Clanfield turn (brown sign). Turn right after Rising Sun in Clanfield. At top of hill, turn left signed Droxford.

CONTACT: Dan and Sam
Tel: 01730 823549
accommodation@sustainability-centre.org www.sustainability-centre.org
The Sustainability Centre, Droxford Road, East Meon, Hampshire, GU32 1HR

Situated mid-way between Alton and Petersfield in glorious Hampshire countryside, the Privett Centre offers lowest cost, comfortable short-stay accommodation in a unique rural setting. The centre is a picturesque converted Victorian school and schoolhouse located next to the church in a farming hamlet which lies within the East Hampshire 'Area of Outstanding Natural Beauty'. Sleeping a maximum of 29 dormitory style with 1 twin bedroom (with disabled access en suite) and one single room, the centre is designed to accommodate small to medium-sized groups who prefer the freedom of hiring a small centre all to themselves. The centre provides the basics – a self-catering kitchen, bunk beds mainly in bedrooms, a large common room, games room and shower rooms all under one roof. Outside a large paddock and asphalt playground provide secure and spacious recreational and parking space. Available for weekday, weekend and day use all year, the Privett Centre is an ideal residential setting

DETAILS

- **Open** - All year.
- **Number of beds** - 29: 1x1, 1x2, 2x4, 1x6, 1x12
- **Booking** - Phone or email
- **Price per night** - From £13 pppn with a minimum charge of £150 per night. (please contact the centre for exact prices applicable to your group)
- **Public Transport** - Nearest train station - Petersfield, approx 6 miles from centre.
- **Directions** - From the A272 follow signs to Petersfield. Go straight across crossroads, centre is signposted on left after approx 2 miles.

CONTACT: Angela Grigsby
Tel: 01730 828238
info@privettcentre.org.uk www.privettcentre.org.uk
Church Lane, Privett, Hampshire, GU34 3PE

GUMBER
BOTHY

Gumber Bothy is a converted Sussex flint barn on a working sheep farm within the National Trust's Slindon Estate. It provides simple overnight accommodation or camping for walkers, horse riders and cyclists, just off the South Downs Way, or a tranquil and remote location to get away from it all.

Five minutes' walk from Stane Street, the Roman Road that crosses the South Downs Way at Bignor Hill, facilities include sleeping platforms in 3 dorms sleeping up to 25, basic kitchen and bathroom facilities, BBQ, drying room, bike racks, payphone. Wheelchair accessible (please phone for details).

Sorry, but as the bothy is on a sheep farm, no dogs and most definitely NO CARS. Not suitable for under fives.

DETAILS

- **Open** - March to October (inclusive), flexible opening hours.
- **Number of beds** - 25: 1 x 16, 1 x 5, 1 x 4 plus overflow area
- **Booking** - Booking by phone or email. Booking for groups with 50% deposit.
- **Price per night** - £12 (adults), £6 (under 16s).
- **Public Transport** -   Train stations, Arundel (urban) 5 miles, Amberley (rural) 5 miles, Chichester (8 miles). National Express stop at Chichester. Buses 84 and 85 from Chichester, stop at Fontwell and then it is a 3 mile walk to the Bothy. Taxi fare from Arundel to Northwood Farm is approx £10, followed by a 2 mile country walk.
- **Directions** - OS Map LR197 or E121 GR 961 119. Nearest car park GR 973 129. No vehicular access. One mile off South Downs Way on Stane Street bridleway

CONTACT: Bothy Ranger
Tel: 01243 814484
gumberbothy@nationaltrust.org.uk www.nationaltrust.org.uk/slindon-estate/
hire-this-venue/
Slindon Estate Yard, Slindon, Arundel, West Sussex, BN18 0RG

Kipps Brighton is situated in the centre of Brighton, with views of the Royal Pavilion and close to all of Brighton's attractions including the beach, Brighton Pier, The Lanes and The Brighton Eye. We offer great value accommodation with excellent facilities, including a lounge, games room, & self-catering kitchen. Staff offer nightly events, from pizza night to pasta night, a great way to meet the other guests and the staff.

Dormitory rooms come with secure free lockers and en suite facilities, suitable for individuals and groups. Private rooms, all feature digital televisions, bluetooth speakers, tea & coffee making facilities and combination safes. Friendly staff look forward to welcoming you to Brighton and to Kipps Brighton.

DETAILS

- **Open** - All year. Reception 8am-2am – No curfew.
- **Number of beds** - 47: 1x1, 6x dbl, 4x twin, 2x3, 2x10.
- **Booking** - Please book by phone, email or online (5% discount if booked online).
- **Price per night** - Dormitory rooms from £15 per person. Private rooms from £21 per person (min 2 people). See website for details of current prices.
- **Public Transport** - Close to Brighton train station and bus station. From train station: exit and walk ahead down the main street for a few minutes, turn into Church Street (on your left) and walk along Church Street until the end, the hostel is opposite. From bus station: exit onto Old Steine Road and turn left towards the Royal Pavilion. At the far end of the Pavilion and opposite is the hostel.
- **Directions** - Take the M23; then A23 towards Brighton town centre. The hostel is opposite the Royal Pavilion on Grand Parade.

CONTACT: Reception
Tel: 01273 604182
kippshostelbrighton@gmail.com www.kipps-brighton.com
76 Grand Parade, Brighton, BN2 9JA

PUTTENHAM
ECO CAMPING BARN

Puttenham Eco Camping Barn offers simple overnight accommodation and a warm welcome for walkers and cyclists - individuals, families or groups - in the Surrey Hills Area of Outstanding Natural Beauty. Located on the North Downs Way and Sustrans NCN22 cycle route, the Barn has a fully equipped self-catering kitchen, a shower, toilets and foam covered sleeping platforms, as well as a garden with picnic benches. Electricity and hot water included but bring your own towel and sleeping bag (or hire one - £3 a stay). Evening meals are available in the village. The Barn has many sustainable features including solar panels and rainwater collection for flushing toilets. NO CARS ON SITE. Excellent cycle shed. Young people are welcome but must be accompanied by a responsible adult. The Barn is wardened. Lights out 11.30 pm.

DETAILS

- **Open** - Easter to October, arrive after 5pm leave before 10am. No access 10am-5pm.
- **Number of beds** - Sleeping platforms for 11.
- **Booking** - Essential. No stag or hen parties.
- **Price per night** - £15 adults; £12 under 18 (accompanied by adult). Sole use by arrangement. £3 `green' refund if arriving by foot, bicycle or public transport.
- **Public Transport** - Trains (08457 484950) at Wanborough (3.5 km), Guildford (7 km) and Farnham (9 km). Bus 65 (0845 1210190) from Guildford and Farnham stops within 1 km of Barn, or bus 46 to Watts Gallery, Compton & follow North Downs Way 2 miles west.
- **Directions** - GR SU 933 479. In Puttenham village (halfway between Farnham and Guildford) the Camping Barn is on North Downs Way - opposite the church.

CONTACT: Bookings
Tel: 01629 592 700 or 0800 0191 700
bookings@puttenhamcampingbarn.co.uk www.puttenhamcampingbarn.co.uk
The Street, Puttenham, Nr Guildford, Surrey, GU3 1AR

COURT HILL
CENTRE

Just 2 miles south of Wantage, and only a few steps from the historic Ridgeway National Trail, The Court Hill Centre enjoys breathtaking views over the Vale of the White Horse.

Reclaimed barns surround a pretty courtyard garden, on the site of a disused rubbish dump! Offering accommodation to families, groups and individuals, a popular year-round destination.

The centre offers evening meals, breakfasts, and picnic lunches. Meals are served in the beautiful high-roofed dining room which retains the impressive proportions and atmosphere of the old barn. There is also the option to self-cater. There is a small sunken lounge to relax in. Camping is an option. A meeting/classroom is also available.

DETAILS

- **Open** - All year, to check availability please call 01235 760253.
- **Number of beds** - 59: 1x15, 1x9, 1x6, 1x5, 6x4, 1x2
- **Booking** - Essential 24 hours in advance.
- **Price per night** - Adult £19.50. Under 18 £15.50
- **Public Transport** - Train, Didcot Parkway 10 miles. Stagecoach, 32/A, X35,36 from Didcot Parkway to Wantage 2 miles. There is no direct connection to the centre.
- **Directions** - From the M4 Jct 14, follow signs to Wantage. From Oxford A420 and A338 through Wantage. The Court Hill Ridgeway Centre is accessed from the A338 close to Letcombe Regis

CONTACT: Reception
Tel: 01235 760253
info@Courthill.org.uk   www.Courthill.org.uk
Court Hill, Letcombe Regis, Wantage, OX12 9NE

PALACE FARM
HOSTEL

Palace Farm Hostel is a relaxing and flexible four star hostel on a family run arable and fruit farm. It is situated in the village of Doddington, which has a pub, in the North Kent Downs Area of Outstanding Natural Beauty. The area is great for walking, cycling (cycle hire available £10 a day) and wildlife. The location is central for exploring Canterbury, Rochester, Chatham, Leeds Castle and the many other historic towns, villages and castles in Kent. The accommodation, in converted farm buildings, consists of ten fully heated en suite rooms sleeping up to 39 guests. The rooms surround an attractive courtyard garden with lawns, patio and barbecue area, ideal for families and groups. The en suite rooms cater for all age groups and those with disabilities. There are quality double beds, single beds and 3ft bunk beds. Duvets, linen and continental breakfast are included. There is also a small tent only campsite. Green Tourism Business Scheme GOLD Award winner.

DETAILS

- **Open** - All year, 8am to 10pm flexible, please ask.
- **Number of beds** - 39: 1x8, 1x6, 2x5, 1x4, 1x3 and 4x2
- **Booking** - Advised.
- **Price per night** - From £16-£30 (all private en suite rooms). Reduction for groups.
- **Public Transport** - Trains: Sittingbourne (London Victoria to Dover). Buses from Sittingbourne to Doddington two hourly (Mon-Sat), last buses from Sittingbourne Station 17.51 Mon to Fri & 17.30 on Sat. No buses on Sundays or Bank Holidays.
- **Directions** - From A2 between Sittingbourne and Faversham turn south at Teynham, signed to Lynsted. Go through Lynsted and over M2 bridge, take 2nd turning right into Down Court Rd. Farm is 90 metres on left.

CONTACT: Graham and Liz Cuthbert
Tel: 01795 886200
info@palacefarm.com   www.palacefarm.com
Down Court Road, Doddington, Sittingbourne / Faversham, Kent, ME9 0AU

KIPPS
CANTERBURY

Kipps is an ideal home-from-home for backpackers, visitors or small groups looking for self-catering budget accommodation in Canterbury. It is a short walk to the town centre and the historic attractions including the renowned Canterbury Cathedral. Canterbury also makes an ideal base for day trips to Dover, Leeds Castle and the many local beaches.

Facilities include dining room, TV lounge with digital TV, a garden, a fully equipped kitchen, a small shop offering breakfast and other food items, bicycle hire. Free WiFi & broadband access. Rooms include single/double/twin/family & dorms of up to 8 beds (most en suite). Camping available in summer. Free on-street parking. Kipps also have a hostel / hotel in Brighton, opposite the Royal Pavilion and close to town.

DETAILS

- **Open** - All year, no curfew, reception 7.30am to 11pm.
- **Number of beds** - 51:- 2x1, 2x2, 1x3, 1x5, 1x6, 1x7, 2x8, 1x9
- **Booking** - Advance booking recommended. Book online.
- **Price per night** - From: dorms £14pp, singles £22pp, doubles £37, quads £50. Weekly and winter rates available. Credit cards accepted.
- **Public Transport** - Canterbury East train station on London Victoria to Dover line, is ½ mile by footpath (phone hostel for directions). The local C4 bus stops by the door of the hostel. Taxi from coach/rail stations is £3.
- **Directions** - By car :- Take B2068 to Hythe from City Ring Road (A28). Turn right at first traffic lights by church. Kipps is 300 yds on left.

CONTACT: Reception
Tel: 01227 786121
kippshostel@googlemail.com www.kipps-hostel.com
40 Nunnery Fields, Canterbury, Kent, CT1 3JT

ALPHA
HOSTEL

A hostel by the sea, next to the Viking way for walkers and cyclists and just 50m from a Blue Flag, safe swimming beach, Alpha Hostel has been providing great budget accommodation in a friendly flexible atmosphere for over 20 years. Children love the beach which is only 50m from the front door- so parents be ready to help build those sand castles! The beach is also used by a number of different water sports enthusiasts. Facilities include; two lounges, a dining room, and large self-catering kitchen, washbasins in rooms, en suite family rooms. Secure bike storage. On street car/coach parking. Risk assessed for council, European schools and group use. Catering available for large groups (20+), exclusive hostel use with classroom available. Group self-catering also an option. Families and individuals also welcome. Why not visit the area or just stay on your way to Europe (1/2 hour to Dover by car)?

DETAILS

- **Open** - All year, 8am to 10am, 5pm to 10pm.
- **Number of beds** - 60: 2x6, 2x5, 4x5, 2x3, 6x2
- **Booking** -   Individuals/families: 25% deposit via website, balance on arrival, Groups: 25% deposit, balance 1 month before arrival.
- **Price per night** - £16.00pp. Accommodation only groups please call/email hostel direct with requirements for meals etc. to obtain the best price.
- **Public Transport** - Train to Margate, bus to central Margate - Stagecoach, taxi, local buses and private hire. 10 minute walk to stations and town centre.
- **Directions** - By car: From A28 follow brown hostel signs. By foot from Margate walk to sea front. Turn left (to the west) and follow the prom. Take second set of stairs to the higher walkway. Hostel is across the road 25m away.

CONTACT: Suzy Shears
Tel: 01843 221616
info@margatehostel.com www.margatehostel.com
3 Royal Esplanade, Westbrook Bay, Margate, Kent CT9 5DL

HARLOW
INTERNATIONAL HOSTEL ENGLAND

Harlow International Hostel is situated in the centre of a landscaped park and is one of the oldest buildings in Harlow. The town of Harlow is the ideal base from which to explore London, Cambridge and the best of South East England. The journey time to central London is only 35 minutes from the hostel door and it is the closest hostel to Stansted Airport. National Cycle Route 1 passes the front door. There are a range of room sizes from single to eight bedded, including two rooms with double beds. Self-catering facilities, refreshments and a small shop are all available. During your visit you can relax with a book or game from our large collection. A children's zoo, orienteering course and outdoor pursuit centre are available in the park as well as pleasant river walks. Meals can be provided for groups. There is even is a free outdoor gym in the neighbouring park.

DETAILS

- **Open** - All year. 8am - 10.30pm (check in 3-10.30pm).
- **Number of beds** - 30: 2x1, 5x2, 1x4, 1x6, 1x8
- **Booking** - Advance booking is recommended (can be taken 18 months in advance).
- **Price per night** - Please check the hostel website for all prices.
- **Public Transport** - Harlow Town rail station is only 800m from hostel with direct links to London, Cambridge & Stansted Airport. Buses connect to London and airports.
- **Directions** - J7 of M11 take A414 into Harlow. At the 4th roundabout take 1st exit (First Ave). Drive to 4th set of traffic lights. Immediately after lights turn right (School Lane). Hostel is on left of Greyhound Pub.

CONTACT: Richard Adams
Tel: 01279 421702
mail@h-i-h.co.uk www.h-i-h.co.uk
13 School Lane, Harlow, Essex, CM20 2QD

CRYSTAL PALACE
LODGE

Located within the grounds of the world famous Crystal Palace National Sports Centre and set within 200 acres of beautiful parkland, The Lodge offers good value hostel accommodation. An ideal place to stay when visiting London.

Specialising in sports bookings, group bookings and tour packages, residents benefit from discounted use of the National Sports Centre, with indoor swimming pool, gym, games room, tennis courts and more. Children and coach parties are welcome.

Accommodation is in single and twin rooms with shared bathrooms or triple rooms with en suite. Facilities in the accommodation include common room, internet access, free WiFi in lobby, free parking, pool table, drink-making facilities, evening entertainment, guest garden or patio, lounge, night porter & 24 hour security. Full catering for meals is available.

DETAILS

- **Open** - All year.
- **Number of beds** - 144: single, twin and family rooms
- **Booking** - Booking advised with payment by debit/credit card.
- **Price per night** - B&B - £32.00, Twin B&B - £48.00, Triple B&B - £64.50. Group bookings - please contact the lodge for pricing information.
- **Public Transport** - 400m from Crystal Palace mainline station which takes you into London in 20 minutes.
- **Directions** - Within Crystal Palace Park, which adjoins Crystal Palace station.

CONTACT: Reception
Tel: 020 8778 0131
the.lodge@gll.org www.better.org.uk
Ledrington Rd, London SE19 2BB

DOVER CASTLE
HOSTEL AND FLATSHARES

Dover Castle Hostel and Flatshares, located close to London Bridge in Central London (Zone 1), offers backpackers great value, short and long stay accommodation. Located in the centre of the city. It is walking distance to sights such as Tower Bridge, St Paul's Cathedral, London Dungeon, Shakespeare's Globe, Tate Modern and the London Eye. Prices include free breakfast and free WiFi. The hostel has a guest kitchen and common room, free luggage room, a laundry service as well as a late guest bar with pool table and super drink offers.

Guests wanting to stay in London for longer can rent rooms in Dover Castle house / flatshares. These furnished houses and flats are a short bus ride to London Bridge in Zone 2 (South East London). Single occupancy double rooms cost £145 per week and twin rooms cost £95 per week per person inclusive of bills and WiFi for a 6 week minimum stay. See www.london99.com for more info on the flatshares. Short or long term guests can find their home in London with Dover Castle!

DETAILS

- **Open** - All year, 24 hours. No curfew.
- **Number of beds** - 86: 1x4, 2x6, 2x8, 3x10, 2x12
- **Booking** - Booking advisable. Credit card secures bed.
- **Price per night** - £15-£28 pp incl. breakfast. Discounted weekly rates available.
- **Public Transport** - Nearest main line station: London Bridge. Take underground Northern Line to Borough Station. Hostel is opposite Borough underground station between London Bridge and Elephant and Castle. 10 mins from Waterloo Station.
- **Directions** - From Borough station cross to Great Dover Street, 1 min on right.

CONTACT: Reception
Tel: 020 74037773
stay@dovercastlehostel.com   www.dovercastlehostel.com
6A Great Dover Street, Borough, London, SE1 4XW

CLINK78

Clink78 is a social backpacker's hostel, providing simple yet comfortable accommodation in the centre of London. The hostel provides a basic breakfast and free WiFi throughout. Set in a 200 year old courthouse, original Victorian features combine with bold and colourful interior design to create a unique, characterful hostel. There's plenty to explore in King's Cross - a creative, up and coming area which is also one of London's main transport hubs so you are just minutes away by tube from all of the city's attractions. Discounted tickets for tours and attractions are available at reception. The friendly Clink78 team will happily recommend their favourite places in the city. Clink78 has everything you need to make you feel at home in London: a well equipped self-catering kitchen, games area, a TV / film lounge, a computer room and laundry facilities. Head down to ClashBAR in the basement for happy hour, DJs, live music and games. Perfect for meeting fellow travellers. No curfew, guests have key card access.

DETAILS

- **Open** - All year, 24 hours - no curfew or lockouts.
- **Number of beds** - 500: 4-16 bedded, triple, twin, single, en suite, cell rooms(for 2)
- **Booking** - Online, by email or phone. With full payment by credit or debit card.
- **Price per night** - From £13pp incl FREE breakfast, FREE bed linen, FREE WiFi and FREE London walking tour. Group discounts.
- **Public Transport** - King's Cross/St Pancras has Underground, national and Eurostar trains and links to Heathrow, Luton, Gatwick & Stansted airports.
- **Directions** - King's Cross station is 10 minutes away by foot. Exit the station, walk down King's Cross Road for 500m and you'll find Clink 78 on your left.

CONTACT: Reservations
Tel: 020 7183 9400
reservations78@clinkhostels.com www.clinkhostels.com
78 Kings Cross Road, King's Cross, London, WC1X 9QG

One of London's best established backpacker hostels. Clink261 offers simple, comfortable accommodation in the centre of London in a renovated Student Union building. A great place to return to after a day spent exploring the city. Backpackers love the laid back, welcoming atmosphere. A basic breakfast is provided, along with free WiFi. The Clink261 team are friendly and international and happy to recommend great places in the city. King's Cross is a creative, upcoming area with lots to explore and just a stone's throw from the British Museum, Covent Garden, Bloomsbury and Camden Market or minutes from the bright lights of Piccadilly Circus and Leicester Square by tube. Discounted tickets are available at reception. With a well equipped self-catering kitchen, comfortable sofas and regular movie nights, you'll have everything you need to make Clink261 your home from home. Clink261 guests are welcome to head round the corner to Clink78 for the nightly entertainment and good value drinks at the lively ClashBAR. No curfew, guests have key card access.

DETAILS

- **Open** - All year (except for Christmas), 24 hours - no curfew or lockouts.
- **Number of beds** - 170: 4-6 8-10 & 18 bed dorms, 4 private rooms (up to 3 beds)
- **Booking** - Advanced booking recommended.
- **Price per night** - From £13pp including FREE breakfast & WiFi. Group discounts.
- **Public Transport** - King's Cross/St.Pancras has Eurostar, UK trains, Underground, local buses and direct links to Heathrow, Gatwick, Luton and Stansted.
- **Directions** - With the stations behind you turn to the left along Euston Road, Take the right fork onto Greys Inn Road, Clink 261 is on the right, opposite the hospital.

CONTACT:
Tel: 020 7833 9400
reservations261@clinkhostels.com www.clinkhostels.com
261-265 Gray's Inn Road, King's Cross, London, WC1X 8QT

TRAVEL JOY
HOSTEL

Travel Joy Hostels are relaxed and chilled-out hostels which focus on personal service. Travel Joy is the only London hostel overlooking the river, centrally located between Chelsea and The Houses of Parliament. There is bicycle dock and a 24-hour bus outside the door that goes every ten minutes to Victoria Station, Houses of Parliament, Trafalgar Square, Soho, Oxford Street and Camden. On-site European & Thai restaurant and tour/theatre-tickets desk. Laptop available at reception and € exchange with 5% commission. Free tea/coffee/soft drinks at all times, free linen/towels, free WiFi in the entire building and free continental breakfast + soya milk and gluten free options. There are no hidden costs. Other facilities include post, washing machine/dryer/iron, hair dryers, on-street free parking during the week (pre-book by email and subject to availability) and free luggage storage. The hostel has a large bar, a great place to relax and socialise, with guest drink specials. You can BBQ on the terrace or hang out in the common room.

DETAILS

- **Open** - All year, reception open 7:30am - 5am. Contact in advance if arriving later.
- **Number of beds** - 74
- **Booking** - Recommended, by email or online
- **Price per night** - Dorm beds from £18. Includes breakfast, bed linen & towel.
- **Public Transport** - Pimlico tube station (Victoria Line) is 5-7 minutes' walk away. Victoria Station 10-15 minutes' walk. Bus 24 runs into central London 24 hours a day.
- **Directions** - From Pimlico tube take Bessborough St South exit, follow Lupus St, turn left onto Claverton St and then right onto Grosvenor Rd. Look for King William IV.

CONTACT: Reception
Tel: 0207 834 9689
info@traveljoyhostels.com   www.traveljoyhostels.com
111 Grosvenor Rd. London SW1V 3LG

STOUR VALLEY
BUNKHOUSE

Opened in 2007, and fitted with a wide range of modern facilities, Stour Valley Bunkhouse is set in peaceful surroundings on an historic 1000 acre working farm, an ideal base for exploring Constable Country. Close to the Stour Estuary, there are excellent opportunities for bird watching, walking and cycling on the doorstep. Alton Water is only 3 miles away for sailing and windsurfing. Ipswich is 6 miles away. For children of all ages there is a huge choice of local attractions, such as Jimmy's Farm or Colchester Castle. Colchester Zoo and Sutton Hoo are good options for a wet day, and there are excellent beaches at Dovercourt, Frinton and Walton. The bunkhouse sleeps up to 20 in 5 rooms. It is self-catering, with a shop and pub within a mile. The bunkhouse is unsuitable for stag parties or groups that are likely to be very noisy or drink heavily.

DETAILS

- **Open** - All year round (sole use groups only). Arrivals 4pm-9pm, depart by 10 am.
- **Number of beds** - 20 beds: 2 x 6, 1 x 4, 2 x 2
- **Booking** - Advance booking essential. Sole use group bookings only.
- **Price per night** - 2 nights from £430 - £620, 3 nights from £530 - £825 for a maximum of 20 guests.
- **Public Transport** - Manningtree Station 2.4 miles (less using bridle-path) with regular service to London Liverpool St (1hr), Harwich Port and Ipswich. Taxis from Manningtree Station about £6.
- **Directions** - Grid Reference: TM120340. Six miles south of Ipswich on A137. Look out for The Bull pub, then cross the railway bridge and turn left after 200 yards, between white railings. Follow the drive to the crossroads, turn left and the bunkhouse is on the right hand side.

CONTACT: Caroline
Tel: 01473 327090 / 07857 630692
stourvalley@yha.org.uk   www.yha.org.uk/hostel/stour-valley-bunkhouse
Brantham Hall, The Chase, Brantham, Nr Manningtree, Suffolk, CO11 1PT

OLD BROODER
BUNKHOUSE

The Old Brooder Bunkhouse is situated in Milden in Suffolk, down a quiet drive three miles from historic Lavenham but only about an hour from London. Surrounded by ancient wildflower meadows and hedged countryside it is one of the Grade II listed Milden Hall farm buildings. The bunkhouse has two 8-bed dorms and two 2-bed rooms. The beds are comfortable "bunk-pods" and conventional beds. There is a self-catering kitchen, sitting room, drying room and plenty of showers. The bunkhouse provides quirky, comfortable group self-catered accommodation for 20 and a separate Tudor barn provides unusual self-catering for 22+ if the bunkhouse is full and you have a bigger budget!. Perfect for friends, walkers, cyclists and civilised hens to get together, BBQ on a summer evening, play croquet, badminton, ping-pong or table football. Enjoy the wildlife, explore the local historic towns on the peaceful village roads of the South Suffolk Cycle Route (bike hire available) or hire boats on the River Stour.

DETAILS

- **Open** - Reception times vary check your booking arrangements
- **Number of beds** - 20: 2x2, 2x8
- **Booking** - By email or telephone, non refundable deposit required.
- **Price per night** - 1 nt w/e from £400, 2 night w/e from £600. 3 nt Bank Holidays £1200. Xmas-New Year (4 nts) £1750 Additional nights either side of w/e from £150. Midweek 2 nts from £500 (2 night min booking). Individuals can book at short notice.
- **Public Transport** - Train: from south to Sudbury (15mins) change at Marks Tey on Liverpool St-Colchester line, from north and west to Bury St Edmunds (25 mins).
- **Directions** - Back drive is opposite telephone box in village of Milden go down 0.6 mile drive, fork left in farm yard, bunkhouse on the right.

CONTACT: Juliet Hawkins
Tel: 01787 247235
hawkins@thehall-milden.co.uk www.thehall-milden.co.uk
The Hall, Milden, Lavenham, Sudbury, Suffolk CO10 9NY

CROFT FARM
WATERPARK

Croft Farm is located just outside Tewkesbury in the scenic River Avon Valley, with a caravan and camping park adjacent to the site's own lake. Accommodation is in cabins, a pod village, chalets and camping. The wide range of watersports activities and tuition on offer provide added interest for those wanting a more active holiday. A footpath meanders through the meadow to the River Avon, and free river fishing is available to all our guests.

Croft Farm is ideally placed as a centre for touring, with the Cotswolds, Malverns, Bredon Hill and the Forest of Dean within easy reach. Local towns include Pershore, Evesham, Cheltenham, Gloucester and Tewkesbury. We also offer a full range of activity holidays and events, from corporate team-building events to stag and hen groups.

DETAILS

- **Open** - All year, 0900-2100.
- **Number of beds** - 250: 58x4 9x2
- **Booking** - £15 deposit on individual bookings. £50 deposit on groups.
- **Price per night** - Bed £12, B&B £18, half board £24, full board £30
- **Public Transport** - Bus stop 100 yards from site entrance. Train station 2 miles Ashchurch for Tewkesbury
- **Directions** - M5 jnct 9. towards Tewkesbury. Turn right at the lights, (Shannon Way). At next lights turn right and go over the motorway bridge. Take the first turning left, through housing estate and over the motorway again. Turn right onto the B4080 and then first left into Croft Farm. From Tewkesbury take the B4080 north (Bredon). Croft Farm is on the left hand side after about 1.5 miles.

CONTACT: Martin Newell
Tel: 07736036967
alan@croftfarmleisure.co.uk www.croftfarmleisure.co.uk
Bredons Hardwick, Near Tewkesbury, Gloucestershire GL20 7EE

GREEN MAN
BACKPACKERS CHEPSTOW ENGLAND

Situated in the heart of Chepstow close to the Wye and Severn Estuaries, Green Man Backpackers offers comfortable accommodation in a Grade 2 historic building. Chepstow is a medieval walled town featuring a hill top castle. It is the starting/finishing point for Offa's Dyke path, the All Wales Coast Path and the Wye Valley Walk. The Forest of Dean, the Vale of Usk and the Wye Valley AONB are all close by. The building has had many past uses including medieval moot hall, former telephone exchange and British Legion building. It has been newly renovated to a very high standard and offers a selection of rooms: mixed dorms, male or female dorms, en suite doubles & triples, family 5 bed rooms and twin rooms with private bathrooms. Visitors have access to the private members' bar and the television lounge. All prices include a free continental breakfast. The en suite rooms feature TV & tea and coffee making facilities. This family run hostel provides a warm welcome to Chepstow.

DETAILS

- **Open** - All Year, all day. Closed New Year's eve/day.
- **Number of beds** - 49: 28 in dorms of 6 or 4 beds, 5 en suite family/twin rooms.
- **Booking** - Via email or phone, online booking coming soon. Groups of more than 5 dorm beds please book by phone
- **Price per night** - Dorms from £22pp, family/4 bed rooms from £65, family/4bed en suite from £75, 5 bed from £75, family/double en suite (sleeps 3) from £55.
- **Public Transport** - Chepstow train station 6 mins' walk, bus station 5 mins' walk.
- **Directions** - Postcode NP16 5LL brings you to Wilkos store on Welsh St. Take road beside Wilkos into car park, go almost to bottom and head for flag and car park.

CONTACT: Mick and Ness
Tel: 01291 626773
info@chepstowbackpackers.com www.chepstowgreenman.co.uk
13 Beaufort Square, Chepstow, NP16 5EP

YE OLD FERRIE INN
BUNKHOUSE

This beautiful riverside pub has been standing on the banks of the River Wye since the 15th Century. With charming traditional features, warming open fires and stunning views across the valley, Ye Old Ferrie Inn is the ideal base for your exploration of the Wye Valley.

Ye Old Ferrie Inn Bunkhouse, adjoining the inn, is the perfect place for you to hang up your rucksack, kick off your walking boots and relax. There are two bunkrooms, sleeping 6 and 12, which are cosy, practical and affordable. You can watch the world float by on the two riverside terraces and meals are available in the inn which serves traditional pub food, locally sourced.

The inn also has double B&B rooms with riverside views. The area is ideal for canoeing, walking and rock climbing.

DETAILS

- **Open** - All year, all day.
- **Number of beds** - 20 (1x14, 1x6) plus double B&B rooms
- **Booking** - Book by phone or email.
- **Price per night** - From £15 per person. For sole use please ring to enquire.
- **Public Transport** - Train stations at Newport, Lydney, Hereford or Gloucester. Regular buses from Monmouth or Ross-on-Wye.
- **Directions** - From A40 Ross-on-Wye to Abergavenny road take junction signed Whitchurch/Symonds Yat West (B4164). Stay on B4164 and take slight left at Ferrie Lane and continue onto Washings Lane.

CONTACT: Jamie
Tel: 01600 890 232
hello@yeoldferrieinn.com www.yeoldferrieinn.com
Ferrie Lane, Symonds Yat West, Herefordshire HR9 6BL

Located on a working family farm, Haye Farm Sleeping Barn offers bunkhouse accommodation finished to a very high standard. It has a fully equipped self-catering kitchen, dining room and lounge. Bedrooms range from double/twin en suite to a 6 bedded dormitory. The barn is central heated throughout. Covered decking, patio, lawn and a BBQ provide ample opportunity to enjoy the quiet rural location. A great location to enjoy the surrounding countryside, the Wyre Forerst being one of the largest remaining ancient forests in England. The Worcestershire Way footpath follows the boundary of the farm and both the Severn Way and Mercian Way (NCN route 45) pass through Bewdley.

The georgian town of Bewdley located on the river Severn is just 1 mile away, the West Midland Safari Park and Severn Valley Railway are also very close.

DETAILS

- **Open** - Open all year, 24 hour access.
- **Number of beds** - 15: 1x2, 1x3, 1x4, 1x6
- **Booking** - Advance booking required
- **Price per night** - From £20pp. Can book bed in dormitory, private room or exclusive use of whole barn. Visit website for full prices.
- **Public Transport** - Train station Kidderminster 4 miles. Bus stop Bewdley 1 mile
- **Directions** - One mile from Bewdley town centre, within 30 minutes' drive of both the M5 and M42. From Bewdley town centre take the B4194 southbound for ½ mile. At top of bank turn right (signposted Heightington/outdoor centre). Farm entrance on the right after ½ mile.

CONTACT: Stuart Norgrove
Tel: 01299 403371
enquiries@haye-farm.co.uk www.haye-farm.co.uk
Haye Farm, Ribbesford, Bewdley, Worcestershire, DY12 2TP

BERROW HOUSE
BUNKHOUSE & CAMPSITE

Berrow House is situated between Rugged Stone Hill and Midsummer Hill in the Malvern Hills. An Area of Outstanding Natural Beauty close to the Forest of Dean, the Welsh border and the start of the Worcestershire Way Walk. In the garden around Berrow House there is a selection of simple accommodation and camping with a wildlife picnic area, woodland, star gazing and grass sledging. The Bunkhouse has two rooms and shares the toilets and showers with the campsite. It's kitchen has a table and benches, hot water, fridge freezer, microwave and a cooker. It's sitting room has easy chairs, four beds and steps leading up to a small loft area with 3 beds. The Fold has a toilet and shower and two small bunkrooms each sleeping two. Adjacent is a kitchenette with fridge, toaster, small cooker and utensils. The Bandsaw Barn is a meeting room for use by groups on request. (seats 16) and can also be used as overflow accommodation for 3. The Nook (caravan) has one double and a single bed (sharing main bunkhouse cooking and toilet facilities). Heating provided (fan heaters). Bring you own sleeping bag or can be hired.

DETAILS

- **Open** - All year, 24 hours.
- **Number of beds** - 7 (Bunkhouse), 4 (Fold), 3 (Nook), 3 (Bandsaw Barn) & 8 tents.
- **Booking** - Not required for individuals
- **Price per night** - £13 per person
- **Public Transport** - Trains and National Express in Ledbury (3 miles/£5 in a taxi).
- **Directions** - Take A449 from Ledbury towards Malvern. Turn right on to A438 through Eastnor. Berrow House is behind phone box in Hollybush (yellow sign).

CONTACT: Bill or Mary Cole
Tel: 01531 635845
berrowhouse@tiscali.co.uk www.berrowhouse.co.uk
Hollybush, Ledbury, Herefordshire, HR8 1ET

Woodside Lodges is a landscaped park with lakes, grass and woodland managed to encourage wildlife. In addition to the Scandinavian lodges, campsite and camping pods there is a modern barn converted into 5 self-catering units. 3 units sleep 2, 1 unit sleeps 3 and 1 unit sleeps 4 (additional camp beds are available). Each unit has a cooking area with kettle, toaster, microwave, 2 electric rings, fridge and basic utensils. Electricity is by coin meter and bedding can be provided for an extra charge (or bring your own sleeping bag). The bunkhouse has a small common room, the toilets and showers are shared with the campsite. Close to the Herefordshire Trail, the Malvern Hills and the Forest of Dean the area is ideal for walkers. Nature lovers will enjoy the site with its backcloth of mixed woodland, wild flowers, pools and waterfalls where fishing, wild swimming and picnics can be enjoyed. The nearby town of Ledbury is famous for its black and white buildings, cobbled streets and Poetry Festival.

DETAILS

■ **Open** - 365 days a year, all day.
■ **Number of beds** - 15 : 1x2, 3x3, 1x4 (max 20 using camp beds)
■ **Booking** - Booking in advance advised.
■ **Price per night** - From £15.00 pp based on 4 sharing a room, weekend supplement, phone or check website for full prices. Can be booked for exclusive use.
■ **Public Transport** - Public transport is available within 1/2 mile.
■ **Directions** - From Junction 2, M50 take the A417 to Ledbury. At the first roundabout turn left following Leadon Way (the by-pass). At the third roundabout turn left into Little Marcle Road. Go past the cider factory and take the right turn signposted Falcon Lane & Baregains Lane. Woodside Lodges is the sixth on right.

CONTACT: Woodside Lodges Country Park
Tel: 01531 670269
info@woodsidelodges.co.uk www.woodsidelodges.co.uk
Woodside Lodges, Falcon Lane, Ledbury, Herefordshire, HR8 2JN

LUDLOW MASCALL
CENTRE

Located in the heart of this beautiful market town, with ample free parking, Ludlow Mascall Centre is within walking distance of the restaurants, markets, shops, pubs, museum, castle and church. The Shropshire Hills are close by, with miles of beautiful countryside and stunning landscapes to explore. Built in 1857 as a national school, this beautiful Victorian building has been extended to provide residential accommodation with twin rooms, a family room, and a room which has been designed for those with limited mobility in mind. All rooms have en suite toilets, basins and showers. Continental breakfasts are included and home cooked breakfasts using locally sourced produce are available for a small extra charge. Packed lunches, half board and full board are also available by arrangement. Tea and coffee making facilities are available in the residents' lounge along with a television. The pretty courtyard garden with seating, won 'Best Community Garden' during 'Ludlow in Bloom 2012'. Guided cycling routes are available by prior arrangement.

DETAILS

■ **Open** - All year except Christmas.
■ **Number of beds** - 19: 7x2, 1x1, 1x4
■ **Booking** - Bookings taken via telephone, email or website.
■ **Price per night** - From £44.00 B&B single per night.
■ **Public Transport** - Ludlow railway station is five minutes' walk away.
■ **Directions** - From A49 take Sheet Road towards Ludlow (The first roundabout from the south and second from the north) Continue along Sheet Road towards the town centre. The Centre is on the left hand side after the police station.

CONTACT:
Tel: 01584 873882
info@ludlowmascallcentre.co.uk www.ludlowmascallcentre.co.uk
Lower Galdeford, Ludlow, Shropshire SY8 1RZ

WALKERS WELCOME WALKERS

CYCLISTS WELCOME CYCLISTS

Foxholes Castle Bunkhouse at Bishops Castle is situated within a relaxed, family-run campsite, surrounded by glorious views of South West Shropshire's beautiful hill country. Within a few minutes' walk of the Shropshire Way, Offa's Dyke Path, the Sustrans cycle network and the lively town of Bishops Castle it is ideal for families, couples, walkers, cyclists and photographers. The bunkhouse is heated, divided in half by a partition with an open doorway. There is a single bed and 3 sets of bunks (no bedding is provided) and television. In a heated buildings next to the bunkhouse (shared with the campsite) you will find 3 wet rooms, and a room with fridge, kettle and washing-up sink. A second set of showers and toilets are 30 seconds' walk away. There is good accessibility for wheelchair users. There is an outside table seating area and space for a BBQ. There are no cooking facilities but there are lots of pubs, restaurants, cafés and take-aways 10 minutes' walk away in Bishops Castle.

DETAILS

- **Open** - All year.
- **Number of beds** - 7
- **Booking** - Bookings by email.
- **Price per night** - £10 per person or £60 for whole bunkhouse (sleeps 7).
- **Public Transport** - Trains at Craven Arms (12 miles). Buses from Shrewsbury to Bishops Castle (5 minutes' walk from bunkhouse) every 2 hours.
- **Directions** - Bishops Castle is on the A488 about 20 miles south of Shrewsbury, and 35 miles from the M54. Foxholes is on the B4385 Montgomery Road just north of the town. Look for our sign, and follow our driveway for half a mile. GR SO 324 897

CONTACT: Chris or Wendy Jones
Tel:
foxholes.castle@googlemail.com www.foxholes-castle.co.uk/bunkhouse.html
Foxholes Camping, Montgomery Rd, Bishops Castle, Shropshire, SY9 5HA

Broughton Bunkhouse offers comfortable accommodation in a 17th century barn with a wealth of exposed beams and full of character. The bunkhouse is clean and cosy. Central heating, hot water and showers are all inclusive. There is a fully equipped kitchen with cookers, fridge-freezer, dishwasher and all the utensils you will need. Clothes washing and drying facilities are also provided.

Broughton Bunkhouse is just outside Bishops Castle in South Shropshire, an excellent area for walking on the nearby Stiperstones and Long Mynd. Ideal for cycling around Clun or just enjoying the real ale brewed in two of Bishop Castle's own pubs.

DETAILS

- **Open** - All year, 24 hours.
- **Number of beds** - 12: 2 x 6
- **Booking** - Check availability and arrange check in by phone or email. A deposit is required for advance bookings.
- **Price per night** - From £10pp. Sole use hire by groups for a night, weekend or week is welcomed. Please telephone for prices.
- **Public Transport** - National Coach stop in Shrewsbury. Train station at Craven Arms (12 miles). Local bus service from Craven Arms to Bishops Castle. Ask hostel about free collection from Bishops Castle. You may also be able to arrange collection from Craven Arms by the hostel for a fee of £10.
- **Directions** - GR 313 906. From Bishops Castle take B4385 (signed Montgomery). Lower Broughton Farm is 2 miles out of town on the right (on the B4385).

CONTACT: Kate
Tel: 01588 638393
lbrfarm@fastmail.co.uk www.broughtonfarm-shropshire.co.uk
Lower Broughton Farm, Nr Bishops Castle, Montgomery, Powys SY15 6SZ

BRIDGES

ENGLAND LONG MYND YOUTH HOSTEL

This small hostel, once the old village school, is tucked away in the Shropshire hills with the Long Mynd to the east and Stiperstones to the west. It is an ideal spot for ramblers with the Shropshire Way passing close by and a great network of uncrowded paths to explore. Ideally situated for the End to End cycle route and plenty of mountain biking opportunities. The nearby small towns of Church Stretton, Ludlow, Much Wenlock, Bishops Castle and sleepy Montgomery are all worth a visit. There's also the Acton Scott working farm museum and Snailbeach former lead mines close by. The hostel has a good kitchen, lounge with wood fire, books and games, a drying room, a food shop and a large garden. One en suite room has some facilities for the disabled, phone to discuss your requirements. Meals are available, camping is allowed and there is a pub nearby.

DETAILS

- **Open** - All year. Reception open 8-10 am and 5-10 pm. Hostel closes at 11pm.
- **Number of beds** - 38: 2x4 en suite, 1x6 or 8, 1x10, 1x12
- **Booking** - Telephone to book. No credit or debit cards accepted. Cheques must be made payable to Bridges Youth Hostel not YHA.
- **Price per night** - Adults £19 single night, £16 two or more nights. Under 18's £13 single night, £11.50 two or more nights. Camping £8
- **Public Transport** - Trains at Church Stretton (5 miles) with a shuttle bus to Bridges at weekends from April to September.
- **Directions** - From Church Stretton, take 'The Burway' road uphill. Take right fork at top of Long Mynd (this route is not advisable in bad winter weather). From Shrewsbury take road via Longden and Pulverbatch, then left by Bridges Pub.

CONTACT: Bridges Youth Hostel
Tel: 01588 650656
bridges@yha.org.uk
Ratlinghope, Shrewsbury, Shropshire, SY5 0SP

BUNKHOUSE

Womerton Farm Bunkhouse is situated right next to the Long Mynd, an Area of National Beauty in the heart of the Shropshire Hills. It offers small select accommodation to sleep eight; six in bunks downstairs and two in a double sofa bed upstairs. There is a fully equipped kitchen and living area upstairs. The bunkhouse is 3 miles from Church Stretton, 12 miles from historic Shrewsbury and 15 miles from Ludlow, food capital of Shropshire. There are many local attractions such as Acton Scott Working Farm Museum, Stokesay Castle, Museum of Lost Content and Discovery Centre. The Long Mynd is fantastic for walking, mountain biking and horse riding. Horses can be field-accommodated if arranged in advance. Well behaved dogs that are not moulting allowed. For photo gallery, directions and details please visit website.

DETAILS

- **Open** - All year, all day. Closed from 11 am to 4pm on change over days.
- **Number of beds** - 8: 1x6, plus double sofa bed in living area .
- **Booking** - Booking recommended to guarantee a place.
- **Price per night** - £80 Christmas / New Year, £80 Easter to Sept, £60 off peak. Stay 3 nights get next 1 to 3 nights half price. Phone or email for midweek offers.
- **Public Transport** - Nearest train and bus station is Church Stretton (3 miles). Taxi fare is about £10.
- **Directions** - From Church Stretton follow A49 north. Past coffee shop and craft centre take a left turn signed Lower Wood. From Shrewsbury on A49 south, pass though Leebotwood then take the right turn signed Lower Wood. Follow this road for 1 mile, cross a cattle grid onto the Long Mynd and we are the first farm on the right.

CONTACT: Ruth or Tony
Tel: 01694 751260
ruth@womerton-farm.co.uk www.womerton-farm.co.uk
Womerton Farm, All Stretton, Church Stretton, Shropshire, SY6 6LJ

BIG MOSE
BASECAMP

Situated on the Dudmaston Estate, a National Trust property 4 miles east of Bridgnorth, Big Mose Basecamp accommodates groups of up to 20 people in 4 bunkrooms of varying sizes. The converted Tudor farmhouse offers a large living area with a TV/DVD and lots of games for those rainy days, a dining area where everyone can sit together and enjoy reflecting on the day's adventures and a fully equipped kitchen area. Sleeping bags required.

Situated next to the Basecamp is a large camping area which, with the outside toilet block attached to the Basecamp, can accommodate additional members to your group. Having your annual meeting where you decide your events for the year? Then why not hire the meeting room, this beautiful airy room is perfect for all occasions.

DETAILS

- **Open** - All year.
- **Number of beds** - Basecamp 20: 1x2, 1x4, 1x6, 1x8
- **Booking** - Essential
- **Price per night** - £150 per night (Mon-Thur). £170 per night (Fri-Sun).
- **Public Transport** - Train stations at Telford, Wolverhampton or Kidderminster.
- **Directions** - From Bridgnorth take A458 towards Stourbridge. Travel 3 miles and after a small pine wood on right, take right hand turning to Mose. Approx 1/4 mile along take a left down a track with a small National Trust sign leading to the basecamp.

CONTACT: Sarah Bailey
Tel: 01746 780866
bigmosebasecamp@nationaltrust.org.uk www.nationaltrust.org.uk/dudmaston-estate/features/places-to-stay-on-the-dudmaston-estate
Big Mose Basecamp, Quatford, Bridgnorth, Shropshire, WV15 6QR

ALL STRETTON
BUNKHOUSE

All Stretton Bunkhouse offers comfortable self-catering accommodation with underfloor heating for individuals and small groups of up to 10 people. It has easy access to the Long Mynd which offers walks and bike rides for all levels of fitness. It is within easy reach of the busy town of Church Stretton and all its facilities, and just 10 minutes' walk from the local pub (but please always book meals as it is not very big). Take-away food is available in Church Stretton. There are three bedrooms in the bunkhouse: Synalds and Cardoc have two bunks (sleeping 4) and Novers has two singles. A cot is also available. The well equipped kitchen has cooker, microwave, toaster, kettle and fridge. There is a shower, two toilets and a tumble dryer. The track up to the property is steep and rough so wheelchair access is difficult. Groups booking the complete bunkhouse may bring dogs.

DETAILS

■ **Open** - All year. Winter 4:00pm-10:30am; Summer 5:00pm-10:30am. Extra access negotiable.

■ **Number of beds** - 10: 2x4, 1x2 + 1 cot

■ **Booking** - Book by phone, post or online.

■ **Price per night** - £19 per person per night; children half price; under 5s free. £1 per person per night discount for those arriving without a vehicle.

■ **Public Transport** - Trains to Church Stretton from Shrewsbury, Hereford and Cardiff. Station 1.2 miles walk (or taxi) from bunkhouse. National Express buses to Shrewsbury, hourly local buses from Shrewsbury to Church Stretton via All Stretton.

■ **Directions** - 300m on right going up Batch Valley bridleway (off the B5477, a mile north of Church Stretton).

CONTACT: Frankie Goode
Tel: 01694 722593   Mob: 0781 5517482
info@allstrettonbunkhouse.co.uk   www.allstrettonbunkhouse.co.uk
Meadow Green, Batch Valley, All Stretton, Shrops, SY6 6JW

STOKES BARN
BUNKHOUSES

Stokes Barn is located on top of Wenlock Edge, An Area of Outstanding Natural Beauty, in the heart of Shropshire countryside. Two bunkhouses are available; the Threshing Barn (sleeping 28) and the Granary (sleeping 16). These offer comfortable, centrally heated, dormitory accommodation for a wide range of groups and provide an ideal base for corporate groups, field study groups, universities, schools, stag and hen parties, walkers or just a relaxing reunion with friends or family. The Ironbridge World Heritage Site is only 6 miles away and is a great attraction. Walk to the historic town of Much Wenlock to visit shops, pubs and sports facilities. Situated only a few miles from Church Stretton and the Long Mynd, the barns are in a walking and cycling haven. Many activities available. Have a relaxing and enjoyable stay.

DETAILS

- **Open** - All year, all day.
- **Number of beds** - Threshing Barn 28: 1x12,1x10,1x6 Granary 16: 1x10,1x4,1x2
- **Booking** - Deposit required. Minimum stay 2 nights.
- **Price per night** - Minimum of two nights. Barn: £560 two nights mid week, £910 two nights weekend. Granary: £398 two nights mid week, £615 two nights weekend. Hire both units for 2 nights at the weekend for £1365.
- **Public Transport** - Trains at Telford (10 miles) and Shrewsbury (10 miles). National Express coaches call at Shrewsbury from London, call 0839 142348 for information. Midland Red buses stop in Much Wenlock, enquires 01952 223766.
- **Directions** - GR 609 999. From the M6 take M54 Telford following Ironbridge Gorge signs. A4169 to Much Wenlock, joining A458 for Shrewsbury. The Barn is signed at Newton House Farm (TF13 6DB) on the Much Wenlock to Shrewsbury Rd.

CONTACT: Chris
Tel: 01952 727491
info@stokesbarn.co.uk www.stokesbarn.co.uk
Stokes Barn, Newtown Farm, Much Wenlock, Shropshire, TF13 6DB

SPRINGHILL FARM
BUNKHOUSE

Springhill Farm Bunkhouse is on a Welsh hill farm at 1475ft above sea level, on the Welsh/Shropshire border with beautiful views over the Ceiriog Valley and Berwyn Mountains. Great for walking, riding, cycling, team building, meetings, or just to relax.

Self catering, the main bunkhouse sleeps around 25 in 6 bedrooms. The 2 smaller self catering cottages can sleep 12 more. There is also a heated games and lecture room. The bunkhouse has under-floor heating, entrance hall with w/c and drying room, large kitchen, dining room and sitting room. Outside is a large patio and lawn, BBQ and hot tub. Available on site, horse riding for all ages and abilities, archery. Horses and pets welcome on request.

DETAILS

- **Open** - By arrangement.
- **Number of beds** - 30+: 25 (bunkhouse) + two cottages
- **Booking** - Advisable, deposit required
- **Price per night** - £20pp (including bedding but not towels)
- **Public Transport** - Nearest train station Chirk (8 miles). Nearest bus service is in the village Glyn Ceiriog (2.5 miles). Transfer can be arranged.
- **Directions** - GR SJ 210 346. On the A483 from Wrexham, take the third exit on the first roundabout (McDonalds). At the next roundabout take the first exit, continue into Chirk, and then turn right for Glyn Ceiriog. After 6 miles you will arrive at Glyn Ceiriog. At the mini roundabout turn left, go over the bridge, and then straight away turn right into a small lane. Continue up the hill for about two miles, do not turn off.

CONTACT: Sue Benbow
Tel: 01691 718406
sue@springhillfarm.co.uk www.springhillfarm.co.uk
Springhill Farm, Selattyn, Oswestry, Shropshire, SY10 7NZ

Your ideal choice for city central accommodation, Hatters Birmingham has combined hotel quality en suite rooms with the social atmosphere of an international travellers' hostel. Catering for groups of all sizes and independent travellers, you can enjoy the comforts of FREE WiFi, breakfast, en suite rooms, large communal areas and enthusiastic, informative staff. Full board or half board options are available for groups of over 15 people. Conveniently located for all city centre attractions and transport links, ask our reception staff about discounts to Cadbury World, Warwick Castle, Sealife Centre, and many other FREE adventures, including our FREE city walking tours and quiz nights. If you are into the outdoors we have the largest bouldering complex just around the corner, or try out your mountain biking skills at Cannock Chase (30 mins' drive). So come and stay with us and we'll show you what's fun in Brum.

DETAILS

- **Open** - All year. Reception available, 24 hours. Check in 2pm, check out 11am.
- **Number of beds** - 100: single, double, twin, triple, 4, 6, 8 and 12 bed rooms.
- **Booking** - Booking not essential but recommended, especially at weekends. Photo ID (ie passport, ID card or driving license) required at check in.
- **Price per night** - From £12 dorms, from £32 private rooms, inc b/fast & linen. For group prices and bookings see www.hattershostels.com/groups or email: groups@hattersgroup.com
- **Public Transport** - Easy walking distance from all public transport hubs: New Street Station 15mins, Snow Hill Station 5mins, Digbeth Coach Station 20mins. Local taxi service @ £5.00 for all city centre travel. Taxi service: BB's Taxi 0121 693 3333
- **Directions** - Please contact the hostel reception for directions.

CONTACT: Reception
Tel: 0121 236 4031
birmingham@hattersgroup.com www.hattersgroup.com/#bham
92-95 Livery Street, Birmingham, B3 1RJ

IGLOO
HYBRID

Located on Market Square, right in the centre of Nottingham, Igloo Hybrid is Nottingham's most popular choice for budget-minded travellers. Opened in 2015, it offers a clean, safe and warm overnight stay for great value prices. Facilities include a fully equipped self-catering kitchen, free WiFi throughout, power showers, lockers, lounge with internet access, outdoor courtyard and laundry facilities. There are dorms beds with memory foam mattresses and reading lights, inspired SleepBox quarters for 1 or 2 people as well as twins, doubles, triples, quads and family rooms (some en suite). Igloo Annexe & Pods (100 Mansfield Road NG1 3HD), also centrally located, offers further accommodation with the same standards and facilities. All rooms are inspired by travelling, fellow explorers and a real passion for value. Created using locally sourced, up-cycled and second-hand furniture (with added touches of personality and top notch comfort) and featuring local street art murals.

DETAILS

- **Open** - All year, all day. Reception open 7am-1am weekday, 24hrs Fri / Sat.
- **Number of beds** - 49: singles, twins, doubles, triples, quads and family rooms.
- **Booking** - Essential - especially during summer months. Groups require deposit.
- **Price per night** - Dorms: £18pp. £95 per week after 10 nights' stay. Singles from £32.00. Other private rooms from £18 pp. Seasonal discounts.
- **Public Transport** - 5 mins' walk from the train and Broadmarsh bus stations or take FREE Centrelink bus to Market Sq. Direct trains/coaches from London etc.
- **Directions** - From the Tourist Info Centre in Market Square turn left, walk across the square to Starbucks and Costa Coffee. Take the road between coffee shops (Wheeler Gate). Hostel on right in a courtyard, between Cafe Nero and Specsavers.

CONTACT: Igloo Hybrid
Tel: 01159 483822
hybrid@igloohostel.co.uk www.igloohostel.co.uk
Igloo Hybrid, 4-6 Eldon Chambers, Wheeler Gate, Nottingham, NG1 2NS

HUNSTANTON
BACKPACKERS & YHA ENGLAND

Available for sole use, family rooms or individuals. Hunstanton Backpackers and YHA is suitable for schools, family & friends get-togethers & uniformed groups. Greatly improved recently, including adding en suites, 3* VisitEngland approved.

An ideal affordable family break or activity getaway for walking, cycling, bird watching or fun on the beach. The Norfolk Coast Path, serviced by Coasthopper Bus, goes through stunning beaches, great for wildlife, or catch a boat to Seal Island. Rooms are bunkrooms of various sizes or family rooms, some doubles, some en suite. Self-catering kitchen, large lounge, conservatory dining area and an optional classroom/training area. Meals and drinks (including alcohol) can be provided (5* food hygiene). The garden has patio, benches & sea views.

A 3 minute walk will take you to the sea front or town centre with a Sealife sanctuary, fantastic beaches and cliff top walks. A friendly, family welcome awaits you in 'Sunny Hunny' a great home-from-home on the east coast.

DETAILS

- **Open** - All year (call if online booking not available). Reception 8-10am 5-9:30pm.
- **Number of beds** - 47: 1x double (e/s), 1x 3 bed, 1x3 bed double/WC, 2x4, 1x4 (e/s), 1x4 double (family) inc WC, 1x5/6, 2x6/8 (e/s). 1 ground floor 2 bed (e/s)
- **Booking** - By phone or email
- **Price per night** - Adults from £24. 2 bed from £55, 4 bed from £80. Enquire for multi night discounts, family rooms & sole use, schools/groups full board packages.
- **Public Transport** - Coast Hopper. Trains at Kings Lynn with bus to Hunstanton.
- **Directions** - Follow the coast road to Hunstanton, then signs for South Beach (Southend Rd). Turn right into Park Road, then first left, hostel is 20 yds on the left. Brown youth hostel signs on route

CONTACT: Neal or Alison Sanderson
Tel: 01485 532061 Mob: 07771 804831/07737 642828
enquiries@hunstantonhostel.co.uk www.norfolkbeachholidays.co.uk
15-17 Avenue Road, Hunstanton, Norfolk, PE36 5BW

DEEPDALE
GROUPS HOSTEL

Deepdale Groups Hostel offers self-contained, comfortable, self-catering accommodation for groups all year round on the beautiful North Norfolk Coast. Sleeping up to 18 people in 4 bedrooms, it is the perfect location for a group or larger family gathering or reunion. A great base for a group walking break or cycling tour, or for bird or wildlife watching groups. There are two 6 bed, one 4 bed and one twin room, providing flexible sleeping arrangements. All bedding is provided; just bring your own towels. There are two showers, two toilets and two wash areas, plus a drying cupboard. Situated in an 'Area of Outstanding Natural Beauty', the village of Burnham Deepdale occupies a very special place on the North Norfolk Coast. Each of the staff at Deepdale have their own passion, whether it be the wild beauty of the saltmarshes on a spring morning; long Winter walks along the Norfolk Coast Path; lying in the grass gazing up awe-inspired at a summer night sky, or an autumn day spent watching birds migrate to their winter home. Join them to discover your passion.

DETAILS

- **Open** - All year, all day. Collect key from Deepdale Visitor Information Centre
- **Number of beds** - 18: 2x6, 1x4, 1x2
- **Booking** - Essential, 20% deposit, balance in advance.
- **Price per night** - From £216 per night, for up to 18 people
- **Public Transport** - Trains/coaches: King's Lynn (25 miles). Coastal Hopper bus to Burnham Deepdale. This bus runs from Kings Lynn to Cromer inc Sandringham.
- **Directions** - On A149 coast road, halfway between Hunstanton and Wells-next-the-Sea. Beside Dalegate Market & opposite Deepdale Church.

CONTACT:
Tel: 01485 210256
stay@deepdalebackpackers.co.uk www.deepdalebackpackers.co.uk
Deepdale Farm, Burnham Deepdale, Norfolk, PE31 8DD

Deepdale Backpackers offers a range of comfortable self-catering rooms (double, twin, triple, quad and family) all with private en suite shower and toilet facilities, plus single sex dorms. All bedding is provided, just BYO towels. With underfloor heating throughout, a laundry & drying facilities, all rooms have shared access to a large well equipped kitchen, communal dining area and living room with TV. Free WiFi throughout. Reception is the Deepdale Visitor Information Centre, with lots of info on the local area, the team can help you decide what to see and do during your stay. Situated in an 'Area of Outstanding Natural Beauty', the village of Burnham Deepdale occupies a very special place on the North Norfolk Coast. The staff at Deepdale each have their own passion; the wild beauty of the saltmarshes in Spring, long winter walks on the Norfolk Coast Path, an awe-inspiring summer night sky, or watching migrating birds in autumn. They invite you to visit and discover your passion with them.

DETAILS

■ **Open** - All year, all day, collect key from Deepdale Visitor Information Centre
■ **Number of beds** - 50: 5xdbl, 1 twin, 1quad, 1 family quad, 2 female dorms, 2 male dorms
■ **Booking** - Pre-booking recommended. Max group size 12.
■ **Price per night** - From £12 in a shared dorm room. From £30 twin/double room.
■ **Public Transport** - Train / coaches at King's Lynn (25 Miles). Coast Hopper bus from King's Lynn to Cromer stops at Burnham Deepdale. Traveline 0870 6082608.
■ **Directions** - On A149 coast road halfway between Hunstanton and Wells-next-the-Sea. Beside Dalegate Market, opposite Deepdale Church.

CONTACT:
Tel: 01485 210256
stay@deepdalebackpackers.co.uk www.deepdalebackpackers.co.uk
Deepdale Farm, Burnham Deepdale, Norfolk, PE31 8DD

This Grade 2 listed flint cottage is located within the picturesque harbour of Brancaster Staithe on the North Norfolk Coast. Guests are never disappointed by the stunning sea views across the beautiful marshes. Brancaster Activity Centre offers group accommodation for up to 22 guests, in 4 newly furbished bedrooms with en suite facilities. Larger groups of up to 48 are also welcome, across 9 bedrooms. Your group can be creative in the self-catering kitchen, or sample the local flavours in nearby pubs and cafés. The upstairs 'snug' has a TV and wood burner and there is a garden with seating and gas BBQ. The perfect spot for activities such as sailing, walking, kite surfing and more; the Norfolk Coast Path runs by the door, as does the Coasthopper bus service and some of Norfolk's finest birdwatching reserves are only a stones' throw away.

             GROUPS ONLY

DETAILS

- **Open** - All year, by arrangement.
- **Number of beds** - 48: 1x8, 1x7, 2x6, 3x5, 1x4, 1x2
- **Booking** - Booking is essential. Call booking office on 0344 335 1296.
- **Price per night** - Oct-Mar: Half centre from £668 (2 nights) to £1909 (7 nights). Full centre from £889 (2 nights) to £2541 (7 nights). Apr-Sep: Half centre from £853 (2 nights) to £2436 (7 nights). Full centre from £1341 (2 nights) to £3830 (7 nights).
- **Public Transport** - Train: King's Lynn 25 miles away. The Coasthopper bus stop is 200 metres away.
- **Directions** - Situated on the seaward side of the A149 in Brancaster Staithe. Turn down Harbour Way and we are located 200m down, on the left hand side. Visitors are encouraged, where possible to share cars.

CONTACT:
Tel: 0344 335 1296
bunkhouses@nationaltrust.org.uk www.nationaltrustholidays.org.uk
Dial House, Harbour Way, Brancaster Staithe, Nr Kings Lynn, Norfolk PE31 8BW

Visitors to Castle Acre are entranced by the special atmosphere of this medieval walled town which lies within the outer bailey of an 11th century castle. Castle Acre is on the Peddars Way, an ancient track now a long distance path. The Old Red Lion, a former pub, is centrally situated and carries on the tradition of serving travellers who seek refreshment and repose. Guests can stay in private rooms or dormitories, where bedding and linen are provided free of charge. There are quiet areas (with wood burning stoves) for reading, meeting other guests and playing. There are two large areas: the flint and timber walled converted pub cellar, suitable for yoga and The Garden Room with kitchen and toilet adjacent, ideal for group use: celebrations, classes, courses, workshops and retreats. There is a ground floor room with double bed. Drying facilities. Local shops and pub. No smoking. Dogs by arrangement.

DETAILS

■ **Open** - All year, all day access. Arrival times by arrangement.
■ **Number of beds** - 22: 1x8, 1x6, 1x double, 2 x double en suite, 2 x twin
■ **Booking** - Useful but not essential
■ **Price per night** - Price includes self service, wholefood breakfast, bedding, towel, all day access and parking. Twin £50, double en suite £65, double £60 per room. Single occupancy supplement. Dorm beds £22.50.
■ **Public Transport** - Trains at King's Lynn & Downham Market . Peterborough to Lowestoft X1 bus by Excell stops at Swaffham. Daily National Express coach between London Victoria & Swaffham. Norfolk Bus 0500 626116.
■ **Directions** - GR 818151. Castle Acre is 3.5 miles north of Swaffham (A47) on the A1065. The hostel is on left, 75yds down from Bailey Gate in village centre.

CONTACT: Alison Loughlin
Tel: 01760 755557
oldredlion@yahoo.co.uk www.oldredlion.org.uk
Old Red Lion, Bailey Street, Castle Acre, Norfolk, PE32 2AG

BROOK HOUSE
BARN

Comfortable, self-catering accommodation ideally suited for families, groups or individuals. This high standard barn conversion has a fully equipped kitchen/dining area, drying room, utility and a large lounge with panoramic views over the Wolds countryside. There are 2 bedrooms on the ground floor and 3 bedrooms and a small lounge on the first floor. The bedrooms have a mix of beds and bunks, bed linen is provided and all have en suite shower rooms. A two bedroom (4/5 person) cottage converted to a similar standard (graded VisitBritain 4*) is also available. The village of Scamblesby, at the heart of the Lincolnshire Wolds and on the Viking Way, has footpaths, bridleways and meandering country lanes. The historic market towns of Louth and Horncastle are 10 minutes' drive, 1/2 hour to Lincoln, Boston and the coastal beaches. Cadwell Park racing circuit, Market Rasen racecourse and the Battle of Britain and Aviation Heritage centres are nearby. See website for activities in the area.

DETAILS

- **Open** - All year, flexible accesss.
- **Number of beds** - 22 (27 including adjoining cottage).
- **Booking** - Booking necessary, 20% deposit, balance 1 month prior to visit.
- **Price per night** - From £25pp, family and group rates available. Whole barn hire: full week £1700, Mon,Tues,Wed,Thurs £300 per night (minimum of 2 nights) reducing to £275 per night for 3rd & 4th night stays. Weekends (Fri, Sat) £900 for 2 nights. Sundays £300. Bond of £150 required.
- **Public Transport** - Trains: Lincoln, Grimsby. Coaches: Louth, Horncastle. Interconnect 6 (0845 234 3344) calls at Scamblesby and other villages in the Wolds.
- **Directions** - Scamblesby village is just off the A153 Horncastle to Louth road.

CONTACT: The Strawsons
Tel: 01507 343266
enquiries@brookhousefarm.com www.barnbreaks.co.uk
Watery Lane, Scamblesby, Nr Louth, Lincolnshire, LN11 9XL

The Glenorchy Centre is situated in the Derbyshire Dales on the edge of the Peak District National Park. It is situated on a cobbled street in the picturesque market town of Wirksworth. A few minutes' walk in any direction will find you in the rolling Derbyshire hills. Close to the High Peak Trail for walking, pony trekking and cycling and Black Rocks for bouldering and climbing. Nearby Cromford has the historic Arkwright's mills and Cromford Canal. Suitable for self-catering groups, the fully heated accommodation comprises 8 and 12 bed dormitories, one 4 bed and one 2 bed room, all with showers and toilets. Sheets and duvets are provided, but not towels. There is a fitted kitchen with dining area and a large multi-purpose room with a large stage, ideal for recreation, conferences etc. There is a TV, DVD player, table tennis and a snooker table. Disabled access is possible to the main hall and dining area. Car parking available next to the centre, overnight charge £1, 24 hours for £5.50.

DETAILS

- **Open** - Mid Feb to early Dec, 24 hours.
- **Number of beds** - 26: 1x12, 1x8, 1x4, 1x2
- **Booking** - Book with 25% deposit. Booking form on website or ring 01629 824323. WDURC, Coldwell Street, Wirksworth, Derbyshire, DE4 4FB
- **Price per night** - Mon 12am - Fri 12am £950; Fri 4pm - Sun 4pm £590; Sat 2pm - Sat 10am £1360. Smaller groups £17pppn, minimum £390 over 2 nights. Incl. 9hrs heating per day, extra heating £5 per hour. Sole use only- only your group will be in the building during you stay.
- **Public Transport** - Frequent buses to Belper & Matlock. Train:Cromford (2 miles).
- **Directions** - From the town centre go down past Red Lion pub then take next left.

CONTACT: The Secretary
Tel: 01629 824323
secretary@glenorchycentre.org.uk www.glenorchycentre.org.uk
Chapel Lane, Wirksworth, Derbyshire, DE4 4FF

THE RECKONING
HOUSE

The Reckoning House camping barn has been renovated to a high standard including double glazing and insulation. It is situated on the edge of Lathkill Dale, 3 miles from Bakewell. Lathkill Dale is a nature reserve managed by English Nature to protect a variety of flora and fauna as well as some outstanding geological features. Horse riding, fishing, golf and cycle hire are all available locally. There are also many local walks including the Limestone Way.

It has a cooking area, 4 calor gas rings (gas supplied), a washing up sink with hot water, a toilet, wash basin, storage heaters in all rooms and shower inside the barn. Upstairs there are two separate rooms with bunkbeds.

DETAILS

- **Open** - All year, by arrangement.
- **Number of beds** - 12
- **Booking** - Sole use bookings only, in advance (min 2 nights at weekends). £50 deposit, balance 4 weeks before arrival.
- **Price per night** - £15 per person. Sole use £95 per night.
- **Public Transport** - Train stations at Buxton (10 miles) and Matlock (13 miles). National Express drop at Bakewell. Local buses (enquiries 01332 292200) go to Bakewell from Monyash, Over Haddon, Matlock and Buxton.
- **Directions** - GR 184 666. Take the B5055 out of Bakewell towards Monyash. Continue for 3 miles. After passing Haddon Grove Farm holiday cottages (the second set of cottages on right), take the first turn left at the signpost to Haddon Grove. Bear left at the bottom of the lane. The camping barn is the first on the left in a half mile.

CONTACT: Rachel Rhodes
Tel: 01629 812416 / 07540839233
mandalecampsite@yahoo.co.uk www.mandalecampsite.co.uk
Mandale Farm, Haddon Grove, Bakewell, Derbyshire, DE45 1JF

BARN FARM
BARNS AND CAMPSITE

Barn Farm is in the village of Birchover with fine views over the Derwent valley. A few minutes' walk from the farm is Stanton Moor with Victorian stone carvings and the Nine Ladies stone circle. Robin Hood's Stride and other bouldering and climbing are an easy walk away. The Limestone Way passes by the village and there are two local pubs serving food. Barn Farm has four camping barns - Sabine Hay sleeps 15 in triple bunk beds, Hill Carr and Warren Carr sleep 12 in single beds, Stables sleeps 6 in bunk beds. All the barns have fully fitted kitchens, TV, heating and some have private bathrooms and showers. The Gatehouse, a double bed unit with kitchen, bathroom and lounge/living area, is also available. Camping is available (no single sex groups). Caravan, motorhome and campervan pitches available with electric hook ups. Laundry facilities, games room, childrens' play area, shop, showers & toilets are on site. AA 5 star rated and VisitEngland 4 star rating.

DETAILS

- **Open** - 1st April - 31st October, enquire for opening hours.
- **Number of beds** - 47: 1x15, 1x12, 1x12, 1x6, 1x2 plus camping.
- **Booking** - Deposits required: barns 50%, camping £10/tent/ngt all non refundable
- **Price per night** - Hill Carr £160, Sabine Hay £150, Warren Carr £240, Stables £100, Gatehouse £85, all per night (min. 2 nights). Camping £8.50pppn (£5.50pppn D of E groups).
- **Public Transport** - The 172 bus runs from Bakewell to Matlock.
- **Directions** - From the A6 Matlock to Bakewell take the B5056. Follow signs for Birchover, go through the village, Barn Farm is on the right at the top of the village.

CONTACT:
Tel: 01629 650245
gilberthh@msn.com www.barnfarmcamping.com
Birchover, Matlock, Derbyshire, DE4 2BL

THORNBRIDGE
OUTDOORS

Thornbridge Outdoors offers excellent flexible accommodation for family and friends' reunions, parties and retreats. In a fantastic location in the heart of the Peak District, Thornbridge Outdoors is a perfect base to access the wonderfully diverse countryside and interesting towns/villages of the Peak District. The Monsal Trail is accessible from the grounds; popular with walkers and cyclists, a flat, traffic free route of 8.5 miles between Bakewell & Blackwell Mill near Buxton. The gritstone edges of Froggatt and Stanage are within easy reach. The Lodge and the Farm House buildings sleep 38 and 34 people respectively and are self contained, each having its own kitchen and dining/lounge area. The Lodge is all on one level and has a disabled toilet/shower room, making it suitable for wheelchair users, whilst the Farm House, a Grade 2 listed 19th century building is characterful with some quirky shaped rooms in the attached roundhouse. The campsite & teepees can be booked along with the Base Camp building that contains toilets, showers, kitchen and dining room. Outdoor activities led by qualified instructors can be provided.

              GROUPS ONLY

DETAILS

- **Open** - All year, all day.
- **Number of beds** - 72 plus camping: Lodge 38: 4x5, 4x3, 1x6; Farm House 34: 2x8, 2x6, 1x5, 1x3, 1x2 (38 beds max capacity 34); Teepees & camping; 45: 9 x 4/5.
- **Booking** - Via website contact form, phone or email.
- **Price per night** - Weekend breaks from £960 per building. Ask for activity costs.
- **Public Transport** - Buses from Bakewell. Trains at Grindleford (7 miles).
- **Directions** - Between Great Longstone and Ashford in the Water on Longstone Ln

CONTACT: Reception
Tel: 01629 640491
info@thornbridgeoutdoors.co.uk www.thornbridgeoutdoors.co.uk
Great Longstone, Bakewell, Derbyshire, DE45 1NY

SHEEN
BUNKHOUSE

Sheen Bunkhouse is a newly converted barn in a quiet corner of the Peak District, close to the beautiful Dove and Manifold valleys. Comprehensively equipped, it offers a large TV lounge, well equipped self-catering facilities and two bunkrooms with wash basins. Toilets and showers are conveniently located for both rooms.

Passing close by the barn, the Manifold Valley Track, Tissington Trail and High Peak Trail provide easy access to beautiful countryside, ideal for families and cyclists. Dovedale, the Upper Dove Valley and the remote and mysterious moorlands around Flash and Longnor offer stunning scenery for walkers. Visit the markets and parks at Buxton (8 miles), Leek (10 miles) and Bakewell (12 miles) for a great day out. Other attractions include Alton Towers (20 mins by car) and the famous Opera House and show caves at Buxton.

DETAILS

- **Open** - All year, 24 hours access, reception 8am - 9pm.
- **Number of beds** - 14: 1x8, 1x6
- **Booking** - Book by phone or email
- **Price per night** - From: adults £16, under 16s £11.
- **Public Transport** - Train station at Buxton. Daily bus operated by Bowers from Buxton to Hartington passes close to bunkhouse.
- **Directions** - On the B5054 between Hartington and Hulme End take the turning to Sheen (also signposted for 'Staffordshire Knott'). The bunkhouse is on the right 200yds after the pub.

CONTACT: Jean or Graham Belfield
Tel: 01298 84501
grahambelfield@fsmail.net
Peakstones, Sheen, Derbyshire, SK17 0ES

Located on a working farm near Alstonefield on the Derbyshire/Staffordshire border, Alstonefield camping barn is near Dovedale, the Manifold Valley, Hartington, Leek and Ashbourne. A perfect base to visit Alton Towers or spend the day exploring the wonderful White Peak landscape. Great for quiet parties (but not stag and hen dos), group get togethers or team building events. The barn welcomes families, cyclists, walkers, DofE, Scouts and school groups.

This is camping in the comfort of a remote cosy barn with unrivalled views. You need to bring usual camping equipment including camping mats or blow up air bed, sleeping bags, cooking stove and fuel, pots and pans, crockery and cutlery. As there is no electricity in the barn you will also need to bring torches and flat safety night/tea light candles and logs for the WOODBURNING STOVE. Self catering holiday cottages are also available at Gateham Grange

DETAILS

- **Open** - All year, all day apart from Christmas and New Year.
- **Number of beds** - 12
- **Booking** - Via email or phone. Dogs welcome with prior arrangement only.
- **Price per night** - 8.50pp
- **Public Transport** - Nearest rail Buxton, nearest bus station Ashbourne or Leek. Moorlands Connect bus goes to Leek.
- **Directions** - From A515 take turning signposted for Alstonefield just by the Newton House Hotel. Keep right through Alstonefield (Hulme End road). At first crossroads turn left towards Wetton. The farm is immediately on your right.

CONTACT: Robert or Teresa Flower
Tel: 01335 310349
Gateham.Grange@btinternet.com www.gatehamgrange.co.uk
Gateham Grange, Alstonefield, Ashbourne, Derbys. DE6 2FT

ILAM
BUNKHOUSE

Ilam bunkhouse is located in an 18th century stable block which originally formed part of the Ilam Hall Estate. The estate is now managed by the National Trust and the bunkhouse sits within the grounds of Ilam Park. Ilam bunkhouse provides high quality group accommodation for up to 16 people. There are 3 bedrooms with bunk beds, with each bunk provided with a locker, night light and plug socket, there is also a hand basin in each room. There is a sociable main living area comprising of a large dining table with benches, an open plan kitchen area with dishwasher and 2 large comfortable fitted sofas in the sitting room area. There are 3 individual toilet and shower rooms and an additional toilet room. A good base to explore the Peak District National Park, in particular the limestone hills and gorges, meandering rivers and beautiful woodland of the White Peak. Explore Dovedale with it's famous stepping stones and our own Ilam Park with it's beautiful views, popular tea room and shop. Dogs welcome.

DETAILS

- **Open** - All year, all day.
- **Number of beds** - 16: in three rooms
- **Booking** - Via National Trust central booking system 0344 335 1296
- **Price per night** - Weekdays £170pn. Weekends £250pn. A minimum of 2 nights at a weekend and 3 nights on Bank Holidays. Dogs £15 per dog per stay. Prices subject to review during for 2017.
- **Public Transport** - Trains at Uttoxeter (12 miles). Bus; Moorlands Connect service – bookable service stops in Ilam village 0300 111 8003.
- **Directions** - In Ilam follow signs for National Trust Ilam Park. Use main car park.

CONTACT: National Trust Holiday Bookings
Tel: 0344 335 1296
bunkhouses@nationaltrust.org.uk www.nationaltrustholidays.org.uk
Ilam Bunkhouse, Ilam Park, Ilam, nr Ashbourne, DE6 2AZ

PEAK DISTRICT
HOLIDAY BARN

This extremely impressive holiday barn with 6 bedrooms comfortably sleeps up to 24. Situated in the heart of the Peak District, perfectly positioned for large groups to stay together and celebrate: wedding parties, family re-unions, birthdays, stag and hen parties, walking holidays etc. Also perfect for corporate residential or team building courses. Converted to an extremely high standard while retaining many of the barn's original features. Fully insulated with double glazing and central heating throughout. 6 bedrooms including king sized 4 poster bed (all bed linen included), 3 bathrooms, a large multi-fuel log burner, plenty of off-road parking. Outside is a lawned garden with BBQ, fire pit and outdoor pizza oven. One all year round price with no additional increases for seasonal variations, school holidays, bank holidays etc (excluding Christmas and New Year's Eve). During midweek periods no matter what the size of your group the barn is the perfect venue with our 'midweek flexibility package.

               GROUPS ONLY

DETAILS

- **Open** - All year round. All day access. Check in is available from 4pm.
- **Number of beds** - 24 : 2x king size, 3x double, 14 large bunks
- **Booking** - Deposit of 30% with final invoice including returnable security bond of £300 due 6 weeks prior to arrival.
- **Price per night** - Weekends: Fri/Sat £2250, Fri/Sat/Sun £2800. Midweek: (Mon-Thur) £850 per night. Midweek sleeping 12 or less: £600 per night. Great deals for midweek breaks of 1-4 days. Wedding from £3250 including 2 nights in the barn.
- **Public Transport** - Rail: Sheffield to Manchester line Hope or Grindleford stations (7 miles). Transpeak bus Nottingham to Manchester stops at Ashford (4 miles).
- **Directions** - Situated on the A623 in Wardlow Mires, next to the pub. OS 182757

CONTACT: Amanda or Mark
Tel: 07525 051226 or 07791 667027
bookings@peakdistrictholidaybarn.co.uk www.peakdistrictholidaybarn.co.uk
Wardlow Mires, near Tideswell, Buxton, Derbyshire, SK17 8RW

ST MICHAELS
CENTRE

At the heart of the bustling Peak District village of Hathersage in the Hope Valley. With limitless walking from the door, it is close to the popular Derwent Valley reservoirs, the gritstone edges, Chatsworth estate and the caverns of Castleton. The Hope Valley train line and a good network of bus routes pass through the village making it possible to explore the area without a car. Providing high quality, warm and welcoming accommodation for groups, the centre can accommodate up to 38 people in dorms with 4 extra beds available in an adjacent cottage. There is a well equipped self-catering kitchen, a dining room and lounge area with TV/DVD and WiFi, a classroom, showers, toilets, drying room and secure parking for up to 12 cars. Shops, pubs, cafés, rail station, bus route, tennis court and an open air heated swimming pool are all a few steps away. Suitable for family groups, friend re-unions, training and team-building. Outdoor activities, climbing and caving may be available on request.

DETAILS

■ **Open** - All year. Office open Monday – Friday 8.30 am – 4pm
■ **Number of beds** - 38: 2x2, 1x4, 2x6, 1x8, 1x10. Plus 4 in adjacent cottage.
■ **Booking** - Advanced booking only.
■ **Price per night** - £21.40pp minimum £428 a night, bookable for a minimum of 2 nights. Activities: £280 per day (for maximum of 12 people) plus cost of transport.
■ **Public Transport** - The Hope Valley line has regular trains from Manchester and Sheffield. Buses daily to Sheffield, Hope,Castleton, Eyam, Bradwell and Bakewell
■ **Directions** - On main A6187 road just west of junction with B6001. From the station walk uphill to main road and turn left. Alight buses at shops and walk downhill

CONTACT: Gary Richards
Tel: 01433 650309
stmichaels@nottscc.gov.uk www.nottinghamshire.gov.uk
Main Road, Hathersage, Derbyshire, S32 1BB

THORPE FARM
BUNKHOUSES

Thorpe Farm Bunkhouses are situated a mile northwest of Hathersage, on a family-run mixed dairy farm which makes its own ice cream.

The bunkhouses are 2 miles west of Stanage Edge. Other popular climbing and walking areas are nearby. Castleton is 6 miles up the Hope Valley and Eyam is 6 miles southwest. Each bunkhouse has dormitories with individual bunks or mattresses on the floor. There is some sleeping space in the sitting rooms and room for camping outside. The bunkhouses have heating, drying facilities, hot showers, toilets, electric / gas cooking, fridges, freezers, electric kettles, toasters etc. The Byre is all on one level with disabled facilities.

DETAILS

■ **Open** - All year, no restrictions.
■ **Number of beds** - Old Shippon 32: 2x12, 2x4. Byre 14: 1x6, 1x4. Living room 4. Old Stables 14: 1x8, 1x6. Pondside 14: 1x8, 1x6.
■ **Booking** - Essential for weekends.
■ **Price per night** - See own website.
■ **Public Transport** - Train station at Hathersage, 10 mins' walk from bunkhouse. Bus service 272 operates from Sheffield to Hathersage. Details phone Busline 01298 230980 or 01246 250450.
■ **Directions** - GR 223 824. If walking from A6187/A625 in Hathersage turn right (just past the George Hotel) up Jaggers Lane, turn second right up Coggers Lane and fifth turning on left (signed Thorpe Farm). If driving follow the road from Hathersage towards Hope for ¾ mile, then turn right into private drive (signposted Thorpe Farm).

CONTACT: Jane Marsden
Tel: 01433 650659
jane@hope-valley.co.uk www.thorpe-bunk.co.uk
Thorpe Farm, Hathersage, Peak District, Via Sheffield, S32 1B

ROYAL OAK
BUNKBARN

Eat, drink, be merry and stay in a refurbished stone barn with a traditional award winning Peak District country pub on site. The Royal Oak serves fantastic pub grub and local cask ales (Multiple Winner of 'Derbyshire Pub of the Year Awards'). The Royal Oak has direct access to the High Peak and Tissington Trails which use disused railways to provide easy off road cycling. The area is also ideal for climbing and walking with stone circles and limestone gorges to explore. The bunk barn is perfect for any number from 1 to 34 (small and large groups welcome) wanting comfortable, clean, private bunk bed style rooms. The five separate bunk rooms are all heated and lockable. All the bunk beds have comfortable mattresses, a pillow and fresh linen, just bring a duvet or sleeping bag. There is a small communal kitchen ideal for basic meals with fridge, oven and kettle and seating for 5/6 people. Separate ladies and gents toilets and hot showers are included in the simple per person tariff. Campsite and holiday cottages (some sleeping large groups) available.

DETAILS

- **Open** - All year, all day.
- **Number of beds** - 34: 3 x 8 (bunks), 1 x 6 (bunks), 1 x 4 (bunks)
- **Booking** - Booking in advance by phone or email
- **Price per night** - April to Sept £17pppn, Oct to March £15pppn.
- **Public Transport** - Nearest trains Buxton (8 miles). Local bus no.42 (Buxton to Ashbourne) drops off 15 minutes' walk away on A515
- **Directions** - From the A515 Buxton to Ashbourne road take road to Hurdlow oposite to B5055 road to Bakewell.

CONTACT: The Royal Oak
Tel: 01298 83288
hello@peakpub.co.uk www.peakpub.co.uk
The Royal Oak, Hurdlow, Nr Buxton, SK17 9QJ

High Peak and Tissington Trails

Managed by the Peak District National Park Authority and Derbyshire County Council, these are former railway lines converted for use by walkers, cyclists and horse riders. Please respect other users. Cyclists give way to walkers and horse riders - keep to the left of the Trail and overtake others slowly in single file.

Take extra care on bridges and embankments.

You are advised NOT to cycle down inclines

MOORSIDE FARM
BUNKHOUSE

Moorside Farm is a 300-year-old farmhouse set 1200 feet up in the beautiful Peak District National Park on the Derbyshire / Staffordshire border and approximately five miles from the historic town of Buxton. Sleeping accommodation is provided in two areas, one for 14 - this is alpine style with pine clad ceiling and a pine floor with bunk beds. The second area has 6 beds, also in bunks and is an ideal room for a small group or family. Downstairs there are showers, toilets and a large dining / general room. The farmhouse has full central heating and drying facilities are available. Provided at the bunkhouse is a three course breakfast, packed lunch and a substantial dinner in the evening, vegetarians are catered for. A small kitchen is available for making tea and coffee. Ample parking space is provided. All bookings have sole use of the accommodation.

DETAILS

- **Open** - All year, 24 hours.
- **Number of beds** - 20: 1 x 14, 1 x 6
- **Booking** - Deposit required with minimum two weeks' notice.
- **Price per night** - £36.00 per person per night, includes bed, breakfast, packed lunch and evening meal. Bed and breakfast only £25.00 per person per night. Minimum booking 4 persons.
- **Public Transport** - Nearest train station Buxton. Take bus to Longnor or Travellers Rest. Bus enquiries 01332 292200.
- **Directions** - GR SK 055 670. Leave A53, Buxton to Leek road at Travellers Rest, take 4th lane on left, down to T junction, take first left, Moorside Farm is first right entrance.

CONTACT: Charlie
Tel: 01298 83406
charliefutcher@aol.com   www.moorsidefarm.com
Hollinsclough, Longnor, Buxton, Derbyshire, SK17 0RF

'We found it - the most beautiful site we've ever encountered'.

Upper Booth Camping Barn is located adjacent to a small campsite alongside Crowden Clough. It is possible to hire the barn and additional pitches on the campsite. There is space for cooking and tables for eating. Toilets, handbasins, washing up sinks and showers are shared with the campsite.

Upper Booth camping barn is located on a working hill-farm. Walking and biking are available from the farm, the Pennine Way passes through the farmyard. An ideal base for outdoor enthusiasts.

DETAILS

- **Open** - March-November. Arrival between 3pm and 9pm. Departure before 10am. Not suitable for late night parties.
- **Number of beds** - Sleeping space for 12
- **Booking** - Pre-booking essential for weekends & bank holidays. Provisional booking held for 7 days. Confirmed if full payment is received within that time.
- **Price per night** - Exclusive use (up to 12 persons) from £90 per night plus vehicles. Individual spaces from £10 per person per night.
- **Public Transport** - Nearest station, Edale (Sheffield/Manchester line) approx 40 minutes' walk on footpaths to Upper Booth. Nearest bus stop Barber Booth (15 minutes' walk). Service 260 weekdays. 3 buses a day go to Upper Booth.
- **Directions** - GR103 853. Follow signs for Edale village, then for Barber Booth, immediately after river bridge turn right for Upper Booth.

CONTACT: Robert, Sarah or Alice
Tel: (01433) 670250
mail@helliwell.info www.upperboothcamping.co.uk
Upper Booth Farm, Edale, Hope Valley, Derbyshire, S33 7ZJ

PINDALE FARM
OUTDOOR CENTRE

A mile from Castleton in the heart of the Peak District. Pindale Farm comprises a farmhouse pre-dating 1340 and lead mine buildings from the 1850s, which have been completely rebuilt from near dereliction. The centre offers 5 different kinds of accommodation. The farmhouse offers traditional bed and (an AGA cooked) breakfast. The Barn has 6 independent self-catering units, 3 of these can accommodate people with certain physical disabilities. The Old Lead Mine Engine House is a self-catering unit sleeping 8. The Powder House, originally the mine's explosive store, is a small camping barn with basic facilities for up to 4 people. A campsite, adjacent to the centre, has showers, hot water, and toilet facilities. All rooms have Freesat TV, WiFi is available in the barn and most of the camping areas (£2 a day). The ideal base for walking, climbing, caving, horse riding etc. Instruction is available if required. Well behaved pets welcome. Scouts, Cadets and DofE expeditions welcome, camping or in the bunkhouse.

DETAILS

- **Open** - All year (camping March-October), 24 hours.
- **Number of beds** - 64 bunkbeds plus camping and B&B
- **Booking** - Early booking (deposit) is best.
- **Price per night** - Camping £8 pp (£4 for hook up). Barns £16 pp plus £1 electric tokens for cooker, shower and sockets. B&B with four poster bed and AGA breakfast enquire for prices.
- **Public Transport** - Train station in Hope. On local buses ask for Hope. Hope is 15 minutes' walk from the hostel. National Express Sheffield (taxi fare £15-£20).
- **Directions** - GR 163 825. From Hope follow cement works signs, turn off main road between church and Woodroffe Arms.

CONTACT: Alan Medhurst
Tel: 01433 620111
pindalefarm@btconnect.com   www.pindalefarm.co.uk
Pindale Road, Hope, Hope Valley, Derbyshire, S33 6RN

HOMESTEAD
AND CHEESEHOUSE

These two bunkhouses are situated on a small mixed farm in the middle of Bamford, just 3 miles from Stanage Edge. The Derwent Dams are between 1.5 and 7 miles further up the valley. Castleton is 5 miles to the north, Chatsworth House and Park 10 miles to the southwest. Both bunkhouses have individual bunks each with mattress, fitted sheets and pillow (bring your own sleeping bags), gas central heating and drying facilities. Homestead has 22 beds in 3 rooms, and 2 bathrooms with 2 toilets and showers in each, a large dayroom with oak seating and a fully equipped kitchen with gas cooker. Cheesehouse is a self-contained bunkhouse with four bunks, ideal for a small family or group. It has a shower and toilet and is equipped with a kitchen having cooking rings, a microwave oven, toaster and kettle. The bunkhouses are 2 minutes' walk from a pub. Sorry, no dogs (working dogs on site).

DETAILS

■ **Open** - All year, arrive after 2pm on day of arrival and leave by 11am on departure.
■ **Number of beds** - Homestead 22: 1x10, 2x6. Cheesehouse 4: 1x4.
■ **Booking** - Recommended for weekends.
■ **Price per night** - From £15 per person. Sole use: Homestead £195, Cheesehouse £45. Minimum of 2 night booking for Homestead at weekends or phone for a quote for a single night fee.
■ **Public Transport** - Nearest train station Bamford, 10 minutes' walk. Bus 274 & 275 operates Sundays Bamford to Sheffield or Castleton. Bus 272 Bamford to Sheffield and Castleton. Bus 241 Bamford to Bakewell.
■ **Directions** - The farm is in the centre of Bamford on South View Lane (turn off A6013 at the 'Country Stores').

CONTACT: Helena Platts
Tel: 01433 651298

The Farm, Bamford, Hope Valley, S33 0BL

DALEHEAD
BUNKHOUSE

Dalehead Bunkhouse is a renovated gritstone farmhouse on a working hill-farm at the remote head of Edale Valley. Providing basic but comfortable accommodation heated by log burner supplemented by infrared radiant heat. There is a kitchen with fridge/freezer, a lounge, dining room and plenty of parking. Visitors must bring their own sleeping bags, pillows and towels. Edale is a very popular destination for walkers, climbers, mountain bikers, hang-gliders or for just enjoying the magnificent scenery. It lies between the gritstone of the peat-topped Kinder moors to the north and the cave-riddled limestone of the White Peak to the south. Despite its proximity to major cities and the straightforward rail service to Sheffield and Manchester, the Dark Peak remains unspoilt, with many places where it is possible to enjoy a sense of remoteness. Dogs are welcome on the ground floor of the bunkhouse.

DETAILS

- **Open** - All year, 24 hours.
- **Number of beds** - 20: 1x6, 1x8, 1x6
- **Booking** - Via National Trust central booking system 0344 335 1296
- **Price per night** - Weekdays (Mon-Thurs) £190 per night. Weekends (Fri-Sun) £275 per night. Minimum of 2 nights bookings on Fri,Sat and Sun, 3 nights for a bank holiday. Dogs £15 per dog per stay. Prices subject to review for 2017.
- **Public Transport** - Trains at Edale (2 miles) to Sheffield and Manchester. Taxi service only available from Hope Station. Nearest bus station at Castleton (3 miles).
- **Directions** - SK101841 (OS map no. 110). At the western end of the dale 2 miles from Edale church .

CONTACT: National Trust Holiday Bookings
Tel: 0344 3351296
bunkhouses@nationaltrust.org.uk www.nationaltrustholidays.org.uk/
bunkhouses/dalehead-bunkhouse/
Dalehead Bunkhouse, Upper Booth, Edale, Hope Valley, S33 7ZJ

JOHN HUNT
BASE

The John Hunt Base, part of Hagg Farm Outdoor Education Centre, offers comfortable accommodation in a converted 18th century hill farm in the Upper Derwent Valley. With stunning views across the open moors of the Dark Peak, walks from the door lead onto the high moors of Kinder and Bleaklow and around the Ladybower reservoirs and dams. The Hagg Farm descent cycle route passes close by and there is secure storage for mountain bikes and bike washing facilities. The Base has a lounge/dining area with TV/DVD, well equipped kitchen, showers & toilets with good wheelchair access throughout. Sleep in 2 dormitories sleeping 6 and 8 and 2 twin bed rooms. All bedding is provided and groups have sole use of the base during their stay. In the grounds are a wildlife garden, field, artificial climbing boulder, Jacob's ladder, climbing tower and access to woodland. Instructional support for various outdoor activities such as climbing, caving, gorge walking, canoeing etc may be booked in advance. The site is also ideal for quiet pursuits and retreats. A popular base for walking/cycling groups as well as friends and family re-unions.

DETAILS

- **Open** - All year. Office open Mon - Fri 9am - 4.30pm
- **Number of beds** - 18: 1 x 8, 1 x 6, 2 x 2
- **Booking** - Advance booking essential.
- **Price per night** - £275 minimum 2 night stay. Outdoor activity instruction for 12 people from £280 per day. Hire of boots & equipment £5 per person per day.
- **Public Transport** - Trains at Bamford (7 miles away) on the Hope Valley Line.
- **Directions** - From Ladybower Reservoir junction take the A57 3 miles west towards Glossop, lookout for a sign to Hagg Farm on the right.

CONTACT: Tel: 01433 651594
haggfarm@nottscc.gov.uk www.nottinghamshire.gov.uk/haggfarm
Hagg Farm OEC, Snake Rd, Bamford, Hope Valley, S33 0BJ

Nottinghamshire
County Council

FOUNDRY
ADVENTURE CENTRE

Foundry Activity Centre has 2 units, Kinder; 31 beds and Howden; 21 beds, they can be combined to provide total 52 beds. With easy access to all parts of the Peak District National Park, the centre is an ideal location for outdoor activities and touring, welcoming a wide range of groups including schools, universities, corporate, clubs and large families. The spacious centre includes; comfortable lounges with a library, TV and wood burning stove, equipped kitchens and dining areas, four bathrooms and warm drying facilities. Bunks in rooms of 2 - 8 have optional bedding provision. There is parking for 20 plus vehicles with flat hard surfaced and grass areas for activities on site. Surrounding farmland and woodland can be accessed via an extensive network of footpaths. The centre is an AALA licensed provider and can also offer a wide range of adventure activities including abseiling, caving, climbing, hill walking, mountain biking & watersports. These can be combined to create a range of team building and personal development courses.

DETAILS

- **Open** - All year, all day.
- **Number of beds** - 52
- **Booking** - Group bookings for minimum 20 people.
- **Price per night** - From £17 per person per night
- **Public Transport** - Buses and trains via Hope Valley
- **Directions** - A623 (Chesterfield to Chapel en le frith), follow to Tideswell junction. Turn for Bradwell, take first right for Great Hucklow. On approaching the village, turn right at Queen Anne pub, then first right after 100m.

CONTACT: Tim Gould
Tel: 01298 873029 Mob: 07786 332702
info@foundrymountain.co.uk www.greatadventures.co.uk/foundrymountain/foundry_adventure_centre/
The Old Playhouse, Great Hucklow, Derbyshire, SK17 8RF

OLLERBROOK FARM
BUNKHOUSES

Ollerbrook Farm Bunkhouses are located in the heart of the stunning Peak District countryside. Situated on a working hill farm which dates back to the 16th century, the barns are close to the start of the Pennine Way and offer easy access to Kinder Scout. A short walk away is the village of Edale with a village store, two pubs serving food, railway station and Moorlands Info Centre. This is ideal walking country, with a network of footpaths direct from the doorstep, including a walk with stunning views over the Mam Tor ridge to Castleton, a pretty tourist village famous for its Christmas lights, show caves and gift shops. Buxton, Bakewell and Chatsworth House are all within 40 minutes' drive. Nab View, converted in 2016, sleeps 18 in 3 rooms, whilst the Stables Bunkhouse has 4 rooms sleeping 4. The bunks have a bottom sheet and pillow case, bring your sleeping bag. Each bunkhouse has a fully equipped kitchen, dining area, modern showers and toilets, cycle store and car parking. Book sole use or by the bed and share the barn. Weekends reserved for groups until close to date.

DETAILS

- **Open** - All year, all day. Arrive after 4pm depart before 10.30am.
- **Number of beds** - 34: Nab View 18: 3x6, Stables Bunkhouse 16: 4x4
- **Booking** - Deposit required with booking, remainder to be paid 4 weeks in advance of stay. Weekends reserved for groups until 3 weeks prior to stay.
- **Price per night** - Nab View: £300 (min 2 nights), The Stables: midweek £200, weekends £210 (min 2 nights). Enquire for longer stays and prices per room or bed.
- **Public Transport** - Less than half a mile from Edale train station
- **Directions** - Follow signs for Ollerbrook Booth from Edale or footpath from station.

CONTACT: Sheila
Tel: 01433 670235
ollerbrookfarm@gmail.com www.ollerbrookfarm.co.uk
Ollerbrook Farm, Ollerbrook Booth, Edale, Hope Valley, Derbyshire, S33 7ZG

BUSHEY HEATH
FARM

Bushey Heath Farm is a family run smallholding in the heart of the Peak District, central to all the popular visitor centres, offering a pre-booking group summer campsite and bunkbarns for up to 28 people in three self contained units. The farm has been developed in an environmentally sensitive way with ground source heating, a wind turbine for electricity and rainwater harvesting for wc flushing, so visitors can experience practical sustainable ideas. The Hen House bunkbarn has two bedrooms with bunks for 4 in each. The Little Barn has a large single bedroom with bunks for 6 people. Hadfield Barn sleeps 14 in two rooms of 6 and 8. All have luxury shower rooms and a combined fully equipped kitchen/diner open area. Sleeping bags/duvets/sheet required. Well behaved dogs accepted by prior arrangement.

DETAILS

- **Open** - All year. Group only campsite May - October. Opening hours by arrangement.
- **Number of beds** - 8: Hen House, 6: Little Barn, 14: Hadfield Barn.
- **Booking** - Camping: always. Bunkhouse: early with deposit advisable.
- **Price per night** - Bunkbarns: for sole use, Hen House: £160. Little Barn: £120. Hadfield Barn: £280. All per night (min. 2 night)
- **Public Transport** - Nearest trains at Hope (4 miles). Nearest buses in Tideswell (2 miles). Bus numbers 65, 66, x67, 173, 177, 197, 202.
- **Directions** - GR SK 146 785. From Tideswell take Manchester Road past Star Pub and cross over A623, road stops at farm. Going west along A623, 1.5 miles past the Anchor Pub turn right at crossroads in 's' bends.

CONTACT: Rod or Lisa Baraona
Tel: 01298 873007 9am-8pm only.
busheyheathfarm@gmail.com www.busheyheathfarm.com
Tideswell Moor, Tideswell, Buxton, Derbyshire, SK17 8JE

With its own crags, streams, lakes and over 100-acres of mature woodland, the hidden Shining Cliff Hostel has nature on its doorstep. The hostel is ideal for groups wishing to enjoy time away in a peaceful woodland setting. The entrance porch, with space for hanging coats and boots, leads into the open plan kitchen, dining and lounge area. The well equipped kitchen, has a 6 ring gas hob, electric oven, microwave, fridge, freezer, dishwasher and water boiler. The dining area comfortably seats 20 people whilst the lounge provides seating and space to relax. 5 bedrooms sleep up to 20 people in bunk beds. Please bring your own sleeping bags and pillowcases. Three bathrooms each have a shower cubicle and composting toilet (similar to airline toilets not holes in the ground!). Shining Cliff hostel offers a full range of activities; on-site enjoy bushcraft, abseiling, ecology and environmental art, or travel a little further afield for climbing, caving or canoeing. Activities must be booked in advance. There is a ten minute walk, down a very rough track, from the nearest parking area. Paths lead through the woods to the A6 at Ambergate (20 mins' walk) which has a food shop, pubs, buses and trains to Derby. Sole use only.

DETAILS

- **Open** - All year.
- **Number of beds** - 20: 1 x 4, 2 x 6, 2 x 2
- **Booking** - Phone or email
- **Price per night** - Enquire for prices and availability. Sole use bookings only.
- **Public Transport** - Ambergate rail station (1 mile). Transpeak bus on A6 (1 mile)
- **Directions** - See website for directions. Sat Navs NOT recommended.

CONTACT:
Tel: 01433 620377
enquiries@shiningcliff.org www.shiningcliff.org
Jackass Lane, Alderwasley Belper, DE56 2RE

UNDERBANK
CAMPING BARN

Located on Blaze Farm, a dairy farm, café, ice cream parlour and pottery painting studio on the western edge of the Peak District National Park. This lovely little barn overlooks the Wildboarclough Valley and is close to the stunning viewpoint on Shuttlingsloe Fell.

The barn provides the perfect, simple base for walking, climbing, fell-running and mountain biking in and around in this beautiful landscape. The sleeping area is on the first floor, with the living area and a kitchen area with fridge. There is a toilet and shower below. Bring your own sleeping bag, camping mattresses and a stove plus all cooking equipment if you wish to self cater. Blaze Farm ice-cream parlour and café serves snacks and light meals from 10am, and there are several good pubs nearby. Come and explore the farm's own nature trails.

DETAILS

- **Open** - All year, arrive at 4pm leave at 10am (earlier arrivals by arrangement).
- **Number of beds** - 10
- **Booking** - Phone, send a message or email. Booking not available via the YHA.
- **Price per night** - From £9.50. Sole use of 10 bed barn: £95.00 per night. Electricity is metered, so please bring change.
- **Public Transport** - Train at Macclesfield (7 miles)
- **Directions** - 10 miles from Congleton and 7 miles from Buxton and Macclesfield. Travelling on the A54 from Congleton, Blaze Farm is the second farm access on the left hand side after the Rose and Crown pub. When travelling from Buxton, Blaze Farm is the second farm access on the right hand side after the turning for Wildboarclough.

CONTACT: Caroline & Marshall Waller
Tel: 01260 227 266
thesheeponthehill@gmail.com www.underbankbarn.co.uk
Blaze Farm, Wildboarclough, Macclesfied, Cheshire, SK11 0BL

Wandering Duck is a unique fully hosted canal boat experience of 2 or 3 nights on board a 69ft narrowboat. Trips take place around Manchester, Cheshire and Derbyshire. Come on your own or with friends and join a tour, or charter Wandering Duck for your own private small group (max 8 people). These experiences are very hands on and you'll be shown how to work the locks and encouraged to have a go at steering the boat, all under the watchful eye of our experienced crew. Choose between the 2 or 3 Night Canal Boat Adventure travelling between Manchester City Centre and the edge of the Peak District or the 2 Night Canal Boat Escape journeying through stunning Cheshire Countryside between Marple and Congleton. Most meals are included in the price of the trip, as are hot drinks and home-made cake. On board you will find an honesty bar, games, and an ipod dock. As well as many walking options, fishing gear is available free of charge.

DETAILS

- **Open** - March to October, 24 hrs.
- **Number of beds** - 8: 2x4
- **Booking** - Website or phone
- **Price per night** - 2 night tour £145: 3 night tour £195: Charter the boat from £920. Tours include: accommodation on the boat, fully hosted experience, meals & cake.
- **Public Transport** - All trips are one-way and start and finish within walking distance of train stations.
- **Directions** - See website for details. Detailed directions sent with your booking confirmation.

CONTACT: Roberta
Tel: 07584 122614
duckmail@wanderingduck.co.uk www.wanderingduck.co.uk
Wandering Duck, C/O Baileys Trading Post, Lyme Road, Higher Poynton, Cheshire, SK12 1TH

HATTERS HOSTELS
ON HILTON STREET

Hatters on Hilton Street brings new meaning to 'flash packing'! Your ideal choice for city centre accommodation in the heart of the bohemian Northern Quarter, with a combination of hotel quality en suite rooms with the social atmosphere of an international travellers' hostel. Catering for groups of all sizes and independent travellers, you can enjoy the benefits of WiFi, breakfast, en suite and standard rooms, large communal and outdoor areas, and enthusiastic, informative staff. Full board or half board options for groups of over 15. Convenient for all city centre attractions and transport links. Ask about discounts to Alton Towers, and about Man Utd and City football stadium tours and, lest we forget, all that is FREE to do in Manchester...We are more than happy to help. Also a great base for day trips to the Peak District. Come and enjoy our hospitality and explore all that Manchester has to offer!

DETAILS

- **Open** - All year, 24 hour reception. Check in 2pm, check out 11am.
- **Number of beds** - 155; single, twin, double, triple, 4, 6, 8, and 12 bed rooms
- **Booking** - Booking not essential but recommended especially at weekends, with credit/debit card. Photo ID (eg. passport, driving license) required on check in. For group bookings please contact groups@hattersgroup.com
- **Price per night** - From £12 dorms, from £32 private rooms. All rooms include en suite, linen and breakfast. For group prices and bookings see http://www.hattershostels.com/groups or email: groups@hattersgroup.com
- **Public Transport** - Only 5 minutes' walk from Picadilly train and bus stations and Shudehill bus station, and 10 minutes' walk from Victoria train station.
- **Directions** - Please contact the hostel reception for details.

CONTACT: Reception
Tel: 0161 236 4414
hilton@hattersgroup.com www.hattersgroup.com/#mcr
15 Hilton Street, Manchester, M1 1JJ

HATTERS HOSTELS
ON NEWTON STREET ENGLAND

Recently refurbished to its 100 year old splendour and winner of the Manchester Tourism Customer Care award, Hatters has firmly established itself as the city's favourite funky hostel. The city centre location makes it the ideal spot to start exploring the north west of England. Hatters caters for independent travellers and groups. It has a fully serviced kitchen with seating for groups of up to 50 and FREE all-day continental breakfast. Enjoy the FREE all-day coffee while using the FREE WiFi, or choose to socialise with other like-minded travellers and staff. We also offer full board or half board options for groups over 15 people. Let the knowledgeable and friendly staff guide you to the best that this great city has to offer, from live music and football to restaurants, shopping, museums, pubs and clubs.

DETAILS

■ **Open** - All year. 24 hour reception. Check in 2pm, check out 11am.
■ **Number of beds** - 170. Private double/ single rooms. Dorm sizes include 18 bed, 10 bed, 6 bed and 4 bed.
■ **Booking** - Booking recommended, with credit/debit card, especially at weekends. Photo ID is required at check in. Group bookings contact groups@hattersgroup.com.
■ **Price per night** - From £12 for dorms and from £32 for private rooms. Overnight price includes linen and breakfast. For group prices and bookings see http://www.hattershostels.com/groups or email: groups@hattersgroup.com
■ **Public Transport** - Easy walking distance from all public transport hubs: Picadilly train station 5mins, Picadilly bus station 5mins, Shudehill bus station 5mins, Victoria train station 10mins
■ **Directions** - Please contact the hostel reception for directions.

CONTACT: Reception
Tel: 0161 236 9500
Manchester@hattersgroup.com www.hattersgroup.com
50 Newton Street, Manchester, M1 2EA

EMBASSIE
LIVERPOOL BACKPACKERS

The Embassie is a terraced house in an unspoilt Georgian square used in the filming of 'In the Name of the Father'. The house was built in 1820 and until 1986 it was the Consulate of Venezuela. Only 15 minutes' walk from the centre of Liverpool, known for its nightlife. A large student population ensures a lively scene, with late night bands and bars. The hostel has been refurbished and there are new kitchen facilities, a brand new shower suite and an all new games room and relax area with Sky Sports and HD television. Hostellers have a key to come and go. The hostel is clean, safe and staffed 24 hours. Bedding is provided (including sheets) and free coffee, tea, toast and jam are available 24 hours, eat as much as you want. International, or UK regional travellers only. Free Beatles guided tour every Thursday night at 8pm including free admission to the world famous Cavern Club (and free piece of Beatle memorabilia). The only tour given by a tour guide who saw the Beatles perform.

DETAILS

- **Open** - All year, 24 hr access.
- **Number of beds** - 50
- **Booking** - not essential for individuals. Groups over 6 should book (25% deposit).
- **Price per night** - £18 (Sunday to Thursday), £24 Friday, £28 Saturday
- **Public Transport** - Liverpool has a train station and is served by National Express Coaches. A £5.00 taxi fare will bring you from the train or bus station to the hostel door, (good idea if you have a heavy rucksack).
- **Directions** - From the Anglican Cathedral (the third largest in the world) continue uphill along Canning Street away from the city centre. This will bring you into Falkner Square (15-20 mins). The hostel has a red door and is by a phone box.

CONTACT: Kevin
Tel: 0151 7071089
embassie@gmail.com www.embassie.com
1 Falkner Square, Liverpool, L8 7NU

EURO HOSTEL
LIVERPOOL
ENGLAND

The newest addition to the Euro Hostel family, Euro Hostel Liverpool is right in the heart of the city. A perfect base from which to experience Liverpool's legendary night life, shopping and waterfront walks. Whether you are a backpacker, couple, family or part of a group Euro Hostel Liverpool has a room for you. Rooms vary from 8 bed dorms (mixed or female only), en suite private rooms for up to 8 people or VIP suites accommodating groups of 6 or 8 in bunks with private TV lounge and en suite facilities. Looking for somewhere to eat or drink? The Hatch bar on the ground floor is right on Mathew Street and is a great live music venue as well as providing good quality food and drink. Breakfast is also available to purchase in the Hatch bar and there are 2 other bars within the hostel building. Discounted car parking is available at NCP at Vernon Street (L2 2AY) you will be provided with a discount ticket from reception on check out.

DETAILS

- **Open** - All year, all day.
- **Number of beds** - 200 approximately.
- **Booking** - By phone or online. 12% non refundable deposit required
- **Price per night** - From £12.50 pp
- **Public Transport** - Train: Liverpool Lime Street (closest station James St). National Buses.
- **Directions** - Walking from James St Station turn left from station entrance onto James St. Turn left onto Castle St and then right onto Harrington St. Turn left onto Rainford Square, right onto Matthew St then turn right onto Stanley St.

CONTACT: Reception
Tel: +44 (0) 845 490 0971
liverpool@eurohostels.co.uk www.eurohostels.co.uk/liverpool/
54 Stanley Street, Liverpool L1 6AU

HATTERS HOSTELS
LIVERPOOL

Your ideal choice for city central accommodation, Hatters Liverpool has combined hotel quality en suite rooms with the social atmosphere of an international travellers' hostel. Catering for groups of all sizes and independent travellers, you can enjoy the comforts of WiFi, continental breakfast, en suite rooms, large communal areas and enthusiastic, informative staff. We also offer full board or half board options for groups of over 15. Conveniently located for all city centre attractions and transport links, ask the reception staff about discounts to Alton Towers, Beatles tours, football stadium tours, Albert Docks, or many other FREE adventures....The perfect base for day trips to the historic city of Chester, Chester Zoo, or the majestic Lake District. Come and stay and enjoy what is making Liverpool one of the UK's top tourist destinations!. Three star graded by Quality in Tourism.

DETAILS

- **Open** - All year, 24 hour reception. Check in after 2pm, check out 11am.
- **Number of beds** - 300 beds; single, double, twin, triple, 4, 6, 8 and 12 bed rooms.
- **Booking** - Booking not essential but recommended, especially at weekends. We require photo I.D (passport/drivers' licence) and credit/ debit card. For all group bookings please contact groups@hattersgroup.com
- **Price per night** - From £12 for dorms and from £32 for privates. Prices include en suite, linen and breakfast. For group prices and bookings see http://www.hattershostels.com/groups or email: groups@hattersgroup.com
- **Public Transport** - Within walking distance of all public transport hubs. Liverpool Lime Street Station – 5mins, Northern Street Coach Station – 15mins
- **Directions** - Please contact the hostel reception for directions

CONTACT: Reception
Tel: 0151 709 5570
liverpool@hattersgroup.com www.hattersgroup.com/#lpool
56-60 Mount Pleasant, Liverpool, L3 5SH

THE OLD SMITHY
CAMPING BARN
ENGLAND

The Old Smithy camping barn was at one time the village fire station. This "stone-tent" is situated in the village of Burwardsley, Cheshire, mid-way along the Sandstone Trail, one of the finest long distance walks in North West England. The barn is also on NCN route 45 Mercian Way. The Old Smithy offers affordable country accommodation for up to 8 people. Ideal for families or groups of walkers, cyclists and others visiting this part of Cheshire or wanting to get closer to nature. There is an area for cooking & washing up, a toilet and an insulated sleeping platform. There is no electricity or hot water, nor beds. Bring your own sleeping bag and roll mat. Lighting is via lanterns (candles and matches provided). You can pre-order bacon and sausage sandwiches at an extra cost when booking. You can also pre-book or buy food and hot drinks at Burwardsley Post Office & Village Shop (5 min walk). The nearest pub is The Pheasant Inn. Also close by is the Candle Workshop, Cheshire Fishery and the Ice Cream Farm. Bikes can be locked away overnight. Dogs welcome.

DETAILS

- **Open** - All year, 24 hours. Pre-arrange arrival times.
- **Number of beds** - 8: 1 x 8
- **Booking** - By phone or email. All bookings must be paid in full to be guaranteed.
- **Price per night** - £8 per person per night. Exclusive use £50 per night.
- **Public Transport** - The nearest train station is Chester (10 miles) with an hourly bus service to Tattenhall (2 miles).
- **Directions** - The Barn is on Burwardsley Road, close to the Post Office. Grid reference: 513 569 OS Landranger No.117

CONTACT: Rachel and Phillip
Tel: 01829 770359
filws@yahoo.com
Burwardsley Post Office & Village Store, Harthill Road, Burwardsley, Cheshire CH3 9NU

SCARBOROUGH
YOUTH HOSTEL

Once a 17th century water mill, set on a quiet riverside, two miles north of the town and 15 minutes' walk from Scalby Mills and the North Bay. Scarborough Youth Hostel provides quality low-cost accommodation for families, school, college, university and sports groups as well as individuals who wish to enjoy, explore, or simply unwind on the beautiful North Yorkshire coast. Two long sandy beaches, miles of rugged coastline, and one of the UK's largest areas of forest and moorland, make Scarborough the perfect base for activity breaks with excellent walking, cycling, surfing and sailing. There is plenty for those interested in birds, wildlife, history, geology and the seashore. Scarborough regularly hosts live concerts and festivals, TT racing, surf competitions and theatre productions. Use our well equipped kitchen or enjoy a cooked breakfast in the dining room. Sole use available for large groups. School/group packages:breakfast, packed lunch & evening meals as required.

DETAILS

- **Open** - All year, 7.30 - 10.00 am and 5.00 - 10.00 pm.
- **Number of beds** - 46: 5x6, 4x4.
- **Booking** - Phone 01723 361176 or search for Scarborough on YHA website.
- **Price per night** - Beds from £13, rooms from £45, discounts for YHA members.
- **Public Transport** - Bus or train to Scarborough, No 3 or 3A bus from York Place to Sea Life Centre, get off at The Ivanhoe. 5 min walk past the Gulf SS and bridge.
- **Directions** - A165 two miles north of town centre, past Gulf service station, then sharp left after the brick bridge (in a car make a U-turn after the hostel and then turn right). By foot: leave the Cleveland Way at the Helmsley sign, walk to Burniston Road turn left down the hill to the hostel drive.

CONTACT: Robert Fletcher
Tel: 01723 361176
scarboroughhostel@gmail.com www.scarboroughhostel.com
The White House, Burniston Road, Scarborough, YO13 0DA

STABLESIDE
YORK
ENGLAND

Stableside is proud to be a 4 Star rated hostel within the historic and beautiful city of York. Guests are afforded a true Yorkshire welcome and can take advantage of easy access by road, rail, bus and bike. Stableside has free car and coach parking, free WiFi and a secure, spacious and self contained location with landscaped gardens. Stableside offers a variety of room options and can cater for all from the single traveller to larger hobby groups.

There's a spacious dining room with cafeteria style seating up to 100 and a large lounge on the first floor suitable for conferences. A sports field adjoins the complex and the centre lies on the NCN Route 65 which gives traffic free access into the centre of town. Stableside has secure bike storage. Meals can be provided for groups, B&B (full English breakfast), D,B&B and full board packages available. From the quality of our breakfasts to the warmth of our welcome. Stableside is an ideal base to visit York and the surrounding county.

DETAILS

- **Open** - All year (except during race meetings), all day.
- **Number of beds** - 133: 2x6, 21x4, 8x triple, 1x twin, 11 x single.
- **Booking** - Booking essential, by phone or email
- **Price per night** - £70 for a twin room including breakfast Towels included. Enquire for school group rates.
- **Public Transport** - Trains: 20 min walk. City centre buses every 10 mins.
- **Directions** - Situated on the right hand side of the A1036 Tadcaster Road as you head towards York city centre, opposite the Fox & Roman pub.

CONTACT: Fay
Tel: 01904 620 911 ext. 284
fay.waudby@yorkracecourse.co.uk www.stablesideyork.co.uk
Stableside, York Racing Stables, York, YO24 1QG

HALIFAX COLLEGE
HOSTEL

Halifax College is situated in a peaceful location in York, within walking distance of Heslington Village and the University of York campus. Halifax College is the perfect base for exploring the city. York is famous for the iconic York Minster, exquisite architecture and a tangle of quaint cobbled streets called The Shambles. York has boutique shopping, a vibrant café and restaurant culture and world class museums such as the National Railway Museum and the unique Jorvik Centre. These all make York a great city break or educational trip.

The accommodation is let on a self-catering basis and no meals are included in the rate. All rooms are single occupancy with a wash basin in each room and the use of shared bathroom and self catering facilities within the house. There are a maximum of 11 bedrooms in each house. Internet access is available with the City of York's free WiFi CityConnect, where guests can log-in using social media or a signup form.

DETAILS

- **Open** - July 2017 - 17th September 2017
- **Number of beds** - 51
- **Booking** - Book online via the website
- **Price per night** - £26.00
- **Public Transport** - York rail station 3.4 miles. The No.66 bus runs to/from campus every 10-15 mins journey time approximately 15 minutes depending on traffic. A taxi to campus from the station takes c.15mins and costs approximately £8.00
- **Directions** - For directions and maps please visit www.york.ac.uk/about/maps

CONTACT: Reception
Tel: 01904 328431
conferences@york.ac.uk www.yorkconferences.com/events/venue
Halifax College Reception, Garrowby Way, York, YO10 5GH

BANK HOUSE FARM
HOSTEL

ENGLAND

A luxury Bunk Barn and a simple Camping Barn on a working organic farm with farmhouse B&B. Set in beautiful Glaisdale Dale, with stunning views of the North York Moors. The Bunk Barn is a modern barn conversion with under-floor heating, large comfy kitchen/dining/living room with sofas, drying room, showers and private toilets. Picnic BBQ area and garden with panoramic views. There is one large dorm with 9 single beds and one bunkbed, each equipped with sheet and pillow. Bring your own sleeping bag/duvet and towel. The Camping Barn provides simple, single-night shelter for those walking or cycling with their own sleeping bags and cooking equipment. Duvet & towel hire £5. DIY breakfast £5. The farm's beef & lamb is available, bring other food with you, or arrange a supermarket delivery. Wainwright's Coast to Coast route 1m (collection possible), Whitby & Jurassic coast 12m, steam trains 3m, Esk Valley walk 3m.

DETAILS

- **Open** - All year. 9am-9pm for phone calls.
- **Number of beds** - Bunk Barn: 1x11
- **Booking** - Booking essential. Deposit required, balance 4 weeks before arrival.
- **Price per night** - Bunkbarn: Weekends £500 (Fri,Sat,stay Sun for free), Bank Hols £700 (3 nights). Saturday £330. Midweek 1 night from £25pp. Ask for multiple day deals.Camping Barn: £12pp & Farmhouse B&B: £35 any night.
- **Public Transport** - Glaisdale train station 3miles. 'M&D Transport' minibus from Castleton to Whitby in Glaisdale village (2.5 miles). Nat. Express coaches at Whitby.
- **Directions** - From Glaisdale station go uphill through village and turn left at T junction 'Glaisdale Dale Only'. After 1 mile turn left by Witchpost Cottage. Pass New House Farm then turn left and follow farm track 1/3 mile to farmyard.

CONTACT: Chris or Emma Padmore
Tel: 01947 897297
info@bankhousefarmhostel.co.uk www.bankhousefarmhostel.co.uk
Bank House Farm, Glaisdale, Whitby YO21 2QA

COTE GHYLL
MILL

Situated in a beautiful and secluded valley in the North Yorkshire Moors National Park, this converted linen mill is perfect for those wishing to explore the Yorkshire moors, dales & coast. Close to walking, cycling and mountain biking routes, orienteering at Cod Beck Reservoir, pony trekking, fishing and golf. Osmotherley village has pubs, a tea room and shops. The stream and woodlands in the mill grounds provide exploration for children and adults. The Mill is bookable as a whole, by room (some en suite) or by bed. Great for educational groups, families, outdoor clubs and friends gatherings in a comfortable, great value venue. Fully catered or self-cater in the well equipped kitchen. Other facilities include licensed bar and lounge, TV/games room, pool table, free WiFi, large garden, bike store, meeting rooms,laundry & drying room. Bedrooms and showers newly refurbished. New self-catering annex, sleeps10.

DETAILS

■ **Open** - All year, 7am -10am, 5pm-9pm.
■ **Number of beds** - 78: Mill 68: 1x2,5x4,7x6 +4 rollout beds, Annex:10.
■ **Booking** - Advanced booking recommended – especially for groups
■ **Price per night** - Adults from £20.00. Under18's from £13. Family rooms from £33. For group and sole occupancy please contact the Mill.
■ **Public Transport** - Train to Northallerton, from the station the 80 or 89 bus (for Stokesley) stops in the centre of Osmotherley the hostel is a 10 min walk (1/4mile).
■ **Directions** - From A19 or Northallerton A684 towards Osmotherley or Teeside into Osmotherley. At the T junction/village cross turn left. Cote Ghyll Mill is ¼ mile out of the village on the right, just after the Caravan and Camping Park

CONTACT: Reception
Tel: 01609 883425
mill@coteghyll.com www.coteghyll.com
Osmotherley, Northallerton, North Yorkshire, DL6 3AH

WEST END
OUTDOOR CENTRE

Situated amidst stunning landscape overlooking Thruscross Reservoir in an AONB on the edge of the Yorkshire Dales National Park, this self-catering centre offers excellent facilities for up to 30 people in 9 bedrooms with bunk beds. The centre is fully centrally heated. Accommodation is in small dorms of 2 to 6 beds and the leaders' en suite accommodation has dining and lounge facilities. The main kitchen is well equipped with a 4-oven Aga cooker, two fridges and a freezer, together with all the cooking utensils and equipment. There are 4 showers, 4 hand basins and 4 toilets. There are no extra charges for heating, lighting and hot water. Ideal for team building courses, schools, Scouts, Guides and family parties etc. Located only 12 miles from Harrogate and Skipton, 30 miles from the City of York. Managed by the owners for 20 years. All groups must be accompanied by an adult (25+). No stag or hens.

DETAILS

■ **Open** - All year, flexible.
■ **Number of beds** - 30: 4x2, 3x4, 1x6, 1 x 4 en suite
■ **Booking** - Advisable at weekends
■ **Price per night** - £15pp (minimum charge £30). Sole use (Fri, Sat & bank holidays) £350 per night (min stay 2 nights). Midweek £230 (minimum stay 2 nights) or £350 for one night. £780 for 4 nights midweek, £1100 for 7 nights not starting on a Saturday.
■ **Public Transport** - Nearest train stations are at Harrogate and Skipton, both 12 miles from the hostel. Taxi fare from either station would be approximately £22.
■ **Directions** - GR 146 575. Leave A59 at Blubberhouses, signed West End 2.5 miles. Do not turn off, centre is on left side.

CONTACT: Hedley or Margaret Verity
Tel: 01943 880207
info@westendoutdoorcentre.co.uk www.westendoutdoorcentre.co.uk
West End, Summerbridge, Harrogate, HG3 4BA

HEBDEN BRIDGE
HOSTEL

Hebden Bridge Hostel provides accommodation in small dorms, private rooms and a 6-bed bunkroom, all en suite. Nestled into woodland only a short walk from the town centre, the hostel makes the perfect base for hiking, sight-seeing, relaxing or experiencing Hebden Bridge's vibrant café, music, arts & culture. Less than 500m from the Hebden Bridge Loop on the Pennine Way, the Calderdale Way, Hardcastle Crags, Route 66, Mary Townley and Le Tour 2014 cycle route. All-day access is to the lobby. No evening curfew but please respect other guests. Bed linen provided in dorms and private rooms. Bring sleeping bag and pillow for the budget bunkroom. Free internet, WiFi. Self-catering, vegetarian-only kitchen. Light breakfast & tea/coffee included.

DETAILS

- **Open** - Easter to November. Whole-hostel bookings possible all year round. Check-in 5-8pm, check-out by 10am.
- **Number of beds** - Up to 33 : 6x4 (or 2), 1x3 (or 2), 1x6
- **Booking** - recommended but not essential (full payment on booking).
- **Price per night** - Bunk-room £15pp. Small dorm £20pp. Twin £55. Double £60. Double+1 £75. Private 4-bed room £75. Midweek single £35. Sole use available.
- **Public Transport** - 15 minutes' walk from Hebden Bridge train station (frequent, quick service to Leeds and Manchester). Buses from the station stop outside the Birchcliffe Centre (Dodd Naze Circular). Coach stations in Bradford and Leeds.
- **Directions** - From train station turn left onto main Burnley Rd, then right (towards Keighley), right again (Birchcliffe Rd). Hostel is 400m up hill, behind Birchcliffe Centre.

CONTACT: Em or Dave
Tel: 01422 843183
mama@hebdenbridgehostel.co.uk www.hebdenbridgehostel.co.uk
The Birchcliffe Centre, Hebden Bridge, W Yorks, HX7 8DG

EARBY
ENGLAND FRIENDS OF NATURE HOUSE

The Friends of Nature (FoN) invite you to stay in this beautiful historic cottage in the peaceful village of Earby, Lancashire. Earby Friends of Nature House is a cosy cottage with a picturesque garden, stream and waterfall close to the Pennine Way. An ideal stop for the Pennine Way walker, as a base for local day hikes and for cyclists and those interested in the countryside and local heritage. Particularly suited to individuals, families and small groups. There are 2 comfortable lounges, a well equipped kitchen and seating for 18 in the dining areas. Real ale pub and meals nearby. Breakfast café in village and late stop Co-op. Secure bike storage. On-line booking. Visit Britain 3* Hostel, 'Walkers Welcome', and 'Cyclists Welcome'. Friends of Nature is one of Europe's oldest environmental groups with 600k members and 800 houses across Europe. Under 16s must be accompanied by adult aged 18 or over and of same sex if in shared dormitory.

DETAILS

■ **Open** - Opening March 2017. Available all year for sole-use bookings. Open from March to November for all guests.

■ **Number of beds** - 22 beds in 1x2, 2x6 and 1x8 bed rooms.

■ **Booking** - Book via website, email or phone. Verbal bookings held until 6pm daily.

■ **Price per night** - Adults from £15 and under 18's from £13. Members of Friends of Nature and IFN pay the discounted rate.

■ **Public Transport** - Skipton-Burnley bus (hourly) drops ½ mile from Hostel. Skipton rail station for Leeds and Settle–Carlisle line, and Colne for Manchester

■ **Directions** - Grid Ref SD915469. Geo-Coords 53.918065, -2.13064. 7 miles west of Skipton. In Earby village off the A56 Skipton-Colne road, 300m past Red Lion pub.

CONTACT: Manager
Tel: 01282 842349
earby@thefriendsofnature.org.uk www.thefriendsofnature.org.uk
9-11 Birch Hall Lane, Earby, Lancashire, BB18 6JX

AIRTON BARN
FRIENDS MEETING HOUSE ENGLAND

The recently renovated Airton Camping Barn offers overnight accommodation for up to 16 people. The barn is situated in the quiet village of Airton in central Malhamdale, on the Pennine Way and the Way of the Roses cycle route. It is an easy walk from Malham Cove, Gordale Scar and Janet's Foss. The Three Peaks and Bronte Country are a short drive away and the barn is in 1652 country where the first Quakers gathered. The Meeting House has been used by Quakers since the 1650s, and now offers a warm welcome to cyclists, walkers, mountaineers and family groups. There is a bunk room with 6 beds and two multi-purpose rooms for which airbeds can be provided. The enclosed garden can accommodate up to 2 medium tents. There are two fully-fitted kitchens, two bathrooms and a separate toilet. Bedding can be hired on request and there is a small store of basic non-perishable food. Food can be ordered in advance and collected from the village farm shop. Secure cycle storage.

DETAILS

- **Open** - All year, warden resident on site.
- **Number of beds** - 6 bunk beds + 10 mattresses. Overflow camping for 2 tents.
- **Booking** - Advance booking essential.
- **Price per night** - £17pp. Larger groups call to discuss requirements and rates.
- **Public Transport** - Trains at Skipton (11 miles) and Gargrave (7 miles by road, 4 miles by Pennine Way). Limited buses from Skipton (via Gargrave) and Malham.
- **Directions** - Entering Airton from Gargrave take the first right. Barn is the 4th house on the right. Leave the Pennine Way at Airton Bridge, walk towards the village. The Barn is the first house on the left. Knock on the white door. GR SD 904592

CONTACT: The Friend in Residence
Tel: 01729 830263
airtonbarn@gmail.com www.airtonbarn.org.uk
The Nook, Airton, Skipton, North Yorkshire, BD23 4AE

WHITEFIELDS
COTTAGE

Situated in a medieval deer park, Whitefields Cottage offers self-catering accommodation within Fountains Abbey and Studley Royal Estate. Cared for by the National Trust and awarded World Heritage Site status in 1986, the estate contains a beautiful water garden, Elizabethan mansion and a Cistercian abbey. Whitefields is a 19th century cottage on the edge of Studley Royal Deer Park, home to around 350 red, fallow and sika deer.

Whether you want to explore the water gardens and impressive abbey, or walk around the North York moors (1hr drive) or Yorkshire Dales, Whitefields is ideal. It offers groups of up to 16 people inexpensive but comfortable accommodation.

DETAILS

- **Open** - All year, except Christmas and New Year, no restrictions.
- **Number of beds** - 16: 1x6, 1x8, 1x2.
- **Booking** - Bookings required 1 week in advance, non refundable deposit £60.
- **Price per night** - Mid week £140. Weekend (Fri/Sat) £180. Bookings of 7 nights or more charged at £140.00 night. £50 extra charge for 1 night stays at weekends
- **Public Transport** - Train station and National Express coaches at Harrogate (15 miles). Regular bus service between Harrogate and Ripon. Taxis Ripon to Whitefields £8 - Harrogate to Whitefields £20.
- **Directions** - From B6265 turn to Studley Roger. Drive through village, bear sharp right, before the National Trust sign, into deer park. Half a mile up main avenue turn right sign-posted 'estate vehicles only'. Turn right up the track at the end of this road, Whitefields is at top of track.

CONTACT: Andrew Moss
Tel: 01765 643172
andrew.moss@nationaltrust.org.uk   www.nationaltrust.org.uk/fountainsabbey
Fountains Abbey and Studley Royal Park, Fountains, Ripon, HG4 3DY

GRASSINGTON
BUNKBARN
ENGLAND

At almost 1000 feet, with spectacular views of Wharfedale, Grassington Bunkbarn offers comfortable accommodation for groups of up to 32 people in a magnificent location. The ground floor has 3 bunk rooms and a leader/disabled bedroom with private toilet/shower. On the upper floor there is a large dining area with open plan kitchen equipped for groups and a lounge/games area with Freeview TV, although you may be content with the dramatic views from the window! The barn has free WiFi and good mobile coverage. The ground floor has 3 bathrooms with 5 showers and 5 WCs along with a large drying room. The barn is heated by an environmentally sustainable wood pellet biomass boiler which fuels radiators in all the rooms and constant hot water. Outside there is a barbecue area, a large locked bike store and a large car park area. With walking, cycling, climbing, fishing, horse riding, archaeology, bird watching, geology, botany and even golf, the area has something for everyone.

 GROUPS ONLY

DETAILS

- **Open** - Reception 9am - 5pm Mon - Fri, Sat Sun 10am - 2pm.
- **Number of beds** - 34: 2 x 12, 1 x 6, 1 x 4
- **Booking** - 25% deposit, with balance 2 weeks before stay.
- **Price per night** - Weekends £980 (2 nights). Bank holidays (Friday 3 pm to Monday 11am) £1250. Mon–Thurs £390 per night. 4 night stay £295 per night. 7 night stay from £2040. Individual beds: please ring for availability @ £25 per night.
- **Public Transport** - Train to Skipton and then an hourly bus to Grassington. The bunkbarn is about 1.25miles from the nearest bus stop.
- **Directions** - Take B6265 to Grassington, turn up Main St. through village to the Town Hall, then carry on up the hill (Moor Lane) for 1/2 mile, bunkbarn is on the left .

CONTACT: Paul or Janet Kent
Tel: 01756 753882
enquiries@grassingtonbunkbarn.co.uk www.grassingtonbunkbarn.co.uk
Spring Croft, Moor Lane, Grassington, BD23 5BD

NIDDERDALE
BUNKHOUSE

Set in the stunning Nidderdale Valley Area of Natural Beauty, overlooking the Gouthwaite reservoir. Nidderdale Bunkhouse was newly opened in the summer of 2016. Matt and Bev, who also own Skirfare Barn (p192), have done a suburb job of converting this grand old shooting lodge. Sleeping up to 20 in 4 rooms, two of which are en suite. With two further bathrooms and 4 showers. There is a well equipped open plan kitchen and beautiful dining and seating areas with fantastic views over the valley and an open fire. There is also a large living room with comfy sofa seating for all. The Nidderdale Way walk goes right past the house. In nearby Ramsgill is the renowned Yorke Arms Michelin star restaurant. Pateley Bridge has pubs serving food and the Nidderdale Museum is a short drive away. Perfect for walkers and wildlife lovers with Gouthwaite Reservoir Nature Reserve a short walk away. Or a great base for starting your Yorkshire adventure. Sorry no dogs.

DETAILS

- **Open** - All year, all day.
- **Number of beds** - 20: 1x8, 3x4
- **Booking** - Please phone or email to book.
- **Price per night** - Week nights £285 (2 night min), Weekend from £850. Groups of more than 20 £20 per extra person.
- **Public Transport** - Buses from Harrogate to Ramsgill (15 min walk).
- **Directions** - From Ripon take the B6265 to Pateley Bridge. After crossing the bridge turn right onto Lower Wrath road (Upper Nidderdale). Follow this through Ramsgill. Nidderdale Bunkhouse is the third turning on the right.

CONTACT: Matt or Bev
Tel: 07597 645254
nidderdalebunkhouse@gmail.com www.nidderdalebunkhouse.com
Ramsgill, Harrogate, North Yorkshire HG3 5RH

KETTLEWELL
HOSTEL

The Kettlewell Hostel has 40 beds spread over eight bedrooms, a large dining room, serving the best cooked breakfasts, a bookshop, a well equipped self-catering kitchen, a lovely lounge with wood-burning stove and a nice garden to sit out in during the summer. There are dormitory rooms and private rooms, most with bunk beds and shared bathroom facilities. The hostel offers really good value, delicious home cooked evening meals and a great range of local ales and carefully selected wines. It is in the heart of Kettlewell which is well served by three great pubs and a village shop. There are lovely walks to be had right out of the front door including Great Whernside and Buckden Pike or you can join the Dales Way for a more gentle walk along the river Wharfe or over to Grassington. Kettlewell also makes a great base for touring the Yorkshire Dales, from here you can easily drive to Hawes, Malham or Skipton. There is a large cycle shed and some of the country's most fabulous riding including Park Rash, Fleet Moss and Buttertubs all right around the corner.

DETAILS

- **Open** - All year. Reception times: 08.00 - 10.30 16.00 - 22.00.
- **Number of beds** - 40: 1x2, 1x4, 2x5, 4x6
- **Booking** - Email to hire whole hostel or via YHA website for individual bookings.
- **Price per night** - Beds from £19, private rooms for 2 from £49.
- **Public Transport** - Bus number 72 from Skipton train station.
- **Directions** - From Skipton travel north towards Grassington then follow signs to Kettlewell. In the village, cross two bridges then turn right in front of the Bluebell pub. At the T junction turn left. The Hostel/Post Office is the second building on right.

CONTACT: Saul & Floss Ward
Tel: 01756 760232
saulward@hotmail.com www.yha.org.uk/hostel/kettlewell
Whernside House, Kettlewell, Skipton, North Yorkshire, BD23 5QU

SKIRFARE
BARN

Skirfare Barn is a traditional stone barn and is a distinctive feature of the beautiful Dales landscape, standing at the confluence of Upper Wharfedale and Littondale with the climbers' challenge, Kilnsey Crag, providing a spectacular backdrop. The area is famous for walking, cycling and touring with several footpaths easily accessible from the barn including the Dales Way. Kilnsey is nearby where you can find The Kilnsey Park providing day fishing and food as well as The Tennant Arms Hotel for those who prefer a bar snack. Pony trekking is available at Conistone. Although altered little on the outside, the Barn has been converted to provide centrally heated accommodation with fully equipped kitchen, common room with TV and DVD player and showers on the upper floor, and 5 bedrooms & drying room on the ground floor. Ample car parking and a grass recreation area. Free WiFi available. Perfect accommodation for cycling or walking holidays or friends and family-get-togethers

GROUPS ONLY

DETAILS

- **Open** - All year.
- **Number of beds** - 20: 2x2 (twin), 2x4, 1x8.
- **Booking** - Essential, in advance for weekend block bookings.
- **Price per night** - From £14 per person.
- **Public Transport** - Skipton trains (12 miles). Buses from Bradford, Keighley and Harrogate.
- **Directions** - From Skipton take B6265 to Grassington then the B6160 towards Kettlewell. In Kilnsey, 400m after the Crag turn into Skirfare Barn just before the T junction.

CONTACT: Matt & Bev
Tel: 07597 645254
skirfarebarn@gmail.com www.skirfarebarn.com
Kettlewell Rd, Kilnsey, North Yorkshire, BD23 5PT

HORNBY LAITHE
BUNKHOUSE BARN

Simple, comfortable accommodation in the Yorkshire Dales National Park, Hornby Laith Bunkhouse Barn has been converted from original farm buildings and occupies a secluded position within easy walking distance of both the pretty village of Stainforth and traditional market town of Settle. The perfect base for groups wishing to explore this beautiful area. Within easy access to a wide variety of routes for both the seasoned walker or climber and those wishing to explore the countryside at their leisure. Sleeping up to 50 there is also space for a marquee for events and weddings & ample parking. Full catering available by arrangement although a fully equipped kitchen is available for self-catering. A separate barn contains a recreational area & camping is available. Stainforth Foss, a picturesque waterfall on the river Ribble, is just a short walk across the fields from the barn and in the right season you can see the salmon leap on their journey upstream to spawn. The owners also have a holiday cottage available in Cumbria. See selfcatering-windermere.co.uk for more details.

DETAILS

- **Open** - All year.
- **Number of beds** - 50
- **Booking** - Book by telephone
- **Price per night** - 36 people - £800 for the weekend, 50 people - £1,050 for the weekend. Please call for prices for other party numbers.
- **Public Transport** - Train at Settle, bus No 11 from Settle to Stainforth from which it is approximately a 12 minute walk to bunkhouse..
- **Directions** - From the A65 follow the B6480 through Settle (B6479) and Langcliffe. After crossing the railway continue for approx 1 mile. Hornby Laithe is on the left down a track.

CONTACT: Neil and Enid Caton,
Tel: 01729 822240
Hornby Laithe, Stainforth, Nr Settle, North Yorkshire BD24 9PB

INGLETON YHA
GRETA TOWER
ENGLAND

A Victorian house in private grounds, Greta Tower is situated on the edge of the Yorkshire Dales, in the pretty village of Ingleton. Surrounded by magnificent countryside with caves, waterfalls and mountains. Dominated by Ingleborough, the best known of Yorkshire's Three Peaks, the area is known for its walking routes and waterfall trail. There is plenty to offer for walkers, climbers, mountain bikers and cavers and it makes a great base for the Yorkshire Three Peaks Challenge. The Yorkshire Dales, Lake District, Forest of Bowland and Morecambe Bay coastline are all only a short drive away. Whatever your agenda, you're sure of a relaxing stay. This licensed hostel serves tasty meals. There's an open-air swimming pool (summer only) and park next door. Great for family breaks and school trips. Dormitory-style bed rooms with bunks and shared bathrooms plus two private en suite rooms with 5 beds (including one double bed). Sole use is available. Free parking on site.

DETAILS

- **Open** - All year (sole use only Nov-Feb). Reception open 8am-12, 5-10pm.
- **Number of beds** - 64: 4x6, 7x4, 1x2, 2x5
- **Booking** - Recommended, essential for groups. By phone, e-mail or website.
- **Price per night** - Beds from £15, rooms from £30. Sole use bookings welcome.
- **Public Transport** - The Leeds to Morecambe train line stops at both Clapham & Bentham. Ribblehead train station is the closest stop on the Settle-Carlilse railway. All are within approx. 10 minutes drive of Ingleton. For convenient bus connections to Ingleton, the best stations are Settle or Lancaster.
- **Directions** - In centre of village, close to the outdoor pool and play area. Off the A65 Skipton to Kendal Road, 30 mins from Morcambe and 25 mins from Lancaster.

CONTACT: Manager
Tel: 015242 41444
ingleton@yha.org.uk www.ingletonhostel.co.uk
Greta Tower, Sammy Lane, Ingleton, North Yorkshire, LA6 3EG

THE OLD SCHOOL BUNKHOUSE

Situated near Ingleton in Yorkshire Dales limestone country, between Ingleborough and Whernside with superb views of both, the bunkhouse makes an ideal base for sporting or nature holidays. Converted from an old stone school, with much of the character remaining. It provides self-catering accommodation for up to 30 people in five rooms. There is a lounge, drying room, 4 shower rooms with hand basins and toilets, well equipped kitchen / dining room with industrial cooker, toasters, fridge, freezer, dishwasher, microwaves and payphone. Nearest pub 100 yds. The area is well known for its scenery including the Three Peaks walk over Ingleborough, Pen-y-ghent and Whernside. Close by are the Waterfalls walk and some of the best caves and potholes in the country including the famous Gaping Ghyll system and the White Scar show cave. Cave and Canyoning UK offer underground and over water adventures at discounted rates for bunkhouse guests.

              GROUPS ONLY

DETAILS

- **Open** - All year, 24 hours.
- **Number of beds** - 30 (5 x 6)
- **Booking** - Early booking advised for popular times. £150 deposit for 2 nights. 25% for 3 nights or over.
- **Price per night** - £320 per night (sole use) for up to 20 people with an extra £16 per person for groups over 20 people. Minimum of 2 nights at weekends.
- **Public Transport** - Ribblehead station 1 mile. No buses.
- **Directions** - 4.5 miles on the B6255 Ingleton to Hawes Road, just after Chapel-Le-Dale village on left hand side. 11 miles from Hawes on B6255.

CONTACT: Debbie Bryant
Tel: 01931 714874 Mob: 0788 4260 815
oldschoolbunkhouse@gmail.com www.oldschoolbunkhouse.co.uk
Chapel-le-Dale, Ingleton, Carnforth, Lancs, LA6 3AR

A stunning location on a busy bridleway with far reaching views to Ribblehead, Park Fell and Ingleborough. Broadrake Bunkbarn has been renovated to a very high standard with bedrooms, showers, toilets and drying room on the ground floor and an upstairs open-plan area with exposed beams, excellent kitchen facilities, dining area and seating area with large, comfortable sofas. A small resources room has a good selection of books, maps and games. There is free WiFi but no mobile phone reception in the area. The Dales High Way long distance path passes directly in front of the barn and the Pennine Journey LDP is just a field away, making it an ideal overnight stop. The Three Peaks can be walked from the door avoiding the crowds at Horton. There are numerous other walking, biking and caving opportunities in the area as well as the Ingleborough NNR across the valley and the limestone pavement of Scales Moor a short walk away. Broadrake is in a fantastic Dark Skies area too.

DETAILS

- **Open** - All year, all day.
- **Number of beds** - 20 beds – 1 x 8 bed; 2 x 4 bed; 2 x twin.
- **Booking** - Confirm availability by phone then download booking form from website
- **Price per night** - Sole use from £400, 8 bed dorm from £160, 4 bed dorm from £80, Twin room from £45. BYO sleeping bag or rent duvet & towel for £3.50 per stay.
- **Public Transport** - Ribblehead Station is about 2 miles away by footpaths.
- **Directions** - From B6255 turn onto Philpin lane. Go through the farmyard and across 5 cattle grids just before 6th cattle grid turn right onto unmade track. Do not attempt Philpin lane if flooded retire to the Hill Inn and phone from there.

CONTACT: Mike & Rachel Benson
Tel: 015242 41357
info@broadrake.co.uk www.broadrake.co.uk
Broadrake, Chapel-le-Dale, Ingleton, LA6 3AX

GAUBER
BUNK BARN

In the heart of Yorkshire's Three Peaks country right on the route down from Pen Y Ghent and just 10 min drive from Ingleton. This warm comfortable bunkbarn sleeps up to 12 in three rooms (one en suite). Downstairs is the main bathroom with shower over bath. The large self-catering kitchen/diner has a farmhouse table whilst the spacious living room has a wood burner for those chilly nights. (Starter log packs are provided, extra logs can be purchased). The secluded garden to rear has stunning views as do the front bedrooms.

Perfect base for walkers, cavers and cyclists or for families to enjoy a fantastic break in the Yorkshire Dales. Close to Ribblehead Viaduct, White Scar Caves, Ingleton Waterfalls, Wensleydale Creamery, the open air pool at Ingleton and the Settle to Carlisle railway. The Lake District is just a 40 min drive and the coast is just over an hour. Dogs welcome for sole use only.

DETAILS

- **Open** - All year, all day.
- **Number of beds** - 12: 1x4/5 (double + bunk) 2x4 (Bunks)
- **Booking** - Via telephone.
- **Price per night** - £18 inc fitted sheet, pillow and case. Bring sleeping bag and towel. Duvet & towel hire one off charge of £5, Simple breakfast by arrangement.
- **Public Transport** - 15 min walk from Ribblehead train station
- **Directions** - From A65 at Ingleton take B6255 (Hawes). Pass Ribblehead station and take next right (Horton in Ribblesdale). Gauber Bunkbarn is on the left after 1/2 mile.

CONTACT:
Tel: 01524 241150
gauberbunkbarn@gmail.com www.gauberbunkbarn.co.uk
Ribblehead, Ingleton, Carnforth, LA6 3JF

HARDRAW
OLD SCHOOL BUNKHOUSE

Adjacent to the Pennine Way, on the edge of the picturesque village of Hardraw, The Old School Bunkhouse offers well-appointed, practical accommodation for individuals and groups of up to 26. The two smaller bunkrooms are ideal for families or staff. The large school hall (with games, table tennis, piano, log burner & sofas) and enclosed field are perfect for communal activities. Off road parking, drying room, secure bike storage and bike wash area are all available. Hardraw has a café, inn and the famous Hardraw Force waterfall, whilst the market town of Hawes is a 1.5 mile walk across fields. Andy and Helen, qualified instructors, offer caving, gill scrambling and other adventurous activities for families and groups. Taster sessions, teambuilding, technical instruction or extreme adventure all possible. The perfect overnight stay for individuals walking the Pennine Way. It is also ideal for groups booking sole use for outdoor pursuits, family get-togethers, educational visits and DofE.

DETAILS

- **Open** - All year, 24 hours. Winter (Mid Nov to End Feb) minimum charge.
- **Number of beds** - 26:1x8,1x9,1x6,1x3. 4 mattresses and 2 tent spaces .
- **Booking** - 25% deposit to confirm or total fee for 1 night bookings. Group or sole use bookings only on Fri and Sat nights. Short notice may be available.
- **Price per night** - £15pp, exclusive use £175 - £295. Winter (Mid Nov to End Feb): minimum of 5 persons or minimum charge of £65.
- **Public Transport** - Trains: Garsdale (6 miles). Little White Bus outside bunkhouse connects with Leeds - Carlisle services. Buses to Bedale & Leyburn from Hawes.
- **Directions** - Turn north off A684 approx. 1 mile west of Hawes and proceed for ½ mile. Hardraw Old School Bunkhouse is on the left as you enter the village.

CONTACT: Andy or Helen
Tel: 01969 666034 Mob: 07546894317
enquiries@hardrawoldschoolbunkhouse.co.uk www.hardrawoldschoolbunkhouse.co.uk
Schoolhouse, Hardraw, near Hawes, Wensleydale, North Yorkshire, DL8 3LZ

THE JONAS
CENTRE

At the heart of Wensleydale in the tranquil beauty of the Yorkshire Dales, The Jonas Centre provides twelve Scandinavian lodges with a communal area in the Granary for groups to gather or dine together. Ideal for escaping to the country, relaxation and sightseeing. There are cycling and walking routes direct from the door and activities can be arranged on or off-site. Close to Redmire station on the Wensleydale Railway and near to Castle Bolton and Aysgarth Falls. Pub meals in Redmire village. The self-catering log cabins each sleep 5-7 people and have a bathroom, TV, night storage heaters and a well equipped kitchen.
The Granary meeting facilities and large group kitchen and dining area are available to hire. Linen and towels can be hired and a freezer, coin operated washing machine and dryer are available. Pets welcome (nightly charge). Children's playground, table tennis hut, ball games area, camp fire area and space to relax in the peaceful surroundings. An ideal venue for conferences, training, teaching, fellowship, wedding receptions and family celebrations.

DETAILS

- **Open** - Open all year. Office open from 9am - 5pm Monday to Saturday.
- **Number of beds** - 60: 12 x 5. 12 lodges each sleeping between 5 and 7 people.
- **Booking** - Minimum 2 nights. The person making the booking must be over 18.
- **Price per night** - See website for special offers. Discounts for full site use.
- **Public Transport** - Train at Darlington & Northallerton (25 miles), local buses
- **Directions** - A684 westbound to Wensley, right toward Redmire. Entrance is on left after railway arch. A684 eastbound follow signs to & through Redmire entrance is directly ahead, drive carefully down to reception, or park by top steps and walk.

CONTACT: Simon Eastwood
Tel: 01969 624900
stay@jonascentre.org www.jonascentre.org
The Jonas Centre, Redmire, Leyburn. North Yorkshire, DL8 4EW

DALES
BIKE CENTRE

In the tiny village of Fremington in Swaledale, Yorkshire Dales, surrounded by the best biking in Yorkshire in a stunning landscape, criss-crossed by ancient lanes, moorland tracks and roads, this is the perfect venue for cycling, mountain biking, trail running and walking. Accommodation, café, bike shop, hire, workshop and secure storage, bike wash, drying room and a wealth of knowledge about the Dales. 14 beds, in smart 2 and 4 bedded rooms, warmly decorated and with amazing views across Swaledale. Bedding is provided, as well as a kitchenette with free tea and coffee. The café lounge can be used by guests, with magazines, free WiFi internet and 24 hour cake access! A hearty breakfast is included. Evening meals are available in pubs and restaurants in Reeth, a five minute stroll away. On route for a Reeth stopover on Wainwright's famous Coast-to-Coast walk, the infamous Woodcocks off-road Coast-to-Coast mountain bike trip and the Yorkshire Dales Cycle Way.

DETAILS

- **Open** - All year, 24 hours.
- **Number of beds** - 14: Old barn 1x4, 1x2; New barn 1x4, 2x2;
- **Booking** - Online via website, by phone or by email.
- **Price per night** - Single room £39, 2 bed bunkroom £58, 4 bed bunkroom £116, 3 people in 4 bed bunkroom £97. All prices include breakfast.
- **Public Transport** - Trains Darlington (25 miles). Buses X26 & X27 every 15 mins from Darlington to Richmond. Bus 30 from Richmond to Reeth (7 per day till 6.15pm).
- **Directions** - 20 mins from A1M: from Richmond take A6108 then B6270 signed to Reeth. Once through Grinton, DBC is on left at end of a row of tall trees.

CONTACT: Stu Price
Tel: 01748 884908
enquiries@dalesbikecentre.co.uk www.dalesbikecentre.co.uk
Parks Barn, Fremington, Richmond DL11 6AW

Situated 3 miles east of Richmond in the picturesque village of Brompton on Swale, this bunkbarn is ideally located for walking, cycling and exploring the Yorkshire Dales and surrounding areas. Swaledale and Wensleydale are easily accessible, Easby Abbey and Church, Richmond Castle, Kipling Hall and the Georgian theatre are local historic places of interest. Ellerton lakes are a short distance away for outdoor swimming and canoeing. Adrenalin, Ariel Extreme, The Forbidden Corner and paintballing are local attractions. The bunk barn is dog friendly and has an area for securing bikes overnight. The village shop is directly opposite and has a large selection of food and drink, there is a pub 200 yards away and a larger pub 1/2 mile away. The barn has a fully equipped kitchen, shower and toilet. An area for BBQs available on request, duvets and pillows are provided but require a sheet sleeping sack (£1 hire), towels are also available to hire and washing and drying facilities available for a small charge.

DETAILS

- **Open** - All year, all day
- **Number of beds** - 12: 3x4
- **Booking** - Book via phone or email
- **Price per night** - £10pp, £120 sole use. Sleeping sack hire £1
- **Public Transport** - Train at Darlington, X34 bus from Darlington to Richmond stops close by.
- **Directions** - From A1 follow signs to Brompton on Swale. Go through the village on Richmond Road, after The Crown pub the sign for the Bunkbarn is on the right. Turn down the farm track and through the gate.

CONTACT: Chris Wilkin
Tel: 01748 818326
chris01748@gmail.com www.fb.com/Bromptononswalebunkbarn/
24 Richmond Road, Richmond, North Yorkshire, DL10 7HE

FELL END
BUNKHOUSE

Overlooking the unspoilt Howgill Fells, these two 18th century buildings provide comfortable bunkhouse accommodation for people wishing to explore this beautiful area. Perfect for mixed groups, DofE, families and people with special needs. Great for walking & cycling, canoeing & caving nearby, the Lake District is only 1 hour away. The Schoolhouse sleeps 8 in bunks in the central area with an extra bed in an adjoining room. There are two toilets, one shower and four wash basins and a fully equipped kitchen with a fridge/freezer, microwave and cooker. The living room has a multi-fuel stove, which also heats the radiators. Greenslack has a further 2 bunks and 1 single bed plus a bathroom for people with mobility problems. Get in touch if your group has fewer than 8 people but require Greenslack for these facilities. Entry into both buildings is by a touch lock system. Dogs allowed under strict supervision. Fell End is owned by the Bendrigg Trust, a charity offering outdoor activities for disabled people.

DETAILS

- **Open** - All year.
- **Number of beds** - 14: 1x8, 1x5, 1x1.
- **Booking** - Completed booking form with 20% deposit to Bendrigg Trust, Old Hutton, Kendal, Cumbria, LA8 0NR. Payment by cheque or BACS
- **Price per night** - £11.50 + VAT. Minimum booking: 6 for Schoolhouse, 8 for both buildings, 12 people if booking 1 night only, (no charge under 5yrs).
- **Public Transport** - Nearest train station: Kirkby Stephen (6 miles) on the Carlisle/Settle/Leeds line. Taxis only to Fell End.
- **Directions** - Bunkhouse 6 miles NE of Sedbergh, just off A683. GR:723983

CONTACT: Lynne Irish
Tel: 01539 723766
lynne@bendrigg.org.uk www.fellend-bunkhouse.org.uk
Ravenstonedale, Kirkby Stephen, Cumbria, CA17 4LN

HOWGILLS
BARN

Set up a winding lane, past open fields with 360 degree panoramic views of the beautiful Howgill fells, "Stay in Style" in seclusion and privacy. Just a short stroll from the historic market town of Sedbergh which oozes an 'old world' feel with sandstone buildings, cobbled alleys, independent cafés, restaurants & shops. The barn offers a base to explore the Dales and Lakes and is a haven for relaxing and unwinding. Flagged floors, underfloor heating, oak beams, large lounge, dining area, drying room, indoor games room, patio & games field set the tone for a quality stay. The hot tub on the patio, looks up the fell with no neighbours or nearby distractions (apart from the odd sheep!) Designed to suit everyone whether you are booking a single bed or room for the evening, or the whole barn for a special occasion or business event. A variety of walks are on the doorstep including the Dales Way. Golfing, horse riding, fishing and cycling are also popular, depending on your adrenalin requirements! The historic towns of Kendal, Ingleton and Kirkby Lonsdale are all close by.

DETAILS

- **Open** - All year, all day.
- **Number of beds** - 35: 6x4 1x5 1x6.(all en suite) plus camping
- **Booking** - Booking is essential (deposit required).
- **Price per night** - From £25ppn inc. breakfast. Duvet hire £6 single, £9 double. Hot tub additional rates, please enquire. Camping £12 per person per night
- **Public Transport** - 8 miles from Oxenholme. Taxis are available from the station.
- **Directions** - M6 Junction 37. In Sedbergh, turn left IMMEDIATELY on seeing Westwood's Books' building, go up small lane through farmyard, over bridge, to barn.

CONTACT:
Tel: T: 015396 21000 M: 07973 947753
enquiries@howgillsaccommodation.co.uk www.howgillsbunkbarn.co.uk
Castlehaw Farm, Castlehaw Lane, Sedbergh, Cumbria LA10 5BA

LONGRIGG
RESIDENTIAL CENTRE

Longrigg Residential Centre, within walking distance of Sedbergh, only 10 miles from Kendal and less than 10 minutes from the M6, is an ideal location for exploring the Lakes and the Yorkshire Dales. Standing in its own grounds and overlooking the unspoilt splendour of the Howgill Fells the centre is perfect for mixed groups or families. Walking, cycling, canoeing and caving are nearby. Recently refurbished the centre has two six bed dorms in the main building and a larger separate building sleeps 20 in dorms of 2,4,6 and 8. There are ample shower and toilet facilities, a drying room and tumble drier. Sleeping bags and pillowcases are required. The large kitchen is equipped for group catering. The lounge has easy chairs and gives access to the patio area. A separate games room has pool table, TV and table football. The centre holds an Adventure Activity Licence and can offer instruction and equipment. Entry is by a touch lock system. The centre is owned by Action4Youth a registered Charity (No 1033626) and complies with relevant health and safety requirements.

DETAILS

- **Open** - All year, all day.
- **Number of beds** - 32: 1x8, 3x6, 1x4, 1x2
- **Booking** - Book by phone or email
- **Price per night** - £17 per head for a minimum of 12 people. £16 per head for 20 or more. £15 per head for groups of 25 or more.
- **Public Transport** - Trains at Oxenholme on the West Coast Line.
- **Directions** - Near the village of Sedbergh which lies on the edge of the Yorkshire Dales and is just 30 minutes from the Lake District. Easy access via M6 junction 37.

CONTACT: Dave Hollingham
Tel: 01539 621161
longrigg@action4youth.org www.longrigg.org.uk
Frostrow Lane, Sedbergh, Cumbria, LA105JT

NEW ING
LODGE

New Ing Lodge is a 18th century grade 2 listed farm. Now operating as a 10 bedroom, 10 bathroom B&B and hostel offering friendly flexible accommodation with food. It has been awarded Gold Green Tourism and is the only winner of the Above & Beyond Outstanding Commitment to Responsible Tourism. Based in Shap in the Eden Valley, on the edge of the Lake District National Park, the Howgills and the Pennine Fells, New Ing Lodge offers comfort at an affordable price just minutes from the M6. Available for exclusive use it is perfect for large groups looking for a peaceful retreat. Situated on Wainwright's Coast to Coast path, the Westmorland Way and the Miller's Way it is ideal for walking and cycling. Run by outdoor enthusiasts who can give advice on what to do. There is an acre of well kept field with volleyball court and a walled orchard. Sole hire gives use of 10 bedrooms, the bar, commercial kitchen, dinning room, volleyball court and the grounds. Quality Cumbria accredited.

DETAILS

- **Open** - All year
- **Number of beds** - 34. 2x twin, 3xdouble, 2x double and single, 1x double and 2 singles, 1x 6 bedded dorm, 1 x 8 bedded dorm.
- **Booking** - Well in advance - deposit 50% via website or card payment by phone.
- **Price per night** - 18pp dorm with bedding, B&B (private rooms) from £30pp. Discounts for larger groups and longer stays. Sole use from only £600 per night.
- **Public Transport** - Bus from Penrith or Kendal station. Pick-up from station is possible. No buses on Sunday.
- **Directions** - North end of Shap village, opposite the Bampton and Haweswater junction. 5th building on the left hand side if travelling from the North.

CONTACT: Scott
Tel: 01931 716719
info@newinglodge.co.uk www.newinglodge.co.uk
New Ing Lodge, Main Street, Shap, Penrith, Cumbria, CA10 3LX

GREENGILL
BARN

A converted traditional barn on the edge of Morland in Cumbria's rolling Eden Valley, close to the Lake District and handy for the M6. Great for weekend gatherings of family or friends wanting to visit the Lake District, the Pennines, the Yorkshire Dales and the Borders. Accommodating 16 in 2 bunk rooms, a large fully equipped kitchen/dining room and a huge beamed recreation room with sofas, armchairs, pool table, library, dartboard and card table and music system. A great space for a party. Night storage heating. 3 Mira sports showers, 3 loos. Small campsite and two self-catering cottages next door. The Eden Valley is an idyllic cycling area with quiet rolling roads and wonderful views. Greengill Barn is on NCN route 71 and new Wiggo's Loop on C2C. Secure bike storage, ideal for road cyclists and mountain bikers. Good local walking and easy access to lakes and fells. BYO food and drink or just 4 mins' walk to The Mill Yard Café for Friday night pizzas, full English breakfasts, coffees, lunches and take-aways. The Crown Inn opposite serves real ale, and weekend meals.

DETAILS

- **Open** - All year.
- **Number of beds** - 16: 2x8
- **Booking** - Exclusive group use only. Minimum 2 nights. 30% non-returnable deposit to confirm. Balance due a month before arrival. Payable online or by cheque.
- **Price per night** - £280 per night so £560 for 2 nights.(£17.50pppn for 16 people). Bunk sheet included. Own sleeping bags free or duvet, pillow, towel £5pp. Dogs £15.
- **Public Transport** - Nearest rail station and bus station in Penrith, 7 miles
- **Directions** - Last building in Morland on road to Great Strickland.

CONTACT: Freddy Markham
Tel: 01931 714244 Mob: 07831 428541
freddy@greengillholidays.co.uk www.greengillholidays.co.uk
Greengill Barn, Strickland Road, Morland, Penrith, Cumbria CA10 3AX

YEALAND
OLD SCHOOL

Yealand Old School hostel is located in the middle of the village of Yealand Conyers, and is part of the Quaker Heritage of the village. The hostel is run on a not-for-profit basis by the adjacent Quaker meeting house.

The hostel offers simple self-catering accommodation for all sorts of groups. Facilites include a well equipped kitchen, which provides good dining space. Upstairs there are 3 good sized spaces used in various ways by different groups. One is a sizable hall, and another a comfortable sitting room. Good WiFi. Room for bike storage inside the building. Duvets available for a small charge per visit. Groups normally have sole occupancy of the building. The hostel is well located for walking, cycling, the RSPB reserve at Leighton Moss and is on the National Cycle Network NCN 6. Camping in the adjacent field may be possible. Resident warden.

DETAILS

- **Open** - All year, all day.
- **Number of beds** - 26: 1x4, 1x2, mattresses for 20+
- **Booking** - Contact warden for booking form.
- **Price per night** - £15/adult/night, £7.50 children 5 and over, min charge £100 for group Friday/Sat, £50 during week.
- **Public Transport** - Carnforth station 3 miles, with a connection by local bus which stops outside the hostel.
- **Directions** - Exactly at the top of the hill on the main road through Yealand Conyers village, 5 mins from J35 M6.

CONTACT: Sue Tyldesley
Tel: 01524 732336
yealandwarden@lancsquakers.org.uk www.lancsquakers.org.uk/simple-hostel.php
Yealand Rd, Yealand Conyers, Carnforth, LA5 9SH

A family run independent hostel since 2014. This large Edwardian house overlooking Morecambe Bay is perfectly situated with great views of the Lake District mountains. In the summer evenings enjoy the spectacular sunsets in the garden with outdoor seating, fire pits, games, picnic tables and BBQ facilities. Spend winter evenings relaxing by the fire in the lounge, playing board games and enjoying a local ale from the licensed bar. Try your hand at pool or darts in the games room or relax into a good Sky film in the TV room. Take advantage of the large refurbished self-catering kitchen or book a delicious home cooked supper in the restaurant. Arnside is an ideal base for activity breaks in the Lake District and Yorkshire Dales. Take a guided walk across Morecombe Bay or around the coast and back over Arnside Knott. Those looking for birdwatching holidays will enjoy the RSPB Leighton Moss reserve and butterfly lovers shouldn't miss Arnside Knott. Great affordable accommodation for families, individuals & groups, especially if you love the Lake District but prefer to avoid the crowds. Field study/conference rooms available to groups

DETAILS

- **Open** - All year except Christmas Day, reception: 07.30 - 10.00, 17.30 - 22.30.
- **Number of beds** - 67
- **Booking** - Book by phone, email or our website .
- **Price per night** - From £18.50
- **Public Transport** - 20 minute walk from Arnside Railway station
- **Directions** - M6 to J35. A6 Milnthorpe. B5282 to Arnside - follow main road through Arnside to YHA sign on right.

CONTACT: Martin or Leigha
Tel: 01524 761781
enquiries@arnsidehostel.co.uk arnsideindependenthostel.co.uk/
Oakfield Lodge, Redhills Rd, Arnside, Cumbria, LA5 0AT

ROOKHOW
CENTRE

Situated in the Rusland Valley, close to the heart of the Lake District, this small beautiful hostel has its own glorious woods where you can have a bonfire/BBQ or explore the woodland walks. Close to Coniston and Windermere and on the edge of the Grizedale Forest Park with its trails and sculptures, Rookhow is the perfect base for walking, orienteering, mountain biking, canoeing and all outdoor activities as well as quiet retreat, relaxation, study and artistic pursuits.

Converted from the stables of the nearby historic Quaker meeting house (available for conferences, seminars and group activities) the three sleeping areas can be rented as private or family rooms. Facilities: kitchen/dining area, cosy wood stove, picnic tables and BBQ. Private parking. WiFi by arrangement. Inn food 2/3 miles. Supermarkets 15mins or will deliver. Electric heating inc.

DETAILS

- **Open** - All year, all day.
- **Number of beds** - 20: 1x9, 1x8, plus extra on bed settees. Also camping.
- **Booking** - Booking is essential (deposit).
- **Price per night** - From :- Adult £16.00, £8.00 for under 16s. Sole use from £190 (minimum) per night. Camping rate half the above. Duvet hire £5 pp.
- **Public Transport** - Trains at Grange-over-Sands and Ulverston. (11 miles, approx £25 by taxi). A seasonal bus service sometimes operates - check with the warden.
- **Directions** - GR 332896. From M6, Junction 36, follow A590, signs for Barrow. Leave A590 at Greenodd (A5092) junction and follow sign for Workington for ¼ mile. Take minor road to right signed Colton / Oxen Park. Continue through Oxen Park for 2 miles. Centre on left. From Ambleside: to Hawkshead, then to Grizedale. Continue beyond Grizedale for 3.5 miles (Satterthwaite - Ulverston Road). Centre on the right.

CONTACT: Warden
Tel: 01229 860231 Mob: 0794 350 8100
straughton@btinternet.com www.rookhowcentre.co.uk
Rusland Valley, nr Grizedale, Ulverston, Cumbria, South Lakeland, LA12 8LA

LOWICK SCHOOL
BUNKHOUSE

Lowick School Bunkhouse is based within the old primary school at Lowick Green which is nestled between Coniston and Ulverston. The bunkhouse has 20 beds in 3 rooms plus a lounge/meeting room with wood-burning stove, kitchen/dining room, great views of the mountains, an outdoor area with campfire and more!

River Deep Mountain High Activity Centre provides a wide variety of outdoor activities from gorge walking to mountain biking, kayaking to sailing and more. Group and family packages include activities in the price. Just 25 mins' drive from the M6 and only 4 miles from Coniston Water. It is less than a mile to 2 pubs – either a pleasant walk down a back lane to the Red Lion or down the main road to the Farmer's Arms.

           GROUPS ONLY

DETAILS

- **Open** - All year.
- **Number of beds** - 20: 2x8, 1x4 (one 8 bed can be expanded to 10)
- **Booking** - Package prices include an outdoor activity with River Deep Mountain High. Schools and youth/college groups can discuss how to fit a stay in their budget.
- **Price per night** - Whole bunkhouse available from £550 at weekends (Club scheme), from £800 Mon-Thurs. £250 deposit required for groups. Shorter stays available by negotiation. Family packages in school holidays
- **Public Transport** - Buses from Windermere and Ulverston
- **Directions** - From the M6, jn36, follow the A590 to Greenodd. Turn right onto A5092, after 2.5 miles Lowick school is on the right after Esps Farm. If you get to Woodgate, you have missed it!

CONTACT: Emma Hoving
Tel: 01539528666
info@riverdeepmountainhigh.co.uk www.riverdeepmountainhigh.co.uk/
Lowick Old School, Lowick Green, Ulverston LA12 8EB

HIGH WRAY
BASECAMP

Situated in the heart of South Lakeland in secluded woodland, 4 miles from the village of Ambleside, High Wray Basecamp provides an ideal base for groups wishing to explore and take part in activities in the Lake District area. Local attractions include rambling, fell walking, climbing and water sports, with the Basecamp ranger being happy to assist with information on local walks and activities. The Longland Block has two separate fully centrally heated dormitories each sleeping 8, with a separate washing and living area/kitchen block. The comfortable living area is heated by a central wood-burning stove and the kitchen has a commercial gas cooker, fridge freezer, microwave and utensils. The Acland block has two separate centrally heated dormitories sleeping 10 each, with toilet and shower room attached. The kitchen / lounge area is fitted with commercial gas cooker, fridges, microwave and utensils.

DETAILS

- **Open** - All year, 24 hours.
- **Number of beds** - 16 + 22
- **Booking** - By email or phone
- **Price per night** - Longland £11.00pp (Mon-Thur), £14.00pp (Fri-Sun). Acland £11.50pp (Mon-Thur), £15.00pp (Fri-Sun).
- **Public Transport** - Nearest train station Windermere 8 miles. Local bus (505 'Coniston Rambler' Windermere - Hawkshead) stops 2 miles away at turning to Wray Castle (Cumbria travel-line 0870 6082608)
- **Directions** - GR: 373 995. Take A593 from Ambleside towards Coniston, bear left onto the B5286 signed Hawkshead, fork left for High Wray village, signed Wray Castle. Basecamp is ¼ mile up dirt road on the left at the end of High Wray village.

CONTACT: Philippa Barber
Tel: 015394 34633
Philippa.barber@nationaltrust.org.uk
High Wray, Ambleside, Cumbria, LA22 0JE

KIRKBY STEPHEN
HOSTEL

Kirkby Stephen Hostel, is a former YHA hostel converted from a Methodist Church and has been independent since 2010. The old chapel has a range of accommodation for individuals, families and groups amongst beautiful authentic features; stained glass windows, arches, oak panels and stone covings. The chapel houses a large dining room and kitchen, with a lounge/reading room in the gallery. The bedrooms and dormitories are in a building at the rear, with ample lavatories and showers, WiFi and a drying room. Kirkby Stephen is a pleasant market town in the upper Eden valley, situated 15 miles from Kendal, 15 miles from Hawes and on Wainwright's Coast to Coast path and the W2W cycle path. It enjoys easy access to the Lady Ann Clifford Walk, the Walney to Wear bike ride, the Howgill Hills, the Dales National Park and the Lake District. Paragliding is also available. The hostel stands prominently on the main street of Kirkby Stephen, with a range of restaurants, cafés, pubs, take-aways (including fish and chips) and food shops on the doorstep.

DETAILS

- **Open** - All year, please arrive after 5pm (or ring to arrange arrival).
- **Number of beds** - 38: 1x8, 3x6, 2x4, 1x2, 1x2 en suite.
- **Booking** - Book by phone or email. Booking advised but not essential.
- **Price per night** - £20pp. Reductions for groups.
- **Public Transport** - One mile from Kirkby Stephen train station on the Leeds-Carlisle line. Regular buses from Penrith, Kendal and Appleby stop outside hostel.
- **Directions** - In the centre of town on main road. From M6 leave at junction 38 and follow signs towards Appleby.

CONTACT: Denise
Tel: 01768 371793 or 07812 558525
kirkbystephenhostel@btconnect.com www.kirkbystephenhostel.co.uk
Market Street, Kirkby Stephen, Cumbria, CA17 4QQ

A Georgian town house next to the Brewery Arts Centre just 300 yards from the centre of the historic market town of Kendal. This family run, friendly hostel is a home from home with a comfortable lounge, free WiFi, well equipped kitchen, dining room seating 26, central heating, hot showers, laundry facilities ,secure cycle shed, drying room and a good selection of books and maps to borrow for walking and cycling routes. Famous for Wainwright, Kendal Mintcake, Postman Pat. Hostel staff are always happy to pass on their local knowledge. Kendal has many attractions with 2 castles, museums, Abbot Hall Art Gallery and only 1 stop from Oxenholme Rail station on West Coast Line. A short drive, bus or train ride will take you to Lake Windermere and Bowness for lake cruises and the famous Beatrix Potter exhibition. A great place to break a journey to and from Scotland as well as discovering this beautiful part of the country. Breakfast available on request. Whole hostel bookings taken.

DETAILS

- **Open** - All year, 7.30am to 10.30am, 4.30pm to 8.30pm and by arrangement.
- **Number of beds** - 70: 1x14, 1x8, 2x7 (family), 2x6, 1x5(family), 1x4, 1x3, 4x2, 1xdouble. All family rooms have private shower room and double bed.
- **Booking** - By phone, email, text or website. Booking preferable but not essential
- **Price per night** - £20 Sunday to Thursday, £22 Friday and Saturday.
- **Public Transport** - National Express to Kendal bus station. (10 min walk), Kendal train station (15 min walk), Oxenholme (The Lakes Station) 5 mins by taxi.
- **Directions** - Junction 36 of M6, A6 into Kendal 300m from parish church on LHS, in front of Brewery Arts Centre. Directions on hostel website under the location tab

CONTACT: Jan or Kristina
Tel: 01539 724066; Mob: 07795 198 197
kristina@kendalhostel.co.uk www.kendalhostel.com
118-120 Highgate, Kendal, Cumbria, LA9 4HE

DACRE'S STABLE
CAMPING BARN

Only 20 minutes' drive from Kendal, Dacre's Stable Camping Barn at Grisedale Farm is in the new Eastern extension to the Lake District National Park, On a very quiet gated road away from the main A6 it is a perfect base from which to explore the Yorkshire Dales, the Lake District and the Eden valley, all within an hour's drive. Great for mountain biking, walking, and cycling on quiet tracks and lanes, surrounded by wildlife and space to gaze, bird-watch, sketch, play, read or do nothing but dream. Dacre's Stable (named after a fell pony who lived at the farm) is a flexible, friendly space for families or groups, with a green ethos. It comfortably sleeps 8 on a sole use, self-catering basis. The ground floor sleeps 2 (double bed) with shower room, wood-burner and well equipped kitchen. Upstairs, reached by outside steps, sleeps 6+ with extra mattresses and pillows and a wood-burner and drying rack. A big barn on the farm provides bad weather play space for children as well as extra storage. BYO towels, sleeping bags/ warm bedding, pillow cases, torches and some dry kindling wood.

DETAILS

- **Open** - All year.
- **Number of beds** - 8: 1x2 1x6.
- **Booking** - Please phone to book and discuss requirements.
- **Price per night** - Sole use only - from £55pn reductions for midweek and longer stays (min 2 night stay, unless by special arrangement). Please phone to discuss.
- **Public Transport** - Trains: Penrith & Oxenholme (30 mins' drive), Kendal (20 mins' drive). Car hire and National Express buses also at Kendal. No local buses.
- **Directions** - 10 mins from A6, 7miles north of Kendal, please phone for directions.

CONTACT: Hilary Fell
Tel: 01539 823208   mobile: 07788 633936
dacresstable@gmail.com dacresstablecampingbarn.blogspot.co.uk/
Grisedale Farm, Whinfell, Kendal, Cumbria, LA8 9EN

RYDAL HALL
YOUTH CENTRE
ENGLAND

Rydal Hall Youth Centre is situated in the centre of Rydal Hall estate, sheltered on three sides by the Fairfield Horseshoe and offering access to the best of Lakeland's activities. Facilities inside provide accommodation for groups of up to 29. There are 2 dormitories sleeping 9 and 10 in each and 2 leader rooms each sleeping 4 and 6. A large common room can be used for dining or recreation. A drying room on the ground floor. A welcoming log-burner provides additional warmth to the ample heating powered by our nearby water turbine. The kitchen is fully equipped for cooking. Guests need to bring sleeping bags, towels and extra blankets during winter.

Rydal Hall also offers camping to groups and families and there is residential accommodation for up to 50 at the Hall in single, twin, double and family rooms with private facilities.

DETAILS

- **Open** - All year, 24 hours.
- **Number of beds** - Dormitories 29: 1x10 , 1x9, 1x6, 1x4.
- **Booking** - Required with deposit. Contact by phone or email.
- **Price per night** - £300.00 per night self-catering. Discounts and late deals subject to availability.
- **Public Transport** - Trains at Windermere. National Express at Ambleside. Local Stagecoach service (555) from Lancaster to Keswick stops 200 yards from Hall.
- **Directions** - GR 366 064. Take the A561 from Ambleside to Grasmere, Rydal is reached after 2 miles. By the church turn right and go up lane for 200m.

CONTACT:
Tel: 01539 432050
mail@rydalhall.org www.rydalhall.org
Rydal Hall, Ambleside, Cumbria, LA22 9LX

ELTERWATER HOSTEL

Elterwater Hostel is located in the peaceful village of Elterwater, in the Langdale valley, 15 minutes' drive from Ambleside. The area has many walks for people of all abilities, from gentle riverside meanders to the challenge presented by the Langdale Pikes, Bowfell and Scafell. Banks, shops and other amenities are available nearby.

The area is also a favourite for both on and off-road cycling, rock climbing and many other outdoor activities. An ideal overnight stop on the Cumbria way. The hostel is an ideal venue for individuals, families, outdoor groups, schools and college trips.

DETAILS

■ **Open** - All year (Nov-Feb Groups only). Access between 7.30am and 11.30pm. Reception open 7.30am to 10am and 5pm to 10:30pm.

■ **Number of beds** - 40: 6 x 2 beds, 1 x 4 beds, 4 x 6 beds

■ **Booking** - Booking advisable all year round, via website or phone.

■ **Price per night** - Beds from £19 pppn. For exclusive hire please call. Low season discounts may be available.

■ **Public Transport** - From Ambleside: Stagecoach-in-Cumbria route 516 toward Dungeon Ghyll.

■ **Directions** - From Ambleside take the A593. After 2 miles, turn right onto the B5343. After a further 2 miles go over cattle grid, then next left. Go through the village, the hostel is right.

CONTACT: Nick Owen
Tel: 015394 37245
enquiries@elterwaterhostel.co.uk www.elterwaterhostel.co.uk
Elterwater Hostel, Elterwater, Ambleside LA22 9HX

THORNEY HOW
INDEPENDENT HOSTEL

Thorney How offers clean and comfortable guest accommodation in Grasmere, the heart of the Lake District. Family-run and welcoming it provides en suite, bed and breakfast and standard self-catering accommodation for individuals, families and groups. With a backdrop of magnificent fells, adjacent to the Coast to Coast path, local village and lake, the tranquil location provides the perfect base to explore the Lake District. The Main House, 26 beds in a gentleman's farmhouse, is charming with well proportioned rooms and fabulous views. There are 7 en suite rooms ranging from doubles to family 6-person rooms. Grasmere bunkhouse is ideal for groups of up to 16 with 4 bunk rooms each with shower facilities. All larger groups are automatically offered breakfasts and at least one evening meal. Parking, electric car charging, bike hire, cycle store, drying room, licensed bar, restaurant and spacious grounds complete the experience. Pizza nights Friday. Free films Saturdays. No pets.

DETAILS

- **Open** - Open all year. Closed 10.30am to 3.30pm – check in 3.30pm to 10.30pm.
- **Number of beds** - 42: Main House 26, Bunkhouse 16
- **Booking** - Online booking recommended, Or by phone or email. First night's accommodation non-refundable payment required to secure,
- **Price per night** - Bunkhouse from £20. Main House B&B from £25.50. Double en suite from £77.00. 4 person rooms from £76.00. Larger groups please contact hostel.
- **Public Transport** - National Express coaches stop in Grasmere. Local bus 555 to / from Windermere & Keswick. Train station at Windermere.
- **Directions** - Grid ref: 332084. Half a mile NW of Grasmere village.

CONTACT: Taylor Nuttall
Tel: 01539 435597
enquiries@thorneyhow.co.uk www.thorneyhow.co.uk
Thorney How, Off Helm Close & Easedale Rd, Grasmere, Cumbria, LA22 9QW

GRASMERE
HOSTEL

This small deluxe hostel, situated on a farm, is nestled in the heart of the Lake District National Park and a short stroll from the idyllic village of Grasmere. The only 4 star independent hostel in the Lake District, this family-run hostel is ideal for individuals, couples, families and groups, especially if you want exclusive use of the whole place for a club, school or special event. For groups requiring more space, 3 luxury cottages and a Micro Lodge Pod are also available on the farm. The hostel's extensive facilities include en suite bedrooms, 2 fully equipped self-catering kitchens, dining room, lounge, laundry area, secure bike storage, drying room, LCD TV & DVD, complimentary WiFi, Internet PC, private parking, BBQ area with seating for 24 and even a sauna. A conference/studio room is available for an additional charge. A stunning location midway between Windermere and Keswick makes Grasmere the perfect base for your holiday, whether you are on a quest for adventure, relaxation or celebration. Grasmere Hostel has been praised by the Guardian, The Rough Guide and others.

DETAILS

- **Open** - All year. Reception open until 9pm. 24hr keypad entry system.
- **Number of beds** - 24: 1x3, 1x4, 1x5, 2x6.
- **Booking** - Advisable.
- **Price per night** - From £20 pppn. Sole use from £475 per night.
- **Public Transport** - Trains at Windermere. 555 bus from Windermere or Keswick, ask for Traveller's Rest pub. National Express coach from London to Grasmere daily.
- **Directions** - GR 336 094 1.25 miles north of the village. Stay on the A591 right to our drive, 400m north of Traveller's Rest pub on the right hand side.

CONTACT: Dave Keighley
Tel: 015394 35055
dave@grasmerehostel.co.uk www.grasmerehostel.co.uk
Broadrayne Farm, Keswick Road, Grasmere, Cumbria, LA22 9RU

Noran Bank Farm is situated near Lake Ullswater just through Patterdale in Cumbria. Only 5 minutes' walk away from the Coast to Coast route as well as The Westmorland Way which is a 95 mile walk along generally good paths beginning in the famous horse fair town of Appleby and ending at Arnside, all within the old County of Westmorland.

Shepherd's Crook Bunkhouse is a barn conversion, converted to a very high standard and sleeps 8. Upstairs it has a two bedded room with en suite shower and a 6 bedded room. On the ground floor there is a fully equipped kitchen, seating area in which to relax, toilet and wet room with 2 showers. Duvets, linen and towels are provided. DIY breakfast and packed lunches are available if pre-booked. A well behaved dog considered at owner's discretion. Shepherd's Crook is very popular with overnight stays on the Coast to Coast route and with weekend breaks for walking and cycling enthusiasts. It is also a fantastic meeting place for family and friends get-togethers.

DETAILS

- **Open** - All year.
- **Number of beds** - 8: 1x6, 1x2
- **Booking** - Please book by phone or email.
- **Price per night** - £15pp (6 bed room), £20pp (double room). Sole use £120. Dog £4 per night. DIY breakfast £6. Packed lunch £5. Farmhouse B&B £30pp.
- **Public Transport** - Trains at Penrith (14 miles). Buses at Patterdale (half a mile).
- **Directions** - Take A592 from Patterdale south, farm is on right in half a mile.

CONTACT: Mrs Heather Jackson
Tel: 017684 82327 Mob: 07833 981504
heathernoranbank@fsmail.net
Noran Bank Farm, Patterdale, Penrith, Cumbria, CA11 0NR

FISHER-GILL
CAMPING BARN

Situated in Thirlmere at the foot of the Helvellyn range of mountains, close to Sticks Pass and spectacular Fisher-gill waterfall, with numerous walks, hill and rock climbing from the barn, it's an ideal place for touring the Lake District being just off the A591 road, with local and national bus stops at the end of the lane. Accommodation consists of two rooms: a kitchen/diner with fridge, 4 ring calor gas stove, kettle, toaster, tables and chairs, all pots, pans etc and a sleeping area consisting of 10 bunk beds with mattresses, pillows, blankets and duvets (sleeping bags/liners are required). Both rooms have a wood-burning stove with a daily allowance of wood included (extra is available from the farm). There's also a shower cubicle (metered), toilet, wash basin and a small seating area. Outside there is ample parking with a small patio area, tables and chairs. A pub serving meals is nearby (approx a quarter of a mile).

Keswick is 5 miles, Grasmere 7 miles. Open all year. Pets by arrangement. The barn is ideal for quite country retreats, not suitable for late night drinking parties.

DETAILS

- **Open** - All year, arrival by 9pm unless arranged.
- **Number of beds** - 10
- **Booking** - Advanced booking recommended.
- **Price per night** - £16pp. Sole use £150 from March 2017.
- **Public Transport** - Local and national buses stop at the end of the lane on A591.
- **Directions** - Travelling on the A591 SE from Keswick, after about 5 miles take 1st lane on left after junction with B5322. Barn is after about 100m.

CONTACT: Mrs Jean Hodgson
Tel: 017687 74391
stybeckfarm@btconnect.com www.stybeckfarm.co.uk
Stybeck Farm, Thirlmere, Keswick, Cumbria CA12 4TN

DERWENTWATER
ENGLAND INDEPENDENT HOSTEL

Family run and friendly, Derwentwater Independent Hostel is a Georgian mansion in 17 acres of grounds complete with its own waterfall. The glorious setting near the lake gives wonderful views of the surrounding mountains and is just 2 miles from Keswick. A great base for individuals, families, groups, family parties, reunions and conferences, the hostel has lounges, games rooms and free WiFi. It is licensed and offers a full meal service with a good reputation for home made food. Many of the spacious bedrooms have lovely original architecture. The grounds are teeming with wildlife including red squirrels, with plenty of space for children to play, football goals, picnic tables and open water access to launch canoes and boats onto the lake. Borrowdale has something for everyone; walks along the lake shore, challenging mountains, water sports, mountain biking, climbing, gorge scrambling and tourist attractions. Friendly staff are happy to help you organise your days. The C2C route passes close by.

DETAILS

- **Open** - Most of the year, 7am - 11pm.
- **Number of beds** - 88: 1x4, 2x5, 3x6, 3x8,1x10,1x22.
- **Booking** - Advance booking recommended - especially for groups.
- **Price per night** - From £21.00 (adult), £16.50 (child). Family rooms from £72 (for 4). The smallest rooms are for 4 & 5 but please ask if you want a room for 2 or 3.
- **Public Transport** - Train to Penrith then X4 bus to Keswick. From Keswick take the launch to the Ashness gate jetty; 100m from hostel or bus 78 to hostel drive.
- **Directions** - Two miles south of Keswick on the B5289 Borrowdale road. Hostel entrance is directly off the main road, 150m after the turning to Watendlath.

CONTACT:
Tel: 017687 77246
reception@derwentwater.org www.derwentwater.org
Barrow House, Borrowdale, Keswick, Cumbria, CA12 5UR

GREAT LANGDALE
BUNKHOUSE

Great Langdale Bunkhouse offers great value accommodation for groups, families and individuals. Situated amidst some of the finest mountain scenery in England with immediate access to world class mountain biking, road cycling, walking, fell running and climbing. The whole place is set up to explore the amazing mountains and ideal for those who love the outdoors. The bunkhouse has 21 beds divided into 3 twins, 1 of 7 and 1 of 8 (all bunk beds). There is biomass cental heating throughout with separate male and female shower and toilet facilities. Drying room and secure bike storage (by prior arrangement). No cooking or dining facilities but Sticklebarn Tavern is right next door serving good value lunch and dinners. A hearty breakfast is available at the nearby New Dungeon Ghyll Hotel. Sheet, pillow & pillowcase are provided, BYO sleeping bag and towels. Duvets can be booked via the online room booking system. Well behaved dogs are allowed in a private room with owner.

DETAILS

■ **Open** - All year, all day.
■ **Number of beds** - 21: 3x2, 1x7, 1x8.
■ **Booking** - Booking is advised for all of summer, all weekends and for larger groups. 50% deposit required.
■ **Price per night** - From £15pn.
■ **Public Transport** - Bus service 516 to Great Langdale from Ambleside, ask for New Dungeon Ghyll Hotel, walk 2 mins (timetable 01946 632222).
■ **Directions** - From the A591 Windermere to Keswick road at Ambleside take the A593 turn to Coniston / Torver. After two miles take the B5343 to Great Langdale via Chapel Stile. The bunkhouse is behind the Sticklebarn Tavern.

CONTACT: Ben or Sabrina
Tel: 015394 37725
langdale.bunkhouse@gmail.com www.greatlangdalebunkhouse.co.uk
New Stickle Cottage, Great Langdale, LA22 9JU

Situated in the heart of Windermere and central Lakeland, you will find this cosy, friendly hostel ideally situated for exploring the surrounding area. The owners can advise you on routes for walks and cycle rides and provide you with maps. Staff can also help to organise abseiling, canoeing, sailing, windsurfing, even caving! There is easy access to the lake and fells from our door and the hostel is adjacent to the main 555 bus route through Lakeland.

The hostel with its cosy dormitories provides you with every comfort but at a budget price. The hostel is right next to a number of pubs, restaurants and take-aways and only minutes away from the rail and bus stations. Lockers are available. Internet access with WiFi and Sky TV keep you in touch! A well equipped kitchen and comfortable common room make your stay one to remember.

DETAILS

- **Open** - All year, 24 hours with key code for front door.
- **Number of beds** - 20:- 1x6, 2x4, 2 x double with single above.
- **Booking** - Essential, 24 hours in advance.
- **Price per night** - £16.50 dorms/£19.50 private rooms. £2 discount per night for stays of 3+ nights (Nov-Mar) inc self service continental breakfast & free tea/coffee.
- **Public Transport** - Windermere train station is 2 minutes' walk. National Express coach stop 2 minutes' walk.
- **Directions** - Turn left out of the station, walk to the information centre, the hostel is opposite, between Open Door Properties and the Lamp Lighter Bar, 2 minutes' walk from station.

CONTACT: Paul
Tel: 015394 46374
info@lakedistrictbackpackers.co.uk www.lakedistrictbackpackers.co.uk
High Street, Windermere, Cumbria, LA23 1AF

St John's-in-the-Vale Camping Barn is adapted from an 18th century stable and hayloft, in an idyllic setting. Overlooking St John's Beck, the peaceful hill farm has stunning views to Blencathra, Helvellyn and Castle Rock.

The Barn has a sleeping area upstairs (mattress provided) with a sitting and dining area below. Separate toilet, shower and cooking area (bring your own stove, cooking and eating equipment) are within the building. A wood-burning stove provides a focal point and warmth!

There is a BBQ and seating area outside and, as there is no light pollution, the star-filled night skies are magical. Northern Lights have been seen too! Low Bridge End Farm has a tea garden - all home baking.

To see more and book online go to the Lakeland Camping Barns website.

DETAILS

- **Open** - All year, 24 hours.
- **Number of beds** - 8 : 1x8
- **Booking** - Advised in advance. Credit card booking available on 017687 74301
- **Price per night** - £10.00 per person.
- **Public Transport** - Trains terminate at Windermere. From there take a 555 bus towards Keswick. Get off at Thirlmere Dam Road End (Smaithwaite). Climb over ladder stile and we are ½ mile north along a footpath.
- **Directions** - Leave M6 at junction 40. Take A66 towards Keswick for 14 miles. Turn left onto B5322 St Johns-in-the-Vale Road. 3 miles along the road on the right.

CONTACT: Graham or Sarah
Tel: 017687 79242 (Bookings 017687 74301)
info@campingbarn.com www.campingbarn.com
Low Bridge End Farm, St John's-in-the-Vale, Keswick, CA12 4TS

CARLISLE DIOCESAN
YOUTH CENTRE

Carlisle Diocesan Youth Centre is located near St John's-in-the-Vale just four miles from Keswick. The centre offers flexible accommodation for a variety of groups in modern en suite 4-6 bed bunkrooms. With fell walking, climbing, orienteering, geo-caching and cycling on the doorstep and freedom, space and amazing views from the buildings, this is the perfect place for a group retreat, large family get-together or activity field trips. Projection equipment, flip-chart easel and TV & video/DVD player are available by arrangement with the Chaplain. School House and Chapel House sleep 25 and 14 respectively with well equipped self-catering kitchens, communal spaces and comfortable rooms. The buildings can be hired separately or together. Visitors must bring their own sleeping bag, pillowcase and towel etc. Groups are responsible for providing all consumable items including toilet rolls and cleaning materials.

DETAILS

- **Open** - All year, 24 hours.
- **Number of beds** - 39: School House 25: 1x6,1x5,3x4,1x2, Chapel House 14: 3x4,1x2.
- **Booking** - Book via phone or email. Availability shown on website.
- **Price per night** - £13.50 pp for mixed groups (adults, children, young people, students) from outside Cumbria. £12.00 pp for mixed groups (adults, children, young people, students) from Cumbria. £17pp for all adult-only groups.
- **Public Transport** - The centre is well signposted from the A66 ('Youth Centre') and from the B5322 St John's-in-the-Vale road ('Diocesan Youth Centre').
- **Directions** - Trains at Windemere and Penrith, bus 555 Windemere to Keswick stops about 40 minutes' walk away.

CONTACT: The Revd. Peter Barnes
Tel: 017687 79714
carlisledyc@gmail.com www.cdyc.org.uk/
Carlisle Diocese Youth Centre, St John's-in-the-Vale, Keswick, Cumbria, CA12 4UB

MAGGS HOWE
CAMPING BARN
ENGLAND

Kentmere is a quiet, unspoilt valley within the Lake District National Park. It's a ramblers' paradise with woods, fields, lanes, a scattering of traditional lakeland farms and dwellings and of course the fells with their walks so favoured by Wainwright. The Lakeland to Lindisfarne long distance path passes this way as well as the mountain bikers' and horse riders' Coast to Coast. Kentmere offers plenty of activities which include biking, riding and fishing, but most of all quiet enjoyment. A pleasant day can be spent in Kendal and Lake Windermere which are only 20 minutes away. Maggs Howe provides B&B in 3 rooms of the farmhouse and a camping barn with two sleeping areas, kitchen, two showers and toilets. Bring a sleeping bag for the camping barn, mattresses are provided. Breakfasts and suppers are available at the farmhouse with notice.

DETAILS

- **Open** - All year, 24 hours.
- **Number of beds** - 22: Camping Barn 14: 1x6, 1x4 + 4 mattresses. B&B: 8: 1x4(family), 1x2 (double), 1x2 (twin).
- **Booking** - 50% deposit for groups. Individuals can book but it is not essential
- **Price per night** - Camping Barn: Mid week £12pp or £120 sole use. Friday and Saturday night must be sole use booking of £240 for two nights or £180 for one night. Full breakfast £8. Evening meals from £14. B&B: £30-£35 per person.
- **Public Transport** - Staveley 4 miles with train and bus service. Oxenholme train station is 10 miles. Kendal / Windermere National Express 8 miles.
- **Directions** - GR 462 041, MAP OS English Lakes South East. Green Quarter. Leave the A591 and come into Staveley, proceed to Kentmere for 4 miles, then take right fork to Green Quarter keeping right until you reach Maggs Howe.

CONTACT: Christine Hevey
Tel: 01539 821689
enquiry@maggshowe.co.uk
Maggs Howe, Kentmere, Kendal, Cumbria, LA8 9JP

DENTON
HOUSE

Denton House is a purpose built hostel and outdoor centre in the heart of the Lake District offering bunkhouse style accommodation designed for groups. There is plenty of hot water for showers, central heating throughout, a self-catering kitchen, a large dining room and solid bunk-beds. All linen provided. Breakfasts, packed lunches and evening meals are all available upon request.

The centre is also available for large groups looking for sole use. There is a car park for 40 cars and the outdoor centre provides traditional activities for groups seeking an adrenaline rush. Activities include ghyll scrambling, climbing, abseiling, via ferrata and mountain challenge events. Storage for kayaks and bikes is available and there's access to the River Greta just across the road.

DETAILS

- **Open** - Open all year round (including Christmas). Office hours 9am - 8pm everyday.
- **Number of beds** - 56: 1x4, 2x6, 1x8, 2x10, 1x12.
- **Booking** - Due to large number of school, youth and military groups, corporate team-builds and celebration weekends, early booking is advised. 25% deposit for groups with the balance due 28 days before arrival.
- **Price per night** - £17 midweek, £19 weekend. Sole use £900 (midweek) £999 (weekend). Breakfast £6. Pack Lunch £6. Dinner £10. Activities £30/half day.
- **Public Transport** - Nearest train station Penrith, buses hourly to Keswick.
- **Directions** - Go out of Keswick towards Windermere, keep the river on your left (approx 10 mins). Denton House is on the right after post sorting office.

CONTACT: Libby Scott
Tel: 01768 775351
keswickhostel@hotmail.co.uk www.dentonhouse-keswick.co.uk
Penrith Road, Keswick, Cumbria, CA12 4JW

THE WHITE HORSE
INN BUNKHOUSE

The White Horse Inn Bunkhouse has been converted from the stables of this traditional Lake District inn at the foot of Blencathra. The White Horse is a country pub with great pub food, open fires, local ales and a warm welcome. Four of the stables have been converted into bedrooms, two sleeping 6 people in bunks, one sleeping eight and one sleeping four. There is a basic kitchen with electric hob, microwave and a coin operated clothes dryer and a communal dining area seating 16-20 people. The toilet block has male and female toilets, basins and showers. Guests are welcome to socialise in the pub which is open from 11am to 11pm and has free WiFi, hot drinks and good beer. Food is served 12-2pm and 6-9pm on weekdays and all day on weekends. The White Horse is just outside the picturesque village of Threlkeld close to Sharp Edge, with paths to the mountains immediately from the beer garden. The Coast to Coast (C2C) passes the front of the inn, a popular stop for thirsty cyclists and walkers. New for 2017 - Bunkhouse for 26 people in 5 x 4 bed rooms and 1 x 6 bed room.

DETAILS

- **Open** - All year, all day access.
- **Number of beds** - 24. 1 x 8, 2 x 6, 1 x 4 (+ 26 beds in new bunkhouse mid 2017)
- **Booking** - Book by phone or email.
- **Price per night** - £12 pppn, 4 bunk room £48, 6 bunk room £72, 8 bunk £96, sole use £220. Pillow, sheet and duvet £5 for the stay. Enquire for Xmas/New Year prices
- **Public Transport** - From Penrith train station, 15 mins by taxi or catch the X5 or X4 bus from Penrith to Keswick and ask for Scales, stops outside pub on the A66.
- **Directions** - Just off A66 Penrith to Keswick road, 4m from Keswick (see signs).

CONTACT: Phil or Cozmin
Tel: 017687 79883
info@thewhitehorse-blencathra.co.uk www.thewhitehorse-blencathra.co.uk
The White Horse Inn, Scales, Nr Threlkeld, Keswick, CA12 4SY

BLAKEBECK FARM
CAMPING BARN

Blakebeck Farm Camping Barn is set amidst wildflower meadows in Mungrisdale with panoramic views. It is on the C2C cycle route, the Cumbrian Way passes close by and there are many Lake District Peaks within easy reach. It is ideal as an overnight for cyclists and weekend breaks for walkers and families. There is a large upstairs room where up to 10 people can sleep on the mattresses provided (BYO sleeping bags) and there is a farmhouse table and chairs. Next to this room is a kitchen with hob, microwave, toaster and sink. Utensils, tea towels and washing up liquid are provided. Downstairs are two shower rooms each with a toilet and handwash basin and a third room with sink and drying facilities, ideal for bike storage. For those travelling light, towels, bedding and DIY breakfast and packed lunches can be pre-booked. The Barn has great WiFi. Showers cost £1 and electric oil heaters are available for a small charge. One dog is welcome when a group has sole use. Not suitable for partying groups. There are also two self-catering cottages on the farm.

DETAILS

- **Open** - All year all day
- **Number of beds** - 10: 1x10
- **Booking** - by phone or email
- **Price per night** - £10 per person. Sole use £100. Dog £10 per stay.
- **Public Transport** - Train station at Penrith, buses to Mungrisdale. Road End, about 15 minutes walk from the barn.
- **Directions** - A66 Penrith to Keswick take turning to Mungrisdale and Caldbeck, after half a mile take left turn to Blakebeck Farm.

CONTACT: Judith
Tel: 017687 79957 mobile: 07789287121
j.egan001@btinternet.com blakebeckfarm.co.uk
Blakebeck, Mungrisdale, Penrith, CA11 0SZ

Skiddaw House is a remote, mountain hostel, accessible only on foot or by mountain bike. At 1550 feet (470m), it is the highest hostel in Britain and is an ideal base for exploring the quiet Northern Fells.

A former shooting lodge and shepherd's bothy on the Cumbria Way, the hostel offers simple, yet comfortable accommodation. Solar panels provide hot water and lighting, whilst wood-burning stoves provide the only heating. There is no mains electricity, phone signal, internet or TV to distract from the tranquil surroundings. The hostel is self-catering, but our small shop stocks everything you need to make a simple meal. The nearest road is 3.5 miles away. Walkers and cyclists are advised to bring a map and torch. Camping available with use of hostel facilities.

DETAILS

- **Open** - March to Oct. Group bookings only over winter. Check in from 5pm, check out by 10am.
- **Number of beds** - 22 : 1 x 8, 2 x 5, 1 x 4
- **Booking** - Book on the YHA website or email/phone the hostel
- **Price per night** - From £18 (adult), £9.50 (under 18). YHA members £1.50 - £3 discount. Camping £8. Credit / debit cards not accepted.
- **Public Transport** - Nearest trains and National Express coaches at Penrith. From Penrith take X4 or X5 bus to Keswick. From Keswick it is a 5 mile walk to the hostel.
- **Directions** - Grid reference: NY 288 291. No access for cars, nearest road 3½ miles. Vehicles can be left at Fell car park by Blencathra Centre above Threlkeld, at Lattrigg car park (end of Gale Rd near Applethwaite) or at Whitewater Dash Falls south of Bassenthwaite.

CONTACT: Martin or Suzy
Tel: 07747 174293
skiddawhouse@yahoo.co.uk   www.skiddawhouse.co.uk
Bassenthwaite, Keswick, Cumbria, CA12 4QX

CATBELLS
CAMPING BARN

Catbells Camping Barn is part of a traditional set of farm buildings dating back to the 14th century. The barn is on the slopes of Catbells in the tranquil Newlands Valley, with magnificent views over the Lake District. The Cumberland Way passes through the farmyard. Keswick is only 4 miles away and both Borrowdale and Buttermere are within walking distance. The camping barn is on the ground floor and has sleeping accommodation for 10, with mattresses provided. Bring your own sleeping bags. The barn is heated with a multi-fuel stove (not suitable for cooking) and wood can be bought at the farm. In the adjacent building is a toilet and a cooking area suitable for a camping stove. Bring your own stove, cutlery, crockery and cooking utensils. It is possible to walk to a pub which serves food.

DETAILS

- **Open** - All year, 24 hours.
- **Number of beds** - 10: 1x10
- **Booking** - Advisable, groups require deposit.
- **Price per night** - £10.00 per person
- **Public Transport** - Trains at Penrith (20 miles). Regular buses (meet the trains) from Penrith to Keswick. Summer bus from Keswick to Buttermere stops ½ mile from barn. Summer ferry from Keswick to Hawes End (¾ mile from barn).
- **Directions** - GR 245211. Leave the M6 at Junction 40 and follow the A66 past Keswick. At Portinscale turn left, follow the Buttermere road for 3 miles. Turn sharp left at Stair, follow the sign for Skelgill, up the road for ½ mile and right into farmyard. Please follow these directions and not those from 'sat-nav'.

CONTACT: Mrs Grave
Tel: 017687 74301
info@lakelandcampingbarns.co.uk   www.lakelandcampingbarns.co.uk
Low Skelgill Farm, Newlands, Keswick, Cumbria, CA12 5UE
Hawse End Centre, Portinscale, Keswick, Cumbria, CA12 5UE

Towards the head of Ennerdale valley, one of the most beautiful, least spoilt and quietest valleys in the Lake District, at the foot of Pillar and Red Pike sits Low Gillerthwaite Field Centre. An ideal base for fell walking, classic rock climbs, bird and wildlife watching, mountain biking, orienteering, canoeing and environmental studies.

Originally a 15th century farmhouse, the centre has group self-catering facilities, drying room, a library of environmental books, a large barn for indoor activities (ideal for barn dances), a group lecture room and two lounges with log-burning fires. Due to its remoteness the centre generates its own electricity via a hydroelectric scheme. Vehicle access is by forest track and a BT payphone is on site (most mobiles do not work here). Low Gillerthwaite is an ideal base for clubs, extended family groups, school and youth groups.

DETAILS

- **Open** - All year (except Christmas and Boxing Day), 24 hours.
- **Number of beds** - 40: 2x4, 1x8, 1x10, 1x14.
- **Booking** - See booking link. Always phone to check availability.
- **Price per night** - From £11.50 per person (children and students), £15.50 (adults), camping is £5 per person.
- **Public Transport** - Whitehaven station 12 miles. Buses to Ennerdale Bridge from Cleator Moor or Cockermouth (5 miles).
- **Directions** - GR NY 139 141. From Ennerdale Bridge take road east, via Croasdale, 3.5 miles to Ennerdale Forest. Continue on forest track 3 miles. Hostel is the first building below the RH road, 200m before the YHA.

CONTACT: Ellen or Walter
Tel: 01946 861229
Warden@lgfc.org.uk www.lgfc.org.uk
Ennerdale, Cleator, CA23 3AX

HAWSE END
CENTRE

Hawse End Centre, at the head of the magnificent Borrowdale Valley and directly across Derwentwater from Keswick, has stunning views and access to lakeside, mountains and Keswick (via launch or lakeside walk). The house is a large, comfortable, country mansion, ideal for groups. It has a well equipped and spacious self-catering kitchen with a professional catering oven & hob, a large dining room, lounge, games room, classroom and extensive grounds leading down to the lake shore. The Cottage for individuals, families and groups has a basic self-catering kitchen, living room and a patio with picnic tables and views of the lake. Two yurts with stunning views and transparent domes for star gazing, are on a wooden platform close to the house. These felt and wood structures have electricity, tables and chairs (optional) and mats for sleeping. Picnic tables, a gas barbecue and water are also on the platform with toilets close by. A catering service can be made available by prior arrangement. Outdoor activities can all be booked in advance and are led by experienced and well qualified outdoor leaders.

DETAILS

- **Open** - All year.
- **Number of beds** - House 49: (9 rooms). Cottage 24: (6 rooms). Yurts: 24 (2x12)
- **Booking** - Please book by phone or email. Deposit required.
- **Price per night** - Price on application, subject to availability and season.
- **Public Transport** - Trains at Penrith (18 miles). Keswick Launch passenger ferry from Keswick to Hawse End. Service buses within walking distance in high season.
- **Directions** - 4 miles outside of Keswick.

CONTACT:
Tel: 01768 812280
cumbriaoutdoors.enquiries@cumbria.gov.uk www.cumbria.gov.uk/
Hawse End Centre, Portinscale, Keswick, Cumbria, CA12 5UE

HIGH HOUSE

High House in Seathwaite, at the head of the popular valley of Borrowdale, offers comfortable bunkhouse/hostel self-catering accommodation in a converted 16/17 century farmhouse set within its own grounds. It is popular with walking and climbing clubs and is regularly used by outdoor education and corporate groups. Early booking is advised, especially for weekends. The building is let to one group at a time. Two dorms are available each with toilet, washbasin and shower. There is a third dorm reserved for K Fellfarers members and on some occasions club members may use this room during your stay. There is a common room with stove, easy chairs, library and dining area, a fully fitted kitchen and car parking. You will need to bring sleeping bags or duvets plus sheets, pillows, tea towels, firelighters and food. Basic food (eg. milk) is available from the café in Rosthwaite and the nearest supermarket is in Keswick. Eco friendly washing up liquid is provided to aid the septic tank.

DETAILS

■ **Open** - All year, 24 hours.
■ **Number of beds** - 26: 1x18, 1x8
■ **Booking** - Early booking essential. Groups only. Min. 2 nights at weekends. £40pn deposit. Send to Briarcliffe, Carr Bank Rd, Carr Bank, Milnthorpe, Cumbria, LA7 7LE.
■ **Price per night** - £150, irrespective of numbers, including electricity and heating. £50 key deposit is required.
■ **Public Transport** - The nearest train station is in Penrith 26 miles away. Buses run from Penrith to Keswick, and from Keswick to Seatoller (1 mile from High House).
■ **Directions** - OS Grid Ref NY235119

CONTACT: Hugh Taylor
Tel: 01524 762 067
jhugh.taylor@btinternet.com www.highhouse.talktalk.net/ff.htm
High House, Seathwaite, Borrowdale, Keswick.

Lying in the picturesque Loweswater Valley, Swallow Barn is part of a traditional set of buildings dating back to 1670 on a working beef and sheep farm. The barn accommodates 18 people on mattresses in 4 sleeping areas. There is a cooking and eating area with tables and chairs, 2 metered showers and a metered plug socket and 2 toilets.

The barn is an excellent base for exploring the western fells with both high and low level walks and spectacular views, or you can enjoy the peace and tranquillity of the valley. The Coast to Coast cycle route is right on the doorstep. The Kirkstyle pub provides excellent food, just over a mile away and the market town of Cockermouth is only 8 miles. Check the Lakeland Camping Barns website and book online or ring the booking agent on 01768774301

DETAILS

- **Open** - All year, all day.
- **Number of beds** - 18: 1x9, 3x3
- **Booking** - Book online in advance, especially for school and bank holidays. Book online or ring the booking agents 017687 74301
- **Price per night** - £10 per person.
- **Public Transport** - The nearest train station is Penrith with a bus to Cockermouth, then a taxi costing approximately £40.
- **Directions** - Leave the M6 at junct. 40 and follow the A66 to the Egremont turn off at Cockermouth. Follow the A5086, Egremont road for 6 miles. Turn left at Mockerkin and follow road to Loweswater. The farm is just past the Grange Hotel on the left.

CONTACT: Kath Leck
Tel: Booking office 017687 74301, Farm 01946 861465
info@lakelandcampingbarns.co.uk www.lakelandcampingbarns.co.uk
Waterend Farm, Loweswater, Cockermouth, Cumbria, CA13 0SU

THE OLD SCHOOL
WYTHOP MILL

Once a Victorian village school, The Old School offers simple, heated, self-catering accommodation in a delightful rural setting in the northern Lake District. Ideal for family groups, school/youth groups, cycling/walking groups. Set on the flank of Ling Fell on the C2C cycle route, only a mile from the A66 between Keswick and Cockermouth and a few minutes' drive from Bassenthwaite Lake and Skiddaw. Whinlatter Forest Park is nearby for walking and mountain biking, with western fells, Keswick, Derwentwater, Borrowdale within easy reach. The main building has a fully equipped kitchen, common room, and three bedrooms with bunks. Outside is a Bothy and separate buildings for toilets, washrooms and showers. The Old School is managed by volunteers from the local 'Dewode' charity to fund a health centre in an impoverished Ugandan village, and to support a charitable trust for the educational needs of local children.

DETAILS

- **Open** - All year.
- **Number of beds** - 20: Main building 18: 1x10, 1x6, 1x2   Bothy 2: 1x2
- **Booking** - Book by email. Availability shown on website.
- **Price per night** - £12 per person per night.
- **Public Transport** - Trains at Penrith, buses hourly to Keswick. Bus X4 or X5 towards Workington, alight at Wheatsheaf Inn, Embleton. 1 mile walk to Wythop Mill.
- **Directions** - Leave M6 (Jct 40) and follow A66 westwards towards Cockermouth. Pass Keswick and Bassenthwaite Lake, Wythop Mill is signposted to the left. At crossroads in centre of hamlet, cross bridge and follow road through houses uphill. Turn left after last house, and look on the right. Marked 'school' on OS Maps.

CONTACT: John Atkinson
Tel: 07941 208 356
info@theoldschool-dewode.org.uk www.theoldschool-dewode.org.uk
The Old School, Wythop Mill, Embleton, Cockermouth, Cumbria, CA13 9YP

HILLSIDE FARM
BUNKBARN

A Georgian farmstead in a conservation area just steps away from Hadrian's Wall. Hillside Farm, in the small village of Boustead Hill, near the Solway Coast AONB and RSPB nature reserve, has stunning views over the Solway Firth marshes towards Scotland. Hadrian's Wall National Trail and Hadrian's Cycleway pass right by. Hillside farm is a working farm and the 4th generation of farmers welcome you to to the bunkbarn or the B&B rooms in the farmhouse. The bunkbarn, in a converted stable block, has cooking slabs, cutlery, crockery, a 2 ring gas stove, microwave and small electric oven. There are hot showers. Towels and sleeping bags can be hired if required. The communal downstairs areas are heated but not the upstairs bunkroom. Shopping deliveries can be arranged via the farmhouse and with notice you can have breakfast or bacon sandwiches. Walking, cycling and family groups are most welcome.

DETAILS

- **Open** - All year, 10am to 9pm.
- **Number of beds** - 12
- **Booking** - Book by phone or email.
- **Price per night** - £12 per person including shower. £4 full English breakfast, £2 bacon/sausage sandwiches.
- **Public Transport** - Trains at Carlisle. Bus: Stagecoach 93 (NOT RUNNING ON SUNDAYS or BH's). Ask to get off at Boustead Hill Nr Burgh-by-sands.
- **Directions** - From Jnct 44 of M6 take the western bypass sign posted Workington. Follow until you reach a roundabout signed to Burgh-by-Sands and Bowness on Solway. Follow to Burgh and continue for 2 miles. After crossing cattle grid on to Marsh Road take next left to Boustead Hill then 2nd left under arches into farmyard.

CONTACT: Mrs Sandra Rudd
Tel: 01228 576398
ruddshillside1@btinternet.com www.hadrianswalkbnb.co.uk
Hillside Farm, Boustead Hill, Burgh-by-Sands, Carlisle, Cumbria, CA5 6AA

WAYFARERS
INDEPENDENT HOSTEL ENGLAND

Wayfarers Independent Hostel is situated close to Penrith town centre, providing excellent value accommodation to those visiting Penrith, the Eden Valley and the North Lakes. Penrith is on the edge of the Lake District National Park, close to the M6 and on the West Coast Mainline with shops, pubs, restaurants and a cinema all within 5 minutes' walk of the hostel. The Coast to Coast cycle route passes 100m from the doorstep, secure indoor bike storage, a drying room, and cleaning and maintenance facilities make this an ideal place to stay after a hard day's ride. Newly refurbished in a comfortable, modern style, facilities include a lounge, full kitchen and dining facilities and an outside seating area for guests to enjoy. All bedrooms are en suite with made up beds (sheets & duvets), lockers, bedside lights, towels for hire and have free WiFi. Individuals, small parties and groups of up to 18 are welcome.

DETAILS

- **Open** - All year, reception open 8am-11am, 4pm-9pm.
- **Number of beds** - 16: 1x2, 1x6, 2x4.
- **Booking** - Recommended online, by phone or email.
- **Price per night** - From £22pp (dorm room bed). Sole use available from £320 pn. Family rates available Sun-Thurs from £55. Breakfast and packed lunches available.
- **Public Transport** - Trains and National Express to Penrith train station, 104 bus from Carlisle and X4-5 from Workington to Penrith bus station.
- **Directions** - M6 jcn 40 into Penrith along Ullswater Road. Past the station, bear left at first roundabout, straight over second heading down the hill past Booths and Morrisons. At bottom of the hill follow round to the left and take first turning on left.

CONTACT: Mark Rhodes
Tel: 01768 866011
guests@wayfarershostel.com www.wayfarershostel.com
19 Brunswick Square, Penrith, Cumbria, CA11 7LR

CARLISLE
CITY HOSTEL

Carlisle City Hostel is Carlisle's only independent hostel. Located on picturesque Abbey Street, the building is an old Georgian terrace that can accommodate up to 20 guests. There is a communal kitchen for you to prepare your own meals, communal lounge with TV, DVDs and book swap and a dining room. Free tea, coffee and WiFi is available in communal areas. All prices include a basic breakfast. Secure bicycle and luggage storage is located in the large cellar. Come and explore this wonderful city and its surrounds. The staff look forward to welcoming you as their guest in their hostel and their city. On street parking is free from 6.30pm-8.30am during the week and all day Sunday. Nearest carpark: Devonshire Walk.

DETAILS

- **Open** - All year. Check in is between 3pm – 8pm ONLY (Sunday 4pm-8pm).
- **Number of beds** - 20 : 2x6, 2x4 (family/triple/double).
- **Booking** - By website with first night deposit. Cash only on arrival. Check before booking if you wish to arrive outside of check in times. Deposits are non-refundable.
- **Price per night** - From £18 to £25 pp. Groups of over 8 by pre-arrangement only.
- **Public Transport** - Carlisle City Hostel is located in the city centre of Carlisle. Bus station and train station are 5 minutes' walk from the front door of the hostel.
- **Directions** - From city centre: English Street bears left onto Castle Street, past cathedral. Left onto Paternoster Row which becomes Abbey Street. From M6 Jnc 43: follow signs for city centre. At Nando's traffic lights follow the road left. Get in the right hand lane and take a right through the old city walls. Turn left onto Victoria Viaduct then 2nd right -W Walls this becomes Annetwell Street. Turn right onto Castle Street. Take the first right onto Paternoster Row which becomes Abbey Street.

CONTACT: Jonathan Quinlan
Tel: 07914 720821
info@carlislecityhostel.com www.carlislecityhostel.com
36 Abbey Street, Carlisle, CA3 8TX

BUNKHOUSE & CAMPING ENGLAND

Set in the stunning North Pennines Area of Outstanding Natural Beauty, often described as England's last wilderness, this location is ideal for anyone who loves the great outdoors - walkers, cyclists and mountain bikers . The 36 mile Isaac's Tea Trail walk passes through the site; directly on the C2C and with bicycle hire (including electric bikes) available nearby.The bunkhouse sleeps up to 24 in 3 bunkrooms of 4/5, 9 and 10 and includes a relaxing lounge, self-catering kitchen, modern shower room and large conservatory for chilling out in! Breakfast and evening meals can be provided for larger groups if pre-booked. Nestled between a special nature conservation area and the wildflower meadow, the campsite has been created with tiered pitches to enhance the infinite views across the Nent valley. Electric hook-ups for caravans and motorhomes are also available within the car park. The site has its own private supply of spring water, unique outdoor equipment washing area and secure bike and gear store. It has recently been awarded a Silver Green Tourism Award for commitment to sustainability.

DETAILS

- **Open** - All year, all day access.
- **Number of beds** - 24: 1x4/5, 1x9, 1x10.
- **Booking** - Contact by email or phone
- **Price per night** - £20pp, sole use £380 or 3 nights £1080. Camping £10 (adult), £5 (child). Motorhomes/caravans £20 for up to 2 people.
- **Public Transport** - On 889 / 888 bus routes operated by Wright Bros, Nenthead
- **Directions** - Directly on the A689 between Alston and Nenthead.

CONTACT: Danny Taylor
Tel: 07919 092403/ 01434 382486
info@haggsbank.com haggsbank.com
Haggs Bank Bunkhouse, Nentsbury, Alston, Cumbria, CA9 3LH

ALSTON
YOUTH HOSTEL

Situated in the small town of Alston, Alston Youth Hostel is an ideal place to base your adventures in the North Pennines AONB. Right on the Pennine Way, the South Tyne Trail and approximately halfway on the Coast to Coast Cycle Route, Alston is the perfect destination for cyclists, walkers, families and school and outdoor activity groups. The hostel is run by keen outdoor enthusiasts who know just what you need after a long day in the hills; a hot shower, comfortable bed, hearty home cooked food (evening meals need to be pre-booked but breakfast is always available), large, warm drying room and secure bike storage for 23+ bikes. There is a well equipped kitchen available for self-catering and the dining room and lounge overlook the River South Tyne. The hostel also has a family of red squirrels that they regularly feed and can be seen from the bay window in the dining room!

DETAILS

- **Open** - All year, 8am - 10am, 5pm - 10pm
- **Number of beds** - 30: 2x2, 2x4, 3x6
- **Booking** - Via hostel or YHA website or by phone
- **Price per night** - From £20.50pp, discount for YHA members. Private rooms from £36.00. Sole use from £380 for two nights.
- **Public Transport** - Train – There is no rail link to Alston – nearest stations are Haltwhistle, Penrith, Carlisle, Hexham or Langwathby on the Settle to Carlisle line. Bus – Service 680 from Carlisle via Brampton or the Service 889 to Hexham (Tuesday morning only)
- **Directions** - Car – From the west – A686 from Penrith or A689 from Carlisle. From the east A686 from Hexham (A69 from Newcastle).

CONTACT: Linda, Neil or Jenny
Tel: 01434 381509
alston@yha.org.uk   alstonyouthhostel.co.uk/
Firs Edge, The Firs, Alston, Cumbria, CA9 3RW

Book a bed, a room, or the whole hostel! 4-star rated Ninebanks Youth Hostel is an 18th century cottage in a stunning rural location, recently renovated to a high standard. It's a great place to stay, with high quality en suite bedrooms, a sitting room with log-burner and a spacious dining room - and it has high environmental credentials! This picturesque family-run hostel is open to guests all year round. It has an excellent self-catering kitchen and barbecue area, alternatively catering is available for groups and exclusive hire. In the beautiful county of Northumberland, nestled within the North Pennines and close to the iconic Hadrian's Wall, it provides the perfect base from which to explore this spectacular part of the country. Opening May 2017: two new self-catering high quality chalets, one family and one double to the rear of the hostel.

DETAILS

■ **Open** - All year, open all day, reception from 5pm.
■ **Number of beds** - 28: 2x2/3, 2x4, 1x6, 1x8 + chalets from May 2017.
■ **Booking** - Recommended.
■ **Price per night** - Beds from £10.00, rooms from £34, whole hostel from £200
■ **Public Transport** - Buses are few and get no closer than 1.5miles from the hostel. See the Wright's bus website for the current info. Trains: the nearest train stations are Haydon Bridge 11 miles and Hexham 15 miles (more trains stop at Hexham)
■ **Directions** - In Mohope one mile from Ninebanks village. From A686 take turning signposted Ouston, Ninebanks, Carrshield (left from Northumberland, right from Cumbria) - look out for the blue and white YHA sign. Go down over the cattle grids, turn right at the T junction, follow the road up the hill and the hostel and manager's cottage are the only buildings on the right.

CONTACT: Pauline or Ian
Tel: 01434 345288
contact@ninebanks.com www.ninebanks.org.uk
Orchard House, Mohope, Hexham, Northumberland NE47 8DQ

MILL COTTAGE
BUNKHOUSE

Situated close to the historic Nenthead mines in the centre of the North Pennines Area of Outstanding Natural Beauty, Mill Cottage Bunkhouse sleeps 6 in an upstairs bunkroom. Each "ship's cabin" bunk has blinds for privacy and an internal light and shelf. Downstairs is a small well equipped kitchen and a sitting/dining room. A self-catering continental breakfast is provided and a full english cooked breakfast can be purchased for £4. The local Miner's Arms pub is great for evening meals (please book ahead).

A community shop and bike repair shop are close by in the village.

The bunkhouse is located right on the C2C cycle route in the outstanding countryside of the Roof Of England, making it the perfect base for cyclists and walkers alike. Lockable bike storage is available. Groups please book together to get extra discounts and ensure sole use.

DETAILS

- **Open** - All year all day
- **Number of beds** - 6: 1x6
- **Booking** - via telephone or email.
- **Price per night** - £18 pp. Groups of 6 get a £10 discount when booked together
- **Public Transport** - Nearest train station is at Hexham, there are buses from Hexam to Nenthead just a short walk up the road.
- **Directions** - A689 from Alston, In Nenthead opposite Methodist Church turn right go past Nenthead mines, Mill Cottage is 200 yards further on the left.

CONTACT: Julie or Phil
Tel: 01434 381674
millcottagenenthead@gmail.com www.millcottagebunkhouse.co.uk/index.html
Nenthead, Alston, Cumbria, CA9 3PD

Now owned by a local farming family this hostel is a former 17th century inn with wooden beams and a cosy open fire. It continues to offer friendly accommodation as part of the YHA and IHUK networks in the centre of the Edmundbyers. A self-catering kitchen is available and an in-house bar, serving locally brewed beer as well as a full range of drinks. Enjoy Friday "Pie Night" when a home made pie with something on the side is available. Breakfast can be ordered in advance, as can other meals. There are three pubs close by, all serving food, just ask for a recommendation. Edmundbyers lies in moorland, close to the Northumberland and County Durham boundary, with fine views over Edmundbyers and Muggleswick Commons, two miles from Derwent Reservoir, where sailing and fishing are available and within an AONB. Ideal for walking holidays and there are prehistoric remains to explore. On the Coast to Coast cycle route or for a day out you could visit Hadrian's Wall or the Beamish outdoor museum. The hostel has a campsite within a walled garden, with mature trees and stunning views. Roadside and off-road parking is available.

DETAILS

- **Open** - All year (camping Apr-Oct). Check in 5-10pm, check out 8-10am.
- **Number of beds** - 28: 2x6, 2x5,1x4,1x3. Eight pitches for camping.
- **Booking** - Book by email, phone or online.
- **Price per night** - From £23 (adult), £19 (under 18). Discounts for YHA members: £3 adult, £1.75 under 18. Room for 3 £60, for 4 £70, for 5 £80 and for 6 £90.
- **Public Transport** - Bus 773 twice daily from Consett to Townfield .
- **Directions** - Opposite the shop at the centre of the village of Edmundbyers.

CONTACT: Debbie Clarke
Tel: 01207 255651
info@lowhousehaven.co.uk www.lowhousehaven.co.uk
Low House, Edmundbyers, Consett, Durham,DH8 9NL

ALLENDALE
BUNKHOUSE

The Allendale Bunkhouse opened in October 2014 after being completely refurbished and thoroughly modernised. It sits on the market square in Allendale, overlooking the hustle and bustle of a small countryside town and the fells and river beyond. An oasis for walkers, cyclists, horse riders, families, groups of friends and youth & school groups alike. Allendale is well served with tea rooms, the Forge art gallery & café, a quirky gift shop, pharmacy, Allendale medical practice and the library. Three pubs, all serving food, are a stone's throw away from the bunkhouse. There is also bike hire (electric, mountain and hybrid bikes) and the C2C cycle trail runs close by. Art, heritage and music events run throughout the year across the valley. Book a bunk, a room, a floor (up to 18) or the whole bunkhouse (up to 38) for your group. Downstairs is a large open plan area with a brand new fully equipped kitchen, dining area with seating for up to 34 and a lounge area with comfortable sofas to relax. Double french doors lead onto a BBQ, seating and patio area with steps into the large landscaped garden:

DETAILS

- **Open** - All year, 8am-8pm.
- **Number of beds** - 38: 2x6, 2x4, 1x7, 1x2, 1x3, 1x5
- **Booking** - Via telephone or email. A deposit will be required.
- **Price per night** - From £14 - £30 per person per night.
- **Public Transport** - Nearest train stations: Hexham or Haydon Bridge. Buses available to Allendale Market Place. Pick up service can be arranged.
- **Directions** - On the market place in Allendale, 12 miles from Hexham.

CONTACT: Linda Beck
Tel: 01434618579
info@allendalebunkhouse.co.uk www.allendalebunkhouse.co.uk
Market Place, Allendale, Hexham, NE47 9BD

Situated in the pleasant sleepy village of Rookhope in the stunning surroundings of Weardale. Next door is The Rookhope Inn for a welcome pint and substantial meals. The bunkhouse provides clean, comfortable accommodation with a self service continental breakfast ready for your day's activities. There are kettles, toasters and a microwave with egg poacher. The breakfast bar is stocked with complimentary items for making hot drinks and snacks for breakfast. All welcome, especially cyclists on the Coast 2 Coast (C2C), walkers on the Pennine Journey, Weardale Way, and groups visiting the area. There are 12 bunk beds, each with a personal reading light, and an additional fold-up bed plus a fully fitted disabled wet-room with toilet, basin and shower and one able bodied shower and separate toilet. The large cast iron multi-fuel stove is used from October to March and oil-filled radiators provide extra warmth. There is a tumble dryer and a hair dryer is available on request. Visitors can also camp on the lawns - some camping equipment is available.

DETAILS

- **Open** - All year, all day.
- **Number of beds** - 12 (+1): 1 x 12 plus 1 fold up bed
- **Booking** - Book with deposit by phone/email. Payment in advance for weekends.
- **Price per night** - £24pp incl. snack breakfast. Camping £14 with breakfast, £10 without. Sole use rates negotiable depending on group size and time of year.
- **Public Transport** - Nearest train stations: Hexham 19 miles, Durham 25 miles, Bishop Auckland 23 miles. Buses to Crook, Durham and Bishop Auckland.
- **Directions** - Next door to Rookhope Inn in Rookhope.

CONTACT: Valerie Livingston
Tel: 01388 517656
barrington_bunkhouse@hotmail.co.uk www.barrington-bunkhouse-rookhope.com
Barrington Cottage, Rookhope, Weardale, Co. Durham, DL13 2BG

SLACK HOUSE
FARM

Slack House Farm is a working, organic dairy farm overlooking Birdoswald Roman Fort on Hadrian's Wall. It is on the NCN 72 cycle route and is only 0.5km from the Hadrian's Wall National Trail. The bunkbarn is adjacent to The Scypen café and farm shop and Birdoswald cheese is made on the farm. Accommodation consists of 3 dorms; a 10 bed dorm, a 5 bedded room, and a 3 bed family room (+ child's bed and travel cot). Sheets and shower towels available to hire. Each room has its own shower, toilet, hot water, heated towel rail and electric lighting. There is a worktop with kettle, microwave, fridge and crockery in the shared kitchen/ sitting area, other cooking facilities by arrangement. The wood pellet fired stove warms the shared area and provides under-floor heating. Cooked breakfasts, farmhouse suppers and packed lunches can be provided. There is a laundry with powerful drying room. This is a lovely cosy place to base your Hadrian's Wall stay.

DETAILS

- **Open** - All year. Check in from 17.00hrs, check out by 10.00hrs.
- **Number of beds** - 18: 1x10, 1x5, 1x3 (family)
- **Booking** - Individuals: advisable, credit card confirms. Sole use: essential.
- **Price per night** - Beds £15.00 pp. Sole use of 5 bedded room £60.00, sole use of family room £45.00, sole use 10 bedded dorm £90.00.
- **Public Transport** - Carlisle-Newcastle train line 9km, bus 5km. AD122 bus (April-October) request stop 200m. (Kiln Hill junction).
- **Directions** - On B6318, GR NY670613, From A69, west take turning for Gilsland & Spadeadam. From east take right turn signed Greenhead. Follow Hadrian's Wall signs to Birdoswald. Do not turn left to the fort but continue a further 200 metres.

CONTACT: Dianne Horn
Tel: 016977 47351 Mob: 07900472342
postmaster@slackhousefarm.plus.com www.slackhousefarm.co.uk
Slack House Farm, Gilsland Brampton, Cumbria, CA8 7DB

GREENHEAD
HOSTEL

Greenhead Hostel is a converted methodist chapel in the village of Greenhead on Hadrian's Wall. It is ideal for those walking the Pennine Way or The Wall and is in a great location for those exploring the nearby Roman heritage sites. The church was built in 1886 to serve the village miners and gave its last service in 1972. It has been a hostel since 1978. Greenhead Hostel has a newly refurbished self-catering kitchen with a cooking range ideal for large group catering. There is a lounge with a 50inch TV. There are 40 beds in four rooms of six beds and two rooms of eight beds. These can be booked as family rooms, by groups or by the bed for individuals. Tea and coffee supplies are available and there is a drying room. Above the hostel is a self contained flat with kitchen, lounge, two double rooms and a single room. Evening meals, breakfast and packed lunches are available. The hostel is operated by Greenhead Hotel (over the road) with a welcoming bar and restaurant. VisitEngland approved.

DETAILS

- **Open** - All year (groups only in winter, please enquire), hostel is open all day.
- **Number of beds** - 45: Hostel 40: 4x6. Flat 5: 2dbl, 1 single.
- **Booking** - Book by phone or email.
- **Price per night** - Bunkhouse adult: £15, under 18 £10. Flat £35pp. Reductions for large groups or full rooms. Sole use of hostel £550.
- **Public Transport** - Trains: Haltwhistle 3 miles, Carlisle 19 miles, Newcastle 45 miles. Bus: May to Sept Stagecoach AD 122 from Newcastle to Bowness-on-Solway. Arriva 685 Carlisle-Newcastle passes Haltwhistle station and runs hourly all year.
- **Directions** - On the A69 between Carlisle and Newcastle. Turn off at sign for Greenhead. Turn right at the T junction, the hostel is opposite the Greenhead Hotel.

CONTACT: Diane and family
Tel: 01697 747411
enquiries@greenheadhotelandhostel.co.uk www.greenheadhotelandhostel.co.uk
Greenhead Hotel, Greenhead, Brampton, Cumbria, CA8 7HG

GIBBS HILL
FARM HOSTEL

Gibbs Hill Farm Hostel is a conversion of a barn on a traditional working hill farm near Once Brewed on Hadrian's Wall and close to the Pennine Way. The hostel is designed to reduce energy consumption and is centrally heated throughout. There are 3 bunkrooms, 2 shower rooms, 2 toilets, a well equipped kitchen, comfortable sitting and dining area and a large deck where you can enjoy the evening sun. The hostel has a drying room, lockers, laundry facilities and safe cycle storage. Ideal for families who may take a whole room with private facilities. Study groups welcome. Situated near Hadrian's Wall it is an excellent base for exploring the Roman sites, Hadrian's Wall Trail and Northumberland National Park. Basic items of food may be purchased and evening meals can be ordered the day before. Continental breakfast £5, packed lunches £6.

DETAILS

■ **Open** - All year, hours flexible but no check in after 9pm.
■ **Number of beds** - 18: 3x6
■ **Booking** - Advisable, groups require full payment 4 weeks before arrival.
■ **Price per night** - £18 adult, £12 child (under 12), including bedding.
■ **Public Transport** - Trains at Haltwhistle 6 miles. Regular bus service along A69 between Newcastle and Carlisle, and in summer the Hadrian's Wall bus runs between Newcastle and Carlisle. Alight at Once Brewed Information Centre and walk north to farm. Last bus 5.30pm from Haltwhistle.
■ **Directions** - From the A69, turn north at Bardon Mill, signed 'Once Brewed'. Follow the signs towards 'Housesteads'. At the B6318, turn right and then immediately left towards 'Steel Rigg'. Follow for 1 mile, turn right to 'Gibbs Hill'.

CONTACT: Valerie Gibson
Tel: 01434 344030
val@gibbshillfarm.co.uk www.gibbshillfarm.co.uk
Gibbs Hill Farm, Bardon Mill, Nr Hexham, Northumberland, NE47 7AP

DEMESNE FARM
BUNKHOUSE

This self-catering unit was converted in 2004 from a barn on a working hill farm in the centre of Bellingham in the Northumberland National Park. The farm is situated on the Pennine Way, Route 68, and the Reivers & Sandstone Way cycle routes. The bunkhouse is an ideal base for exploring Northumberland, Hadrian's Wall, Kielder Water and many climbing crags. It accommodates 15 and is perfect for groups, individuals and families. The bedrooms are fitted with hand crafted oak man-sized bunk beds, high quality mattresses, pillows, curtains, cushion flooring and full bed linen. Towels can be hired. Downstairs there is a large living room with wood-burning stove and central heating with leather sofas and WiFi. The large kitchen with under floor heating has electric range cooker, microwave, fridge, freezer, kettle, toaster, crockery, cutlery, cooking utensils and farmhouse table & chairs to seat 15. It has 2 bathrooms with under floor heating, hot showers, basins, toilets. In the courtyard there is ample parking, bike lock up, drying room and a gravelled area with picnic tables.

DETAILS

- **Open** - All year, flexible but no check in after 9pm.
- **Number of beds** - 15: 1x8, 1x4, 1x3.
- **Booking** - Please book in advance.
- **Price per night** - £20 per person, £15 under 18's (including linen).
- **Public Transport** - Trains at Hexham (17 miles), regular bus service from Hexham to Bellingham. Bellingham bus stop 100 metres from bunkhouse. By car: Newcastle 45 mins, Scottish Border 20 mins, Kielder Water 10 mins.
- **Directions** - 100 metres from centre of village, located next to the petrol station.

CONTACT: Robert Telfer
Tel: 01434 220258 Mobile 07967 396345
stay@demesnefarmcampsite.co.uk www.demesnefarmcampsite.co.uk
Demesne Farm, Bellingham, Hexham, Northumberland, NE48 2BS

HOUGHTON NORTH ²⁷⁵
FARM ACCOMMODATION_{ENGLAND}

Houghton North Farm, partly built with stones from Hadrian's Wall, has been in the Laws Family for five generations. It is situated in the beautiful Northumberland countryside right on the Heritage Trail and 15 miles from the start of the Hadrian's Wall Trail. Within the region walkers can enjoy marked woodland trails, rugged moorland & hills and some of the most beautiful deserted beaches in the UK. This newly built, spacious accommodation can take a group of up to 23 and is also ideal for individuals and families. A 4 Star Hostel with Visit Britain, the bunk style rooms (some en suite) are located around the central courtyard and include the use of a self-catering kitchen where a continental breakfast is served. A well appointed TV lounge has a log fire and WiFi access, secure cycle storage and parking. Long-term parking, baggage transfer and packed lunches are available on request. Within 10 minutes' walk are pubs, a restaurant and shops in Heddon-on-the-Wall.

DETAILS

- **Open** - All year. Arrive after 3.30pm depart by 10am.
- **Number of beds** - 22: 1x5, 3x4, 1x3, 1x2.
- **Booking** - Book with a non-refundable deposit of £10 per person per night
- **Price per night** - From £25 to £35 (adult) incl breakfast. Group discounts.
- **Public Transport** - Trains at Wylam (2 miles) and Newcastle (7 miles). The 685/X85/X84/ Newcastle-Carlisle bus stops right outside the farm. Baggage transfer is available.
- **Directions** - From Newcastle take the Heddon turn off the A69 to the B6528. Farm is 1/4 mile outside of the village of Heddon. From Carlisle take Horsley junction and continue approx 3 miles beyond Horsley. Farm is on the left at the top of a hill.

CONTACT: Mrs Paula Laws
Tel: 01661 854364
wjlaws@btconnect.com www.houghtonnorthfarm.co.uk
Houghton North Farm, Heddon-on-the-Wall, Northumberland, NE15 0EZ

TARSET TOR

ENGLAND BUNKHOUSE AND BOTHIES

Tarset Tor's striking timber eco-buildings integrate effortlessly into their natural surroundings deep in the Northumberland National Park close to the Pennine Way, making the most of this remarkable location and providing the perfect base for outdoor adventures. The skies around Tarset Tor are now protected and are an International Dark Sky Reserve, making it the ideal spot from which to gaze at the stars. The stylish bunkhouse is a superb social space, offering comfortable, contemporary sleeping quarters together with shared cooking, eating, showering and lounge facilities. There is also a sauna and pool table. The incredibly versatile floorplan can be quickly adapted to create a welcoming venue for events, conferences and parties. The self-contained Bothy holiday homes enable guests to enjoy the peace and tranquility of Tarset Tor in a more private setting. A small number of campervan/camping pitches are also available.

DETAILS

- **Open** - Mid January - December.
- **Number of beds** - Bunkhouse: 16-20. Bothies: 3x8. 3 campervan bays.
- **Booking** - Booking essential.
- **Price per night** - Bunkhouse £320 to £384 p/n. Lowest rate: Sun-Thur: Bothies: £160-£192pn. Lowest rate Sun-Thur. Campervans £20pn (summer only)
- **Public Transport** - Nearest train station is Hexham 20 miles and a bus runs to Bellingham 3 miles. Pick ups and drop offs can be arranged.
- **Directions** - From A68 to Bellingham follow signs to Kielder Water. After 3 miles at Lanehead junction, look right to see Tarset Tor farmhouse. The bunkhouse and car park is just down the hill on the right.

CONTACT: Rob Cocker and Claire Briggs
Tel: 01434 240980
info@tarset-tor.co.uk www.tarset-tor.co.uk
Greystones, Lanehead, Tarset, Hexham, NE48 1NT

TOMLINSONS
CAFE AND BUNKHOUSE

A former schoolhouse in the historic town of Rothbury overlooking the River Coquet, Tomlinson's is a one-stop shop for low-cost accommodation, wholesome homemade meals and cycle hire. Ideal for families, groups and independent travellers, there are four flexible rooms most with en suite showers. Guests can mix in the communal TV lounge, enjoy the views or a homemade meal in the café. Big windows give beautiful views over the River Coquet. The bunkhouse has laundry facilities, a wash down area for bikes and boots, secure bike storage and drying room. A 50 capacity function room for hire for celebrations and meetings. Rothbury is becoming the Northumberland National Park's cycling hub and the bunkhouse is just metres from a string of off-road cycle tracks and public footpaths. The bunkhouse has a fleet of mountain bikes available to hire and instructors to lead cycle groups of all ages. The Cheviot Hills and the Northumberland Coast are within a 30 minute drive and the area is awash with castles including Alnwick featured in the Harry Potter films.

DETAILS

- **Open** - All year, all day.
- **Number of beds** - 22: 1x8, 1x7, 1x6 plus a double room.
- **Booking** - Book by phone, online or email.
- **Price per night** - From £20 per person, from £400 for the whole bunkhouse.
- **Public Transport** - Trains at Morpeth (15 miles) and Alnmouth. Buses to Newcastle and Morpeth bus station run most days.
- **Directions** - Overlooking River Coquet, on the corner of Bridge Street and Haw Hill off the B6342 in Rothbury.

CONTACT: Christine Nicholson
Tel: 01669 621979
tomlinsonsbunkhouse@gmail.com   www.tomlinsonsrothbury.co.uk
Bridge Street, Rothbury, Northumberland, NE65 7SE

ALNWICK
YOUTH HOSTEL

Once the town's Court House, the accommodation now offered at Alnwick Youth Hostel is much less austere. Opened in 2011, this family friendly 4 star hostel is sure to meet the needs of every traveller, with a variety of en suite rooms, cosy lounge, games room and a bright and airy dining room.

The hostel's town centre location makes it ideal for a visit to historic Alnwick Castle, of recent Downton Abbey and Harry Potter fame, and to The Alnwick Garden, a contemporary pleasure garden in the shadow of the castle. A 15 minute car journey makes the coast, with fantastic castles at Dunstanburgh and Bamburgh, the wildlife haven of the Farne Isles, magical Holy Island and glorious sandy beaches all within easy reach. A short trip inland brings you to the stunning heather clad Cheviot Hills, Hadrian's Wall and Border Reiver country. Great for families, groups, cyclists and backpackers.

DETAILS

- **Open** - All year. Reception open 08:00 to 10:00 and 16:00 to 21:00.
- **Number of beds** - 56: 1xdbl, 2x2, 1x3, 6x4,1x5, 3x6
- **Booking** - Booking advisable by phone or e-mail or book online via our website.
- **Price per night** - Adult dorm beds from £18.50, under 18 from £15. 2 bedded rooms from £49.00. Family 4 bedded rooms from £64.00.
- **Public Transport** - Bus - X15 / X18 / X20 Newcastle - Alnwick. Train station - Alnmouth (4 miles) National Express 591/594 to Alnwick bus station.
- **Directions** - You will find the hostel opposite Alnwick library. A public car park is available at Roxboro Place, to the rear of the Job Centre.

CONTACT: Andrew Clarkson
Tel: 01665 660800
info@alnwickyouthhostel.co.uk www.alnwickyouthhostel.co.uk
34 - 38 Green Batt, Alnwick, Northumberland, NE66 1TU

SPRINGHILL
BUNKHOUSE

Springhill's Lookout & Wigwams are ideal for groups, families or independent travellers looking for great value comfortable accommodation which can be booked as a whole or on a per bed/night basis. Superbly located on the Northumberland heritage coastline and AONB coastal path with stunning views towards the Farne Islands and Cheviot Hills, only 1 mile from Seahouses and 3 miles from Bamburgh. The Lookout has 8 rooms of 4 beds with en suite shower rooms, fully equipped kitchen, dining and sitting area with TV/DVD, free WiFi, BBQ and outdoor seating. The five Wigwams sleep 5 on platform beds with mattresses, electric heating, lights, sockets, fridge, kettle and a separate loo block. The Wigwams have the use of a fully equipped kitchen and dining area with WiFi, TV/DVD and an outdoor seating area with BBQ's and fire pits. Cycle store, drying room and laundry on-site. Pets welcome.

DETAILS

■ **Open** - All year round, arrive 3pm-6pm, departure by 10am. Cleaning 12pm-4pm.
■ **Number of beds** - The Lookout 32: 8x4. Wigwams 25: 7x7.
■ **Booking** - Online, phone or email.
■ **Price per night** - The Lookout £17.50 adult, £15 child (under 16). Wigwams £21.50 adult, £16 child. Prices constant all year round.
■ **Public Transport** - Closest railway stop with easy bus transfers is Berwick upon Tweed. Buses run daily to Seahouses with the nearest bus stop being in North Sunderland which is the top end of Seahouses half a mile from Springhill.
■ **Directions** - Springhill Farm is 0.75miles from the coast road, which runs between Seahouses 1mile and Bamburgh 3.5miles. Alnwick is 15 miles and Berwick 25 miles.

CONTACT: Springhill Accommodation
Tel: 01665 721820
enquiries@springhill-farm.co.uk www.springhill-farm.co.uk
Springhill Farm, Seahouses, Northumberland NE68 7UR

Fly high with the award winning "Albatross"! This clean and modern hostel is located in Newcastle's city centre. All in walking distance from sporting, musical and conference venues, art galleries, historical attractions, food markets and public transport facilities. We are open all year round. The Albatross is primarily designed to provide affordable accommodation in the city centre for the international travellers, walkers, cyclists and bikers. Also ideal for exchange student groups, sports teams, choirs etc. We provide rooms from 2 bed to 12 beds and anything in between for as little as £16.50. The overnight price includes; linen, 24hr reception, fully fitted self-catering kitchen with free tea, coffee and toast, free WiFi access and computer terminals, pool table, satellite TV, free baggage storage and laundry facilities. A young dedicated international team is looking forward to welcoming you.

DETAILS

- **Open** - All year, 24 hours.
- **Number of beds** - 176:
- **Booking** - Recommended. Photo ID at check-in (passport or driving licence).
- **Price per night** - From £16.50pp (dorm).
- **Public Transport** - Five minutes' walk from central train, bus and metro stations.
- **Directions** - Central Station/Megabus drop off point: from main entrance, head right, take the first street on your left (Grainger St), you'll find us on your left 200m uphill. From National Express coach station: head down Scotswood Rd to Central Station. From Airport: take Metro to Central Station (20 mins' travel). From port (ferry): buses travel between the port and Central Station and take 20 mins.

CONTACT: Reception
Tel: 0191 2331330
info@albatrossnewcastle.co.uk   albatrossnewcastle.co.uk
51 Grainger Street, Newcastle upon Tyne, NE1 5JE

Opened in 2016 Calico Barn is perfect for walkers and cyclists passing on the adjacent walking and cycle routes. The barn, designed with these needs in mind, includes secure cycle storage with CCTV, a bike wash / tinkering area and drying room with lockers. All beds are 'cabin' style bunks, fully fitted (so no squeaks) with comfortable, and long, mattresses and bedding. Each cabin has a light, twin socket, USB chargers, shelf and underbed storage. The two twin rooms and two quads are booked by the room or you can book a bed in the 6 bed dorm. These are serviced by 3 wetroom bathrooms (one has disabled access). A fully equipped kitchen has hobs, microwaves, toaster/kettle and all cooking equipment. A dining area is next to the kitchen. Breakfast (cereals) is included in the price, as is tea & coffee. Cooked breakfast packs can be ordered for guests to cook in the morning for a small additional fee. The sitting area has sofas, chairs, a TV and wood-burning stove. Outside there is a veranda and an adjacent paddock where guests can have BBQs and borrow a fire pit.

DETAILS

- **Open** - All year, all day.
- **Number of beds** - 18: 2x2, 1x6, 2x4
- **Booking** - Book online via the website.
- **Price per night** - Twin: £50 Quad: £100. Beds £25. Includes basic self serve breakfast (cereals, porridge, toast, juice). Free tea and coffee provided.
- **Public Transport** - Buses to Berwick upon Tweed and Newcastle at Widdrington.
- **Directions** - At the A1068 roundabout by the Widdrington Inn turn east and follow the road until you see the Calico Barn sign and turning on the right.

CONTACT: Alison
Tel: 01670 458118 Mobile: 07876 344509
alison@hemscotthill.com www.tractorsandtents.com/bunkbarn/
Hemscott Hill Farm, Widdrington, Morpeth, Northumberland, NE61 5EQ

BLUEBELL
FARM BUNKBARN

Bluebell Farm Caravan Park is in the centre of Belford, within walking distance of shops and pubs. It is ideally located for exploring Nothumberland's Heritage Coast, the Cheviot Hills and the historic Scottish Borders. The Bunkbarn sleeps 14, the Studio 4, the Ark 4 and there are 5 self-catering cottages. The Bunkbarn has a family room for 6, an 8 bed dorm and a fully equipped self-catering kitchen. The Studio has a bunkroom for 4 and kitchen, sitting and dining area with outside decking. The Ark has a sleeping platform for 4, fridge, microwave, toaster & kettle, with a patio area where you can use your own camping stove. There is a shared toilet block, renovated in 2015. Pillows and blankets provided and you can hire linen, duvets and towels or a sleeping bag. Activities include golf, climbing, canoeing, diving, horse riding, fishing, cycling and walking. Dogs welcome by arrangement. Duke of Edinburgh welcome. Two 1 man wooden tents are also available for hire with stove & utensils at £7.50 per night.

DETAILS

- **Open** - All year, check in by 9 pm, departure by 10 am.
- **Number of beds** - Bunkhouse 14: 1 x 8, 1 x 6, Studio 4: 1x4, Ark: 4: 1x4
- **Booking** - Recommended throughout school holidays and for weekends.
- **Price per night** - Bunkbarn: £15pp under 16s £8. Studio: £20pp, under 16s £10. Ark : £15pp, under 16s £8. Linen and towel hire £8pp Exclusive use rates available.
- **Public Transport** - Trains at Berwick upon Tweed. Buses from Berwick to Belford. Local bus from Newcastle.
- **Directions** - From the A1 take B1342 into the village. Turn onto B6349 signposted for Wooler. Bluebell Farm is first main driveway on right, almost opposite the Co-op.

CONTACT: Phyl
Tel: 01668 213362
corillas@icloud.com www.bluebellfarmbelford.com
Bluebell Farm Caravan Park, Belford, Northumberland, NE70 7QE

Wooler Youth Hostel & Shepherd's Huts is set in its own spacious grounds on the edge of the town. It has newly refurbished en suite bedrooms & Shepherd's Hut sleeping cabins, a huge dining and common room, excellent drying facilities and a large self-catering kitchen, making it great for groups & families. There is also an excellent value restaurant, on site car parking and secure cycle storage. Wooler has inns, grocery stores and specialist shops, and is an ideal base for exploring the Northumberland National Park, the Cheviot Hills (rich in archaeological sites), local castles and fine sandy beaches. For walkers there is the long distance St Cuthbert's Way and many shorter walks. For cyclists there are the Wooler cycle hub routes, Pennine Cycleway, the Sandstone Way and many quiet lanes to explore. Nearby there are bridleways perfect for mountain-biking, some of the best bouldering in the UK, riding centres and even a gliding school. Bird watchers can take a boat trip to the Farne Islands and visit the Cheviot Hills.

DETAILS

- **Open** - April until end Oct (open for group bookings Nov to March), 7am-11pm.
- **Number of beds** - 52: 3x2, 6x4,1x6,1x8. Shepherd's huts 3x2 & 1x3.
- **Booking** - Booking advised. Always call the hostel in advance of arriving.
- **Price per night** - From £17.00 adults, £12.50 children. Group booking discounts.
- **Public Transport** - Market Place, 400 yards from the hostel. Arriva Northumbria/ Travelsure 464, Border Village 267 from Berwick. Travelsure 470/3 from Alnwick.
- **Directions** - From the Market Place at the bottom of the high street go up Cheviot Street past The Anchor pub. The hostel is 300 yards up the hill on the right.

CONTACT: Mick
Tel: 01668 281365
wooler@yha.org.uk www.woolerhostel.co.uk
30 Cheviot Street, Wooler, Northumberland, NE71 6LW

MOUNTHOOLY
BUNKHOUSE

Nestled at the head of the stunningly beautiful College Valley in North Northumberland, Mounthooly Bunkhouse is a perfect stop off on both the Pennine and St Cuthbert's Way walks. College Valley is a private estate run by the Knott Trust to increase its value as an environmental, social and economic place of excellence. The Bunkhouse was refurbished in 2008 and sleeps 24 in 2 dorms, a 2 bed room and an en suite family annex which sleeps 4. Bedding is supplied. There are well equipped kitchen and living areas with games and toys. A small BBQ is available outside and a TV and DVD are available to hire. There is limited parking and cars need a permit which is provided with the booking. The valley is a haven for wildlife with red squirrels, otters and a thriving population of feral goats. The Bunkhouse is steeped in the history and nature of the area. This is the perfect wild getaway from it all.

DETAILS

- **Open** - All Year, all day.
- **Number of beds** - 24: 2x9 1x2 1x4
- **Booking** - Phone or email. Deposit per person is required.
- **Price per night** - £14.50pp. 20% discount for concessions and whole bunkhouse bookings.
- **Public Transport** - Rail station: Berwick Upon Tweed (37 Miles). Buses at Wooler (8 miles)
- **Directions** - From Wooler take the A697 north, take left onto B6351, take left to Hethpool where there is a free car park. Bunkhouse visitors will be issued with car permits to drive on south to the Bunkhouse.

CONTACT: Pauline Baker
Tel: 01668 216 358
paulineatthetop@hotmail.com www.college-valley.co.uk/Mounthooly.htm
Mount Hooley, College Valley, Wooler, Northumberland, NE71 6TU

Chatton Park Bunkhouse started life as a smithy and has been converted into self-catering accommodation. It is situated on a mixed working farm which nestles around the River Till, half a mile from Chatton village.

Eight miles from the coast and five miles from the Cheviot Hills, Chatton Park is an ideal base for exploring Northumberland's vast empty beaches, heather clad hills & historic castles. Walking, water sports, climbing, fishing, golf and cycling are all available nearby. Accommodating 12, the bunkhouse is perfect for smaller groups, families & individuals. The 2 bedrooms are fitted with large custom made bunks and can be rented separately as secure units. Bedding can be provided at a small extra fee. The living area has a fully equipped kitchen & seating around the original blacksmith's fire. Wash & drying room with hot showers. Secure storage, ample parking. Room for 2 small tents. £10/dog/stay.

DETAILS

- **Open** - All year, flexible times but no check in after 9pm.
- **Number of beds** - 12: 2x6.
- **Booking** - Booking recommended but not essential.
- **Price per night** - £12.50 - £18 pp. Group bookings negotiable. Teenagers need to be accompanied by a responsible adult .
- **Public Transport** - Nearest train station Berwick upon Tweed. Buses to Chatton from Alnwick / Berwick.
- **Directions** - From A1 take B6348 to Chatton. 4 miles at bottom of hill on right is Chatton Park Farm.

CONTACT: Jane or Duncan
Tel: 01668 215247
jaord@btinternet.com www.chattonparkfarm.co.uk
Chatton Park Farm, Chatton, Alnwick, Northumberland, NE66 5RA

SPRUCE COTTAGE
ENGLAND BUNKHOUSE BY FOREST VIEW

Spruce Cottage Bunkhouse is a former forestry worker's cottage in the centre of Byrness on the edge of Northumberland National Park. Byrness is situated on the Pennine Way, and popular cycle routes. The bunkhouse is ideal for exploring Northumberland, Kielder Forest and the Scottish Borders. It is perfect for groups, individuals and families. The 9 full sized single beds (not bunks) in 3 bedrooms have high quality mattresses, pillows, full bed linen, curtains and carpets. There is also a Z bed available as an extra that can go in a choice of locations downstairs. There is a large living room with original open fire and central heating. The kitchen has electric cooker, microwave, fridge, freezer, kettle, toaster, crockery etc. The dining room has another original open fireplace and large pine table to seat up to 10 people. Spruce Cottage is in the heart of Byrness village directly opposite the multi award winning Forest View Inn with its famous real ale bar, food available if booked in advance.

DETAILS

■ **Open** - April to October open to groups and individuals. November to March open to groups only. Opens at 4pm checkout is 9.30am.
■ **Number of beds** - 10: 1x2, 1x3, 1x4 plus a Z bed.
■ **Booking** - Booking is recommended.
■ **Price per night** - Adults from £20. Under 16s £18.
■ **Public Transport** - Nearest rail station Newcastle upon Tyne (40 miles) then National Express to lay-by 200yds from hostel.
■ **Directions** - Spruce Cottage is just off the A68, 4 miles from the Scottish Border, 16 miles south of Jedburgh and 10 miles north of Otterburn.

CONTACT: Colin or Joyce
Tel: 07880711807
joycetaylor1703@hotmail.co.uk
2 Otterburn Green, Byrness Village, Northumberland, NE19 1TS

Maughold Venture Centre Bunkhouse is built of Manx stone, overlooking farmland with views in the distance to the sea. It offers self-catering facilities with the option of purchasing meals from the neighbouring adventure centre if required (subject to availability). All bedrooms are en suite with full central heating.

Facilities include a basic but functional games room and kitchen. The local beach of Port e Vullen, 10 minutes' walk away, is popular with visitors and the bunkhouse is adjacent to the Venture Centre where you may arrange sessions of kayaking, abseiling, air rifle shooting, archery, gorge walking, dinghy sailing, and team events. It has its own stop, Lewaigue Halt, on the Manx Electric Railway giving access to Douglas, Ramsey and to mountain walks and tranquil glens. Ideal for groups, families and individuals.

DETAILS

■ **Open** - January - December, 24 hours.
■ **Number of beds** - 52: 2x2, 1x5, 4x8, 2x10.
■ **Booking** - Telephone reservation essential.
■ **Price per night** - £10-£15 per person.
■ **Public Transport** - No 3 bus or Manx Electric Railway from Douglas or Ramsey. Get off bus at Dreemskerry (5 minutes' walk); get off railway at Lewaigue Halt (nearby). Taxi from Ramsey £5. Taxi from Douglas £25.
■ **Directions** - GR 469922. From Douglas take the A2 coast road. When the road begins to descend into Ramsey the Venture Centre is signposted on the right hand side. Follow the signs - it is the first building on the left.

CONTACT: Simon Read
Tel: 01624 814240
contact@adventure-centre.co.uk www.adventure-centre.co.uk
The Venture Centre, Maughold, Isle of Man, IM7 1AW

KNOCKALOE BEG
FARM BUNKHOUSE

A working farm nestled under Peel Hill with fantastic views along the west coast of the Isle of Man, Knockaloe Beg offers B&B, cottages, bunkhouse and glamping. Heated by wood-burning stove the bunkhouse sleeps 8 in bunkbeds at one end of the room with dining and seating at the other. It has is a microwave, kettle, small fridge and a DVD projector. The Bothy is a twin bed room heated by oil filled radiator with a kettle and microwave. There is a toilet and basin outside the Bothy and there are showers and toilets below the Bunkhouse. Bedding is included and a farmhouse breakfast is sometimes available for £10. In the orchard there are two glamping cabins each sleeping four with integral self-catering and showers. The farm is just 2 miles from the picturesque city of Peel which is well provided with restaurants, walks, pubs and beaches. There is lots to see and do on the farm.

DETAILS

■ **Open** - Bunkhouse: 1 April-30 September, Bothy: all year.
■ **Number of beds** - 18: Bunkhouse 8, Bothy 2. Cabins 8: 2x4
■ **Booking** - Online, phone or email. 20% non-refundable deposit is due on booking with the balance to be paid 8 weeks before arrival.
■ **Price per night** - Bunkhouse: £15pp; minimum charge £30 TT/Classic TT fortnight: £120 per night whole bunkhouse (max 8). The Bothy: £20 pp, min charge £40. Farmhouse breakfast (when available): £10 pp
■ **Public Transport** - There is an hourly bus from 8am – 5pm to the end of the lane.
■ **Directions** - A27 south from Peel. Approx 1/2 mile after the river Neb bridge take the farm track on the right just before the Kirk Patrick sign. Follow this to the farm.

CONTACT: Fiona and John Anderson
Tel: 01624 844279
info@knockaloebegfarm.com www.knockaloebegfarm.com/
Knockaloe Beg Farm, Patrick, Isle of Man, IM5 3AQ

Knockaloe Beg Farm

Guest House ★★★★
Self Catering Cottage ★★★★
Bunkhouse   Farm parties
Contact Fiona or John Anderson
01624 844279 / 01624 475330
info@knockaloebegfarm.com
Part of the Manx Ark Project

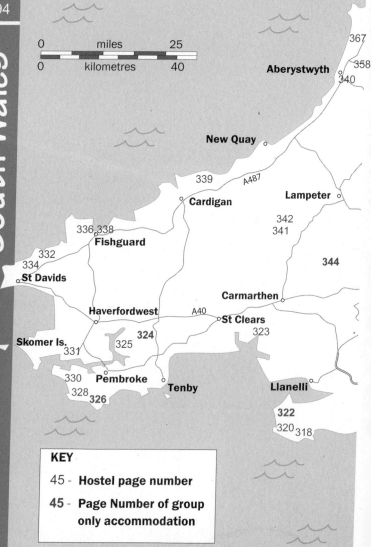

South Wales

0 miles 25
0 kilometres 40

367
358
Aberystwyth 340

New Quay

339 A487
Cardigan **Lampeter**

342
341

336,338
Fishguard

332 344
334
St Davids

Carmarthen

Haverfordwest A40
St Clears
324 323

Skomer Is.
331
325

330
328 326 **Pembroke** **Tenby** **Llanelli**

322
320 318

KEY

45 - **Hostel page number**

45 - **Page Number of group only accommodation**

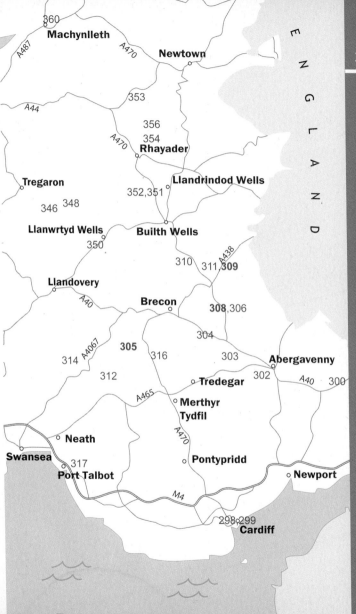

South Wales

North Wales

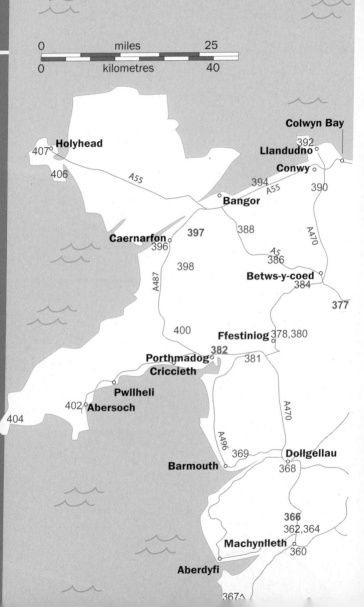

miles 0 — 25
kilometres 0 — 40

Colwyn Bay
Holyhead 407
406
A55
Llandudno 392
Conwy
394 A55 390
Bangor
388 A470
Caernarfon 397
396
398 A5
386
Betws-y-coed
384
377
A487
400
Ffestiniog 378,380
382 381
Porthmadog
Criccieth
Pwllheli
402 Abersoch
404
A487
A496 A470
Barmouth 369 Dolgellau
368
366
362,364
Machynlleth
360
Aberdyfi
367∧

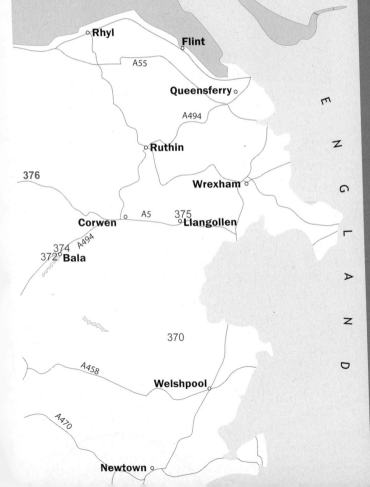

KEY

45 - Hostel page number

45 - Page number of group
only accommodation

Rhyl

Flint

A55

Queensferry

A494

Ruthin

376

Wrexham

Corwen   A5   375 Llangollen

374 A494
372 Bala

370

A458

Welshpool

A470

Newtown

North Wales

ENGLAND

RIVER HOUSE
HOSTEL

This is an award-winning family run 4 star hostel in the heart of Cardiff, voted number 1 in the Hostelworld list of best hostels. Opened in 2007 to rave reviews, the brother and sister team have made sure this will be the best hostel experience you will come across on your travels. With fabulous views of the world famous Millennium Stadium and River Taff and with the central train and bus stations just 5 mins' walk away, what's stopping you?

Facilities include well equipped kitchen, cosy TV lounge, decked garden with barbecue, free lockers and free wireless broadband. Bikes, irons and hairdryers available for hire. Linen, duvets and breakfast are included in the price and the beds are made up for you. Hostelworld awarded best Hostel in UK since 2008.

Treat yourself to a quality stay at budget prices.

DETAILS

- **Open** - All year, 24 hours.
- **Number of beds** - 50: 2 bed private rooms, 4 bed dorms and 6 bed dorms.
- **Booking** - Book by phone or online.
- **Price per night** - From £16pp. Private (twin) rooms from £36 for two people. All prices include breakfast.
- **Public Transport** - Cardiff Central coach and train stations, with regular services to UK cities and airports 5 minutes' walk away.
- **Directions** - From Central train station turn left and cross river on Tudor Street. Once over the river Fitzhamon Embankment is first turn on right.

CONTACT: Reception
Tel: 02920 399 810
info@riverhousebackpackers.com www.riverhousebackpackers.com
59 Fitzhamon Embankment, Riverside, Cardiff, CF11 6AN

The Safehouse Hostel is located in the centre of Cardiff close to the Millennium Stadium and Cardiff Castle and is just a few minutes' walk to Cardiff Central Station. The staff at this friendly hostel are available to offer help over what to see and do and where to eat in the city and they even offer walking tours and cycle hire. Bed and breakfast is available or make use of the well equipped kitchen.

Based in historic former offices of the Windsor Estate, the communal areas have been renovated but retain lots of their original Victorian charm whilst the spacious bed rooms have all the mod cons including USB charging points and deluxe, locally made, bunks. The hostel has a female only dorm and there are 3 family (4 bed) rooms and 3 private (2 bed) rooms with fantastic views of the city. Continental breakfast included, groups welcome but not stag or hens.

DETAILS

- **Open** - All year, all day
- **Number of beds** - 40: 1x12, 1x10, 3x4, 3x2
- **Booking** - book online via website
- **Price per night** - from £15pn. 2 night min booking. Towel hire £1.50 (plus £1 deposit).
- **Public Transport** - Trains and buses at Cardiff Central. Local buses to Westgate Street or walk.
- **Directions** - 2 NCP car parks on Westgate Street or park on or near Cathedral Road (CF11 9LL) mostly free and unrestricted, and is a nice area.

CONTACT: Reception
Tel: 02920 372833
info@safehousehostel.com www.safehousehostel.co.uk/
3 Westgate St. Cardiff, CF10 1DD

RICKYARD
BUNKHOUSE

Rickyard Bunkhouse is set amidst idyllic countryside and well away from the hustle and bustle. Offa's Dyke footpath passes the entrance and it is within 25 mins of Wye Valley, Symonds Yat and the Forest of Dean. Many outdoor pursuits can be enjoyed - canoeing, rafting, potholing, quad biking, rock climbing and paint balling to name but a few. The River Trothy borders the land; kingfishers and otters enjoy the peace and tranquillity of the Trothy valley. Buzzards circle high above, easily recognised by their distinctive call. The Bunkhouse holds 20 easily, has an excellent, very well equipped kitchen, a separate dining/relaxing area with TV, and background heating. Sleeping accommodation is split into several areas. It is totally self-contained, and is ideal for reunions, groups and families. There is a large secure area for camping where children can safely play and ample parking with hard standing. Luggage transfer, breakfasts and packed lunches can be arranged. Bedding supplied, towels £1. Come and enjoy the tranquil surroundings (loud music or wild parties are not welcome). Exclusive use available, please enquire.

DETAILS

- **Open** - All year, all day.
- **Number of beds** - 20: + camping.
- **Booking** - Deposit required, no credit cards. Notice not always required.
- **Price per night** - £16.00pp. Prices include bedding, towels £1. Tents £5pp. Can be booked for sole use.
- **Public Transport** - Trains at Abergavenny (11m). Buses at Monmouth (3m).
- **Directions** - Next to the Hendre Farm House on the same side of the road.

CONTACT: Graham Edwards
Tel: 01600 740128
rickyardbunkhouse@googlemail.com www.rickyardbunkhouse.co.uk
Wonastow, Monmouth, NP25 4DJ

MIDDLE NINFA
BUNKHOUSE

Middle Ninfa Farm, situated on the edge of the Blaenavon Industrial Landscape World Heritage Site in the Brecon Beacons, offers bunkhouse/cottage accommodation, camping and hands-on training in coracle making and willow sculpture. The farm has fine views over the Usk Valley, of the Skirrid and rural Monmouthshire. The Bunkhouse provides comfortable self-catering accommodation for up to 6 people. The rustic charm of the stone building has been retained whilst ensuring modern comforts. The ground floor has a lounge / dining area with double futon and coal-effect gas fire; a well-equipped kitchen and toilet / shower room. Upstairs (mezzanine floor) has 4 single beds, accessed by a spiral staircase. Outside there is a stone barbecue, table and duck pond. Guests should bring food, sleeping bags, towels & pillowcases. Home grown fruit, veg and local produce available.
Walkers and Cyclists Welcome.

DETAILS

- **Open** - All year.
- **Number of beds** - 6: 1x4, 1x2 [double] plus camping.
- **Booking** - Book by phone or email (preferred).
- **Price per night** - £15pp or £60 sole use (Sun–Thurs nights) £70 (Fri & Sat nights). Sole use per week £300-£360. Camping £5 pp + pitch fee of £5/£10.
- **Public Transport** - The nearest bus is at Llanfoist (1.5 miles). The train station is at Abergavenny (3.5 miles). Taxis from the station cost approximately £8
- **Directions** - Approx. 2 miles from A465 (Hereford/Neath), A40 (Brecon/Monmouth and M50) and A4042 (Newport, M4). See website for map. The farm is reached by a steep winding road from Llanfoist, crossing the Monmouthshire and Brecon Canal.

CONTACT: Richard and Rohan Lewis
Tel: 01873 854662
bookings@middleninfa.co.uk www.middleninfa.co.uk
Middle Ninfa Farm, Llanellen, Abergavenny, NP7 9LE

Wern Watkin Bunkhouse is located in the Brecon Beacons National Park, high up on Mynnedd Llangattock. It is also known as YHA Llangattock Mountain. There is direct access on foot to the mountainside and a flat mountain road to a National Cycle Route. The bunkhouse is a converted stone barn with bunks for 30 people in 7, mainly en suite, bedrooms. The massive dining room and seating area opens out onto ancient woodlands. It has under-floor heating throughout, excellent drying facilities and ample hot water. The location is ideal for caving, rock climbing, canoeing, abseiling, orienteering, pony trekking and mountain biking. Outdoor pursuit training can be arranged from local qualified instructors. The bunkhouse is within easy walking distance of Llangattock cave complex (one of Europe's most elaborate cave systems) as well as climbing crags and open moorland. A short drive away are the scenic Wye and Usk river valleys and a wealth of industrial heritage at the World Heritage site of Blaenavon. Catering can be provided for groups.

DETAILS

- **Open** - All year, all day.
- **Number of beds** - 30: 4x6, 1x4, 2x2. All rooms except one are en suite
- **Booking** - Availability online. 20% deposit, balance three weeks in advance.
- **Price per night** - Sole use £450 week nights, £630 weekend nights. Smaller groups by negotiation £16pp week nights, £18.50 pp weekend.
- **Public Transport** - Trains Abergavenny (8miles). Nearest buses Crickhowell.
- **Directions** - Access can be either from Crickhowell or Brynmawr on small mountain roads. Detailed instructions will be sent with your booking.

CONTACT: Andrew Fryer
Tel: 01873 812307
enquiries@wernwatkin.co.uk www.wernwatkin.co.uk
Wern Watkin, Hillside, Llangattock, Crickhowell, NP8 1LG

THE STAR
BUNKHOUSE

Croeso i Fyncws y Seren - welcome to The Star Bunkhouse. An ideal base from which to explore the beautiful Brecon Beacons National Park. Situated in the village of Bwlch, you can expect a warm and comfortable stay in the self-catering bunkhouse. With spacious bedrooms, cosy lounge and dining areas, a fully-equipped kitchen, an outside BBQ area, hot showers, drying room, free WiFi and off-road parking. The Star Bunkhouse can sleep up to 20 people in bunk beds spread over 6 bedrooms, and welcomes bookings from individuals and couples as well as small & large groups. A popular choice for family get-togethers, reunions, birthday parties, hens & stags, school & youth groups, clubs & societies, and with all lovers of the great outdoors. Dog friendly by arrangement. The bunkhouse is situated alongside The Beacons Way long-distance footpath in the gap ('bwlch') between the Black Mountains and the Central Beacons mountain range (which includes Pen Y Fan). Meet and swap stories with fellow travellers if use of the bunkhouse is shared, or please ask if you would prefer exclusive use for your group.

DETAILS

- **Open** - All year, all day
- **Number of beds** - 20: 1×4 (en-suite), 3×4, 2×2
- **Booking** - By email or telephone
- **Price per night** - Standard rate £19 per person
- **Public Transport** - Nearest train station: Abergavenny 13 miles. Bus route: X43 Abergavenny-Brecon. Nearest airport: Cardiff Airport 50 miles.
- **Directions** - On the A40 between Crickhowell and Brecon

CONTACT: Emma or Pete Harrison
Tel: 01874 730 080 Mobile: 07341 906 937
info@starbunkhouse.com www.starbunkhouse.com
Brecon Road (A40), Bwlch, Brecon, Powys, LD3 7RQ

This old stone barn continues the tradition of 900 years when Llanthony Priory next door provided shelter and accommodation. Surrounded by the Black Mountains in the Brecon Beacons National Park, this spectacular setting is a superb base for walking, riding, pony trekking and other mountain activities.

Sixteen bunks are split into three separate areas for sleeping. There is a fully equipped kitchen, hot water for showers, heating throughout and a wood burning stove in the eating area. Small or large groups are welcome, but there is a minimum charge. Two pubs offer real ale and bar food.

Just 50 minutes from the M4 Severn Bridge and one hour from the M5/M50 junction, this must be one of the easiest bunkbarns to reach from the motorways - and yet you feel you are miles from anywhere.

DETAILS

- **Open** - All year, 24 hours, no restrictions.
- **Number of beds** - 16: 1 x 8 ; 1 x 4 ; 1 x 6.
- **Booking** - Booking and deposit required.
- **Price per night** - £30 per person for a two-night weekend, with a minimum charge of £300. Reduction for mid-week bookings.
- **Public Transport** - Abergavenny railway station 12 miles.
- **Directions** - GR SO 288 278 Map on website: Turn west off A465 Abergavenny/Hereford road at Llanvihangel Crucorney (5 miles' north of Abergavenny). Llanthony is 6 miles along country lane - follow signs to Priory. On cycle route 42.

CONTACT: Cordelia Passmore
Tel: 01873 890359
courtfarm@llanthony.co.uk www.llanthonybunkbarn.co.uk
Court Farm, Llanthony, Abergavenny, Monmouthshire, NP7 7NN

BRECON
BUNKHOUSE

Brecon Bunkhouse is a spacious, comfortable and clean bunkhouse in the Brecon Beacons. Offering fantastic value for money with a large self-catering kitchen, big dining room with plenty of tables and separate sitting room with a cosy wood-burner (logs provided). Situated in a small valley in the Black Mountains, the eastern part of the National Park, with mountain walks from the door. The area is ideal for horse riding and mountain bikes, with a white water canoe centre nearby. There is a riding centre on the farm and the bunkhouse has a drying room and storage/cleaning facilities for bikes and canoes. The adult-sized bunk-beds come with a freshly laundered sheet, pillow and pillow-case. Bring a sleeping bag/duvet, or hire a duvet with cover for £5 per stay. The friendly, helpful staff will give advice or leave you to get on with it . The market town of Talgarth, 4 miles away, has Walkers Welcome status and planned walks. Camping available on the farm. Nice pub 15 minutes' walk.

DETAILS

- **Open** - All year. All day.
- **Number of beds** - 28+3: 1x10,1x2,1x2,1x6,1x8. Plus extra 3 bed room available.
- **Booking** - 40% deposit required to book, balance due before arrival.
- **Price per night** - £15 pp, minimum of 4 people. £250 for exclusive use plus £45 for extra en suite family room with 3 single beds.
- **Public Transport** - Train station at Abergavenny. Taxi to bunkhouse costs £25-30 or phone bunkhouse to enquire about minibus transfer (advance notice needed).
- **Directions** - Travelling south from Talgarth on A479 take first left after Castle Inn. The Bunkhouse is on this lane after Trans Wales Trails banner at entrance to farm.

CONTACT: Paul and Emily Turner
Tel: 01874 711500
breconbunkhouse@gmail.com www.brecon-bunkhouse.co.uk
Brecon Bunkhouse, Cwmfforest Farm, Pengenfford, Talgarth, Brecon, LD3 0EU

The Dragons Back (formerly The Castle Inn) is a pub with B&B rooms, camping & 3 self contained bunkrooms, located at over 1000ft above sea level in the stunning Brecon Beacons National Park. The bunkrooms are fully carpeted and centrally heated with en suite wet rooms. Book out the entire bunkhouse from just £350 per night (£12.50pp). A new fully fitted dining/kitchen complete with WiFi and large screen TV, is now located next to the bunkhouse so self-catering is an option, although meals are also available in the pub next door. The pub serves a range of local real ales and home cooked meals using locally sourced ingredients. There's a large log fire, fantastic beer garden, free WiFi in the bar, pool table & 50 inch TV. The bunkhouse's drying room and secure bike storage make it a great base for outdoor activities. Groups welcome including stag/hen parties. Dogs £5 per night in the bunkhouse.

         **GROUPS ONLY**

DETAILS

- **Open** - All year. Arrive after 2pm, depart before 11 am.
- **Number of beds** - 38: Bunkhouse 28:1x6,1x10,1x12, B&B:10: 4 rooms
- **Booking** - Group bookings only. £100 non refundable booking deposit required. 28 days notice required for cancellation, otherwise full value of the booking (less deposit) will be charged.
- **Price per night** - £15pp, £21pp with breakfast. Minimum of 5 people required for 6 bunk room, 7 for 10 bunk room, or 9 for 12 bunk room. Book entire bunkhouse for £350, or £525 with breakfast.
- **Public Transport** - Nearest trains: Abergavenny. Nearest bus: Talgarth (3 miles).
- **Directions** - Located on the A479 approx 3 miles South of Talgarth and 6 miles North of Crickhowell

CONTACT: Jill Deakin
Tel: 01874 711353
info@thedragonsback.co.uk   www.thedragonsback.co.uk
The Dragons Back , Pengenffordd, LD3 0EP

In a converted Welsh Chapel, Wye Valley Canoes Bunkhouse is a warm, modern space with huge sofas and a slide to reach the ground floor. There is a small kitchen area, so it is possible to self-cater, and the River Café next door can feed your group or serve food to you at the big bunkhouse dining table. The luxury bunks are in individual pods and there is a kingsize bedroom area. The beds, the sofas and the kitchen are all within one large first floor open plan area and there are three swanky bathrooms and a table tennis table downstairs. The bunkhouse has been graded 5 star by VisitWales and won the Gold Tourism of Wales Award in 2015.

Canoes, kayaks, mountain bikes and Vespa scooters can be hired from downstairs. Try paddling down to Hay on Wye and walking back along the Wye Valley Walk. It is a beautiful area to explore with the market town of Hay on Wye just 4 miles away. An inclusive package with accommodation, food and activities can be arranged or if you prefer just come and do your own thing!

DETAILS

- **Open** - All year, all day
- **Number of beds** - 14: 12x1 (pods), 1 x double
- **Booking** - Book via website, phone or email
- **Price per night** - From £1176 for a 2 night weekend.
- **Public Transport** - Trains at Hereford and Abergavenney direct bus from Hereford, bus via Brecon from Abergavenney.
- **Directions** - On A438 from Hereford to Brecon.

CONTACT: Jane Hughes
Tel: 01497 847213
info@wyevalleycanoes.co.uk www.wyevalleycanoes.co.uk/bunkhouse.html
The Boat House, Glasbury-On-Wye, Herefordshire, HR3 5NP

RIVER CABIN

River Cabin, a traditional stone building with eco credentials, is set in an old cider orchard overlooking the mill stream. It sleeps up to 4 in a cosy bunkroom with bunk beds & a double futon.

There is a kitchen/lounge area, sunny dining porch, patio & private garden with picnic table, fire pit and BBQ. The price includes heating, hot water, showers, WiFi & use of bike store. From Easter - October a small camp-site is operated alongside the cabin.

Located on Wye Valley Walk & National Cycle Route 8 - fantastic exploration base for walkers, cyclists and anyone wishing to relax and explore this beautiful part of Mid Wales. Canoeing, pony trekking and riding, gliding, bike hire, rope and climbing centre all available locally.

DETAILS

- **Open** - All year, 24 hour access.
- **Number of beds** - 4: 1 x 4 plus camping
- **Booking** - River Cabin (sleeps 4) - minimum booking 2 people for 2 nights.
- **Price per night** - From £19 per person per night.
- **Public Transport** - Trains: Builth (10 miles), Hereford (30 miles), Merthyr (30 miles). Daily bus service, ask for Trericket Mill - cabin is through field gate across the brook from the mill. For info see www.traveline-cymru.info.
- **Directions** - GR SO 112 414. Set back from the A470 Brecon to Builth Wells road between the villages of Llyswen and Erwood.

CONTACT: Alistair / Nicky Legge
Tel: 01982 560312 Mob: 07720 717124
info@rivercabin.co.uk www.rivercabin.co.uk
Erwood, Builth Wells, Powys, LD2 3TQ

WOODLANDS
BUNKHOUSE

Woodlands Bunkhouse is a converted stable in the grounds of Woodlands Centre, a late Regency building, set in 10 acres of grounds. Overlooking the River Wye and with wonderful views of the Black Mountains.

Woodlands is within easy reach of the spectacular limestone area to the south. Nearby is the historic town of Hay on Wye, famous for its vast array of bookshops. With its modern facilities, the Bunkhouse provides comfortable accommodation for families and a variety of groups. With recent renovations increasing the capacity to 22, the ground floor has a well-equipped kitchen and dining room. There are 3 bedrooms on the ground floor, one with en suite facilities and six first floor bedrooms and shared bathroom facilities on both floors. Camping is also available in the grounds. The bunkhouse can arrange courses in outdoor activities which are individually designed to suit groups of all ages and abilities run by their fully qualified instructors.

DETAILS

- **Open** - All year, 24 hours.
- **Number of beds** - 22 in rooms of 1 to 6 plus camping in the grounds.
- **Booking** - Booking essential. Phone or email.
- **Price per night** - £16 pp + VAT. Reduction for children and large group bookings.
- **Public Transport** - Trains to Hereford. A local bus then runs from Hereford to Glasbury on Wye, service 39.
- **Directions** - On the B4350 just through the village of Glasbury accessed via the A438 Brecon road.

CONTACT: Annie Clipson
Tel: 01497 847272
annie.clipson@oxfordshireoutdoors.co.uk www.woodlandsoec.org
Glasbury on Wye, Powys, HR3 5LP

CLYNGWYN
WALES BUNKHOUSE, B&B AND HUT

Clyngwyn Bunkhouse is situated in the Brecon Beacons, in the heart of waterfall country, very near to the caves and waterfalls of Ystradfellte and close to the famous Sgwd Yr Eira waterfalls. The terrain is ideal for mountain biking, gorge walking, canyoning, caving, abseiling, climbing, quad biking, photography and painting. Clyngwyn Bunkhouse is perfect for groups of friends or family. It sleeps up to 19 with camping available to larger groups, three double B&B rooms in the farm house and a romantic shepherd's hut in its own private meadow. There is a fully equipped kitchen, central heating, lounge with TV-DVD, dining room for 20, four acres of land for ball games and a large decked out polytunnel acting as a marquee, lockable storage and drying area. Relax in the evenings and enjoy the mountain views by a fire or BBQ. The villages of Ystradfellte and Pontneddfechan (2½ miles by mini bus taxi) have pubs with restaurants. Four star graded by Visit Wales. Dog friendly.

DETAILS

- **Open** - All year, all day.
- **Number of beds** - Bunkhouse 19, B&B 6, Shepherds Hut 2
- **Booking** - Booking essential. Only groups can book the bunkhouse at weekends. Credit/debit cards not accepted
- **Price per night** - Weekdays: up to 19 people £265, up to 15 people £220 or £18pp. Fri or Sat: up to 19 people £305 up to 15 people £250. Extra charge for bedding or bring your own. B&B in Farmhouse £30pp. Shepherds hut £75 (sleeps 2).
- **Public Transport** - Trains Neath or Merthyr (11 miles). Minibus can be arranged.
- **Directions** - From A465 leave at Glenneath, drive through and take signs for Pontneddfechan. Then 2.5 miles up Ystradfellte road, turn right down small track.

CONTACT: Julie Hurst
Tel: 01639 722930
enquiries@bunkhouse-south-wales.co.uk www.bunkhouse-south-wales.co.uk
Clyngwyn Farm, Ystradfellte Rd, Pontneddfechan, Powys, SA11 5US

CRAIG Y NOS
CASTLE

Craig Y Nos Castle is situated on a sweeping mountain road that crosses the Brecon Beacons. Once a celebrity palace and then a sanatorium providing the fresh air cure, the castle has always been chosen for its location. In the grounds of the castle the Nurses Block has a lounge, a small self-catering kitchen, 10 twin rooms, 1 single room, showers, loos and a disabled bathroom. All the beds are made up with fresh linen and duvets. The kitchen has a 2 ring hob and 2 microwaves, bring your own plates, cutlery and pans. You are welcome in the Castle for hearty meals, cosy evenings by the wood burning stoves and a free history tour (some areas might be restricted if a wedding is taking place). The Castle has a conservatory for parties, a unique period theatre, gardens with views across the river and a hot tub & sports room. The Gwyn Arms is five minutes' walk and there is a pub and other amenities in Pen Y Cae (1.5 miles). Local adventure companies offer outdoor activities, you can enjoy the mountain walks and waterfalls close by or take a 50 min drive to the Gower's sandy bays

DETAILS

- **Open** - 1st April to 31st October 24 hours.
- **Number of beds** - Nurses Block: 21: 10x2,1x1. Plus 64 en suite rooms in castle.
- **Booking** - Bookings only accepted within 6 months of the date of your visit.
- **Price per night** - Nurses Block sole use:- 1 night £350, 2 nights £500, 3 nights £600, 5 nights £700. B&B in Nurses Block per twin room: £67.50pn midweek, £87.50pn weekend. Breakfast for groups £6.50pp. Ask for Castle room rates.
- **Public Transport** - Half an hour by car from trains at Swansea or Neath.
- **Directions** - Between Swansea and Brecon at the foot of the Brecon Beacons.

CONTACT: Reception
Tel: 01639 730725
info@craigynoscastle.com www.groupaccommodationinwales.com
Craig Y Nos Castle, Brecon Road, Penycae, Powys, SA9 1GL

COED OWEN
BUNKHOUSE

Stay on an idyllic Welsh hill farm in the heart of the Brecon Beacons National Park. Coed Owen Bunkhouse can sleep up to 26 guests and provides fully equipped commercial stainless steel kitchen with open plan dining and comfortable sitting area. Coed Owen is a great place for stag, hen and family celebratory parties or gatherings. We can highly recommend our local outdoor activity providers for those adrenaline junkie weekends or places to meditate and chill. Large and small groups will enjoy this beautiful area with the benefit of direct access onto the mountains. Pen Y Fan, the highest mountain in Southern Britain is just 2.5 hours' walk from Coed Owen, we are surrounded by waterfall country and Bike Park Wales is 10 minutes' drive away. Historic Merthyr Tydfil, Penderyn Whiskey and the lovely Georgian town of Brecon are all within easy reach. We have plenty of outdoor space for children, a BBQ area and separate building with a wood burning stove, for those long, cosy night chats. The pub is just at the bottom of our farm drive and serves great food and fine ales.

DETAILS

- **Open** - All year round 8am - 10pm
- **Number of beds** - 25: 2x6 bed dorm, 1x10 bed dorm, 1 double room and 1 single.
- **Booking** - Book by email, phone or we have a booking form on our own website.
- **Price per night** - From £22pp with bed linen. Minimum of two nights at weekends. Prices may increase slightly during winter months for single and small groups.
- **Public Transport** - On bus route T4 around Brecon between Storey Arms & Llwyn-on. Trains Merthyr Tydfil (10 minutes). 1 hour from Cardiff International Airport.
- **Directions** - On A470 between Brecon and Merthyr Tydfil at Nant Ddu.

CONTACT: Molly or Netty Rees
Tel: 07508544044 (anytime) 01685 722628 (after 6 pm)
info@breconbeaconsbunkhouse.co.uk www.breconbeaconsbunkhouse.co.uk
Coed Owen Farm, Cwmtaff, Merthyr Tydfil , CF48 2HY

L&A
OUTDOOR CENTRE

L&A Outdoor Centre is a friendly family-run destination offering affordable accommodation and activities in the Swansea Bay area. The accommodation consists of 6 and 8 person self-catering cabins and bunkhouses which sleep between 10 and 40 with toilets and showers. The high quality cabins have upstairs bedrooms, lounge with TV, kitchenette, eating area, toilet and shower, and are all overlooking a tree-lined mountain stream. There is a 5,000 sq ft activity hall, a large dining hall (300 seats) and a fully equipped commercial kitchen which can be hired to groups. Professional catering is also available. Other facilities include the Watering Hole bar/café, meeting rooms and over 50 acres of woodland and pasture with play area, open air swimming pool, campfire, pets corner, kennels, BBQs and bike wash. Ideally situated for mountain biking with Afan Aergoed and Glyncorrwg Trails just 10 mins away. The Millennium and Liberty Stadia are within 30 mins. For groups from 2 to 250, L&A is the perfect base for conferences, training courses, summer camps and retreats. Activity packages can be arranged. Stag and hen groups welcome.

DETAILS

- **Open** - All day.
- **Number of beds** - Cabin: 117: 6/8 bed units. Bunkhouse: 175:10,16,24,30,40 bed.
- **Booking** - Book or enquire by phone or email.
- **Price per night** - Bunkhouses: £12pp, £15 with bedding. Cabins: 6 bed £90 to £150, 8 bed £100 to £180, depending on length of stay. Groups please enquire.
- **Public Transport** - Nearest rail station is Port Talbot Parkway (two miles).
- **Directions** - One mile from Junction 40 of the M4

CONTACT: Nigel
Tel: 01639 885 509
info@landaoutdoorcentre.co.uk www.landaoutdoorcentre.co.uk
Goytre, West Glamorgan SA13 2YP

EASTERN SLADE
BARN

Eastern Slade Farm Barn is a luxury conversion of a 15 century farmhouse on a working dairy farm in the Gower peninsula. Under floor heating, powered by air source heat pump, provides year round warmth and the barn is ideal for groups of families or friends who like to holiday together. There are 3 wet rooms and 4 bedrooms sleeping 13 people. Two extra fold up beds are available in the lounge when the whole barn is booked. The beds are made up with fresh sheets and pillow cases and you are invited to bring your own sleeping bags or duvet covers (duvets available). The well equipped kitchen has a range style stove (electric oven and gas hobs) and granite work tops. The comfy lounge has leather sofas and a wood burning stove for cosy evenings. The Gower has glorious beaches and castles to explore and a network of traffic free lanes, ideal for mountain bikes. The Coastal Path passes through the farm. Port Eynon seaside village is 30 mins walk west. Oxwich Bay, 20 mins' walk east, has a castle, beach and a hotel with bar and meals. Camping is also available.

DETAILS

■ **Open** - All year, 24 hours.
■ **Number of beds** - 15: 1x5, 2x 2/3 (double with bunk above), 1x2, 2 in lounge
■ **Booking** - Please phone or email to book
■ **Price per night** - £15pp, £180 sole use. High season £20pp, £240 sole use.
■ **Public Transport** - Buses 118 and 114 from Swansea travel to Oxwich Cross once a day. Slade is a 20 minute walk from Oxwich Cross.
■ **Directions** - From Oxwich follow the sign for Slade marked no through road. Pass Oxwich Castle and as the road descends look for Eastern Slade Farm on right.

CONTACT: Kate
Tel: (01792) 391374, Mob: 07970 969814
tynrheol@hotmail.com www.easternsladebarngower.co.uk
Eastern Slade Farm, Oxwich, Gower, Swansea, SA3 1NA

RHOSSILI
BUNKHOUSE

Situated at the end of the Gower Peninsula, in the UK's first Area of Outstanding Natural Beauty, Rhossili Bunkhouse is within easy walking distance of three glorious beaches, including Rhossili Bay (TripAdvisor: UK's #1 Beach 2013) and ideally located for a range of outdoor activities including walking, surfing, cycling, climbing and flying. The Gower Way starts nearby. This 4 star Visit Wales bunkhouse is great for groups of friends or families. It is run for the benefit of the community by Rhossili Bunkhouse Ltd on behalf of Rhossili Village Hall Trustees. Duvets and pillows provided. Bring single bed linen or sleeping bags. Central heating throughout. Self-catering in fully equipped kitchen. Lounge/dining room opens onto patio and garden. Games and books in lounge. Free WiFi. Secure store for bikes and boards, with drying room for coats and boots. Outside area for rinsing/drying wet suits. Card locks on all doors. Hall and meeting room for hire. Car park. No pets. No smoking.

DETAILS

- **Open** - All year except January. Check in 4-9pm; check out by 10:30am.
- **Number of beds** - 18: 1x4, 2x3, 4x2. 4 sofa-beds in lounge (Sole use).
- **Booking** - Advance booking recommended. Check our website for availability. Online form and virtual tour. Deposit 30%. Minimum booking: 2 people for 2 nights
- **Price per night** - Shared (small groups) £16-£20. Full (group of 18) £340. Sole (group of 22) £390.
- **Public Transport** - Regular buses (118) from Swansea stop outside. www.visitswanseabay.com/explorebybus, www.traveline-cymru.info
- **Directions** - On the B4247 in Middleton, Rhossili. GR SS 421 878

CONTACT: Josephine Higgins
Tel: 01792 391509
bookings@rhossili.org www.rhossilibunkhouse.com
Rhossili Bunkhouse, Rhossili, Swansea, SA3 1PL

HARDINGSDOWN
BUNKHOUSE

Hardingsdown Bunkhouse provides comfortable accommodation for families or groups in a tastefully restored stone barn on an organic farm. The Gower has national nature reserves, outstanding coastal scenery, family beaches, castles and ancient monuments. Llangennith beach is one of the best surfing beaches in the south west, Mewslade Bay and Fall Bay are popular with climbers, while walkers and bikers can use the local network of footpaths and bridleways. The ground floor consists of a fully equipped kitchen, 2 shower/toilet rooms, a living room with 2 single sofa-beds and comfy chairs. Off the living room is a bedroom with a bunkbed sleeping 2 people. A spiral staircase leads upstairs where there are 3 bedrooms sleeping 5, 3 and 2 in bunks and single beds. Separate drying room and a lock-up for storing bikes, surfboards, canoes etc. Ample parking and a patio area that catches the evening sun. Shops and pubs nearby. The Chaffhouse sleeping up to 12 is now also available.

DETAILS

- **Open** - All year, 24 hours.
- **Number of beds** - Bunkhouse 14: 1x5, 1x3, 3x2. Chaffhouse: 12.
- **Booking** - Booking essential by phone or email and confirmed by 30% deposit.
- **Price per night** - SOLE USE £220pn (weekends, bank holidays and school holidays), £190pn (midweek). Weekly rates available. INDIVIDUALS mid week, shared use, £18 per person. Enquire for rates in the Chaffhouse
- **Public Transport** - Regular bus 116 from Swansea. Traveline 0871 200 22 33.
- **Directions** - Turn left off the B4295 ½ mile AFTER Burry Green (by bus shelter and post box). Follow lane 400m. End of tarmac road (and before rough track beyond) turn right into Lower Hardingsdown Farm. Bunkhouse is on left of farmyard.

CONTACT: Allison Tyrrell
Tel: 01792 386222
bunkhousegower@btconnect.com www.bunkhousegower.co.uk
Lower Hardingsdown Farm, Llangennith, Gower, Swansea, SA3 1HT

Llansteffan is a beautiful, quaint village set at the tip of the Towi River and Carmarthen Bay. The sandy beaches nestled below the castle offer swimming and relaxation. The virtually traffic free country lanes make this area ideal for cycling. For the walker we are on the Wales Coastal Path. Carmarthen, Wales' oldest city and ancestral home to Merlin of King Arthur's legends, offers most social and cultural activities. The Pantyrathro International Hostel provides dorm accommodation, private rooms, and also has 3 new en suite units of 6, 9 and 12 beds. Facilities include self-catering kitchen, dining area, TV lounge, showers and free WiFi. Our two Mexican bars offer pool, darts, TV, weekly drink specials and food (eat-in or take-out). Horse riding and excursions for trekking, canoeing and surfing offered. Take a day trip, relax on the beaches or have a drink in our bars - something for everyone.

DETAILS

- **Open** - February to January. 24 hours.
- **Number of beds** - 50: 1 x 10, 1 x 9, 2 x 6, 4 x 4, 1 x 3
- **Booking** - Booking recommended. 50% deposit required in advance for groups.
- **Price per night** - £17pp dorm. Group discounts.
- **Public Transport** - Carmarthen has both coach and train stations serving South Wales, SW England and London. Local bus runs six times a day to Llansteffan. Ask driver to let you off at Pantyrathro.
- **Directions** - Pantyrathro is six miles from Carmarthen on the B4312, midway between Llangain and Llansteffan. Two miles from Llangain you will see the hostel signposted, turn right and follow hostel signs to top of lane.

CONTACT: Ken Knuckles
Tel: 01267 241014
kenknuckles@hotmail.com www.backpackershostelwales.com
Pantyrathro International Hostel, Llansteffan, Carmarthen, SA33 5AJ

PENQUOIT
CENTRE

The Penquoit Centre is a welcoming courtyard of historic longhouses converted into hostel accommodation for groups of 10 to 25 people. The land on which the centre stands includes a range of fields, ancient woodland, direct access to the Cresswell river and the Pembrokeshire National Park. The land is rich in birdlife, river, sea and wildfowl and within easy reach of over 20 beautiful beaches as well as the Preselli Hills, castles, Tenby and Caldy, riding and canoeing.

The hostel consists of 2 dormitories (one on the ground floor), communal showers and toilets. There are 2 private rooms, a large dining room with wood burning stove and a long room ideal for group activities, workshops and creativity. The kitchen is fully equipped and the centre is centrally heated. The Centre is ideal for family and friend get-togethers, art, yoga, drama, healing and dancing

DETAILS

- **Open** - All year.
- **Number of beds** - 25+: 1 x 10, 1 x 15, plus 2 private rooms.
- **Booking** - Booking essential, deposit 25%.
- **Price per night** - £16 per person
- **Public Transport** - Trains and National Express stop at Kilgetty or Tenby (7miles). Irish Ferry and Pembroke (6 miles). We can collect if necessary
- **Directions** - M4 to Carmarthen, A40 towards Haverfordwest. At Canaston Bridge (just after Robeston Wathem) take A4075 for Pembroke. At Cresselly (6 miles) turn right, then right again at T junction. After small bridge turn left uphill towards Lawrenny, the Centre is on right (½ mile).

CONTACT: Joan Carlisle
Tel: 01646 651666
joan@penquoit.plus.com
Lawrenny, Kilgetty, Pembrokeshire, SA68 OPL

Set in a picturesque village, surrounded by organic farmland and ancient oak woodland, this relaxed and friendly hostel is a great base for launching into everything Pembrokeshire has to offer. The hostel is warm, clean and comfortable, with modern facilities. There are 22 beds in 5 rooms, all of which can be reserved as family rooms. There's a large open plan kitchen and living room as well as a drying room, large car park and cycle shelter. Once a Victorian village school, the hostel is superbly placed for walking, boating, bird watching and kayaking, and is close to many top family attractions and the beautiful beaches of south Pembrokeshire. Groups are welcome and the whole hostel can be hired for holidays, training courses and events. WiFi is available. The adjoining village hall is available to rent. The hostel is run as a charitable trust and is a Friends of Nature hostel. The village has a community shop, pub and an award-winning tearoom.

DETAILS

- **Open** - All year. Arrange check in with warden/all day access.
- **Number of beds** - 22: 2 x 4 (bunks), 2 x 4 (dbl + bunks), 1 x 6 (dbl/sgl + bunks)
- **Booking** - Online, email or telephone
- **Price per night** - Adults £16, children (4-17) £10. Double rooms £37 (couple), £50 (with children). Sole use of hostel £250 per night.
- **Public Transport** - Not easy! Coach/train to Kilgetty or Pembroke. Get the 381 bus (Tenby to Pembroke Dock) and from Cresswell Quay 2.5 mile walk to the hostel.
- **Directions** - From A40 St Clears to Haverfordwest road take A4075 signed Tenby and Oakwood. Just past the turning to Oakwood, turn right and follow signs to Lawrenny. Bear right in front of church and follow the car park signs.

CONTACT: Laura Lort-Phillips
Tel: 01646 651270
hostel@lawrennyvillage.co.uk www.lawrennyhostel.com
Lawrenny Millennium Hostel, Lawrenny, Pembrokeshire, SA68 0PW

STACKPOLE
WALES OUTDOOR LEARNING CENTRE

The 147-bed, platinum eco-award-winning, Stackpole Centre is in the heart of the Stackpole estate. Just a stone's throw from the banks of the Bosherston lakes. It's the perfect venue for large families, groups, special interest breaks and outdoor activities. The estate of countryside and coast includes a national nature reserve, ancient settlements, towering cliffs, wild woodlands and two stunning sandy beaches. The accommodation has been developed from a range of stone farm buildings. It comprises four large houses, three cottages and a manor house. Facilities include a theatre and bar. Adventurous activities such as coasteering, kayaking and surfing are available by arrangement. There are more than 30km of footpaths that crisscross the estate.

         GROUPS ONLY

DETAILS

■ **Open** - All year, all day. Reception 9am - 5pm.
■ **Number of beds** - Swan House 13 bedrooms (up to 24 persons), Shearwater House 7 bedrooms (17 persons), Kestrel House 12 bedrooms (35 persons), Kingfisher 10 bedrooms (44 persons), Manor House 3 bedrooms (up to 9 persons), 3 cottages 9 bedrooms (18 persons)
■ **Booking** - Bookings are made through reception or National Trust Holidays' website.
■ **Price per night** - Minimum of two night's stay. Please contact bookings team for a quote. Prices range from £30 per person per night.
■ **Public Transport** - Trains Pembroke (5 miles). Bus from Pembroke: 387 Coastal Cruiser (seasonal).
■ **Directions** - On the B4319 from Pembroke to Stackpole and Bosherton (various entry points onto estate).

CONTACT: Stackpole Reception
Tel: 01646 661425
stackpole@nationaltrust.org.uk www.nationaltrust.org.uk
The Old Home Farm Yard, Stackpole, nr Pembroke, Pembrokeshire, SA71 5DQ

WARREN FARM
GLAMPING

Beautiful big bell tents, cosy bunkhouse & unique pods right on the Pembrokeshire Coast Path with great views out to sea, close to fantastic climbing at Castlemartin Range, excellent surfing at Freshwater West & Broadhaven South and within striking distance of many of Pembrokeshire's beaches, countryside, wildlife, castles, river walks, charming pubs, film locations and other places of interest. The well-appointed 6m bell tents, which each sleep up to 8, and pods for individuals & couples are on secluded pitches with their own outside dining area, camp fire, fully equipped camp kitchen, and off grid shower & compost loo. The bunkhouse has purpose-built robust and good-sized bunkbeds for up to 12 adults, complete with wet room, toilets and courtyard campfire cooking. Pedestrianised, step-free & dog-friendly site with plenty of parking, grassy lawns and garden games. All mattresses are orthopedic & hypo-allergenic, so you'll get a good night's sleep even after the most energetic day. Please note: this is a remote rural location near an active military training range with no mobile signal, there is usually WiFi in the farmhouse.

DETAILS

- **Open** - All year. Flexible check in by arrangement.
- **Number of beds** - Bunkhouse: 12. Bell Tents: 6x8. Camping, plus an expanding range of pods for couples & individuals
- **Booking** - via website. Bunkhouse sole use only. Camping also available.
- **Price per night** - Check website for latest accommodation & prices. From £12ppn
- **Public Transport** - Train & Ferry: Pembroke. Bus route: 387/388 Coastal Cruiser
- **Directions** - Take the B4319 from Pembroke and follow red-edged signs to Castlemartin Range. Then turn right through Merrion, Warren Farm is on the right.

CONTACT: Jane, Hannah or Amy
stay@warrenfarm.wales www.warrenfarm.wales
Warren Farm, Warren, near Castlemartin, SA71 5HS

GUPTON FARM

Gupton Farm is the National Trust's new visitor base at Freshwater West, with camping, farmhouse accommodation and community facilities on-site. Whether under canvas or Welsh slate, you can be assured of a warm welcome and a relaxed and informal atmosphere. The simple, rustic setting has great facilities including a heated toilet and shower block, a wet weather barn, communal areas and loads of outdoor space. Gupton Farm is the base from which you can explore Freshwater West and the wider landscape. Nestled in a cwtch-like hollow, our farm feels a million miles away from the hustle and bustle of daily life. It's a place to escape, reconnect with nature and breathe in the salty sea air; wake up to striking sunrises, unwind with equally spectacular sunsets and enjoy stargazing after dark. You can follow our network of footpaths, go wildlife watching at the nearby bird hide or head straight to the beach for sandy adventures. The Stackpole Estate is only a short drive away too, if you want to discover more of the National Trust's special places in Pembrokeshire.

DETAILS

- **Open** - Farmhouse & campervan parking all year. Camping on a seasonal basis.
- **Number of beds** - 10 +camping
- **Booking** - Booking on-line or by phone.
- **Price per night** - From £15pp
- **Public Transport** - Trains: Pembroke (5 miles). Bus from Pembroke: 388 stops at Freshwater West car park (20 mins' walk)
- **Directions** - On the B4319 from Pembroke to Freshwater West. 1 mile after Castlemartin take right turn up farm track.

CONTACT:Campsite Manager
Tel: 01646 661425
guptonfarm@nationaltrust.org.uk nationaltrust.org.uk/gupton-farm
Gupton, Castlemartin, Penfro, Pembrokeshire, SA71 5HW

Environmentally sensitive barn conversions on a small family run sheep farm, close to the Milford Haven Waterway in the Pembrokeshire Coast National Park. Ideal for divers, climbers, walkers or for family and friends having a get-together. The four independent units, all have access to garden/patio, laundry/drying room, wash-down area, secure storage and ample parking. THE COWSHED BUNKHOUSE- single storey with disabled access. Large sitting room and kitchen/dining area, and two bedrooms each with en suite shower rooms. THE BARN BUNKHOUSE has an upstairs sitting room and kitchen/dining area whilst the two downstairs bedrooms have en suite shower rooms. THE GRANARY LODGE also has an upstairs sitting room/kitchen. The ground floor bedroom sleeps up to 3 people and has an en suite shower room. The DAIRY LODGE is single story with bathroom, 2 single beds and diner kitchen. All units have fully fitted kitchens, fridge freezers, microwave, toaster, crockery, TV, CD player and wood burning stove. Graded 5 Star bunkhouse by Visit Wales.

DETAILS

- **Open** - All year, check in from 4pm. Check out before 10.30am.
- **Number of beds** - Cowshed 10 1x6,1x4. Barn 8 1x6,1x2. Granary 1x3. Dairy 1x3
- **Booking** - Provisional booking taken by phone/email and confirmed by deposit.
- **Price per night** - From £16pp (inc linen). Min 2 nights at weekends (3 nights bh). Exclusive use: min 6 Barn, 8 Cowshed. Smaller groups/individuals by agreement.
- **Public Transport** - Puffin coastal shuttle passes farm www.traveline-cymru.org.uk
- **Directions** - Follow A4076 through Milford Haven to roundabout by Docks. Take first exit (signed Hakin). Follow for 2 miles, look for first farm on left (next to layby).

CONTACT: Sean or Mandy Tilling
Tel: 01646 690750
mail@upperneeston.co.uk www.upperneeston.co.uk
Upper Neeston Farm, Dale Road, Herbrandston, Milford Haven, SA73 3RY

OLD SCHOOL HOSTEL
FORMERLY YHA TREFIN

Escape to this wonderful, wild and rugged corner of the Pembrokeshire Coast National Park. Old School Hostel is in Trefin, a pretty village which has a pub and a café, just a quarter of a mile from the world famous coast path. Circular walks from the door take you to stunning wild beaches and interesting small harbour villages. The cathedral city of St. Davids and the popular family and surfers' beach at Whitesands Bay are only 20 minutes by car. This characterful 4 star hostel has unique double and twin rooms from £18 pppn. It also offers that rare find, great value single rooms from only £23 and there are budget family/friends rooms too. All rooms have en suite showers, some are fully en suite, and a light breakfast is included in the price. We offer excellent value for exclusive use of the hostel too. Check our guests reviews on Tripadvisor (134 excellent out of 140 reviews). You can book on-line from our website.

DETAILS

- **Open** - All year but we strongly advise you check availability first.
- **Number of beds** - 22: 1 x 6 (3 bunks, one with 4ft lower bed), 1×2 (bunk), 1 x 2 (bunk with 4ft lower bed), 1×2 (double), 2 x 2/3 (bunk with double lower bed), 1×4 (1 double + 1 bunk). Some rooms available for single occupancy.
- **Booking** - Book on-line via our website or contact us by phone or email.
- **Price per night** - From £18. Kids £10. Exclusive use of hostel from only £150.
- **Public Transport** - Train to Fishguard & Goodwick arriving 13.17 to connect with bus 413 to Trefin. See www.travelinecymru.info
- **Directions** - M4/A48/A40 to Letterston. Turn left onto the B4331 for 5 miles then left onto the A487. After 3 miles turn right after the petrol station/shop for Trefin.

CONTACT: Sue or Chris
Tel: 01348 831800
oldschoolhostel@btconnect.com www.oldschoolhostel.com
Ffordd-yr-Afon, Trefin, Haverfordwest, Pembrokeshire, SA62 5AU

CAERHAFOD
LODGE

Ideally situated between the famous cathedral city of St Davids and the Irish ferry port of Fishguard, the Lodge overlooks the spectacular Pembrokeshire coastline. Within walking distance of the well known Sloop Inn at Porthgain and the internationally renowned Coastal Path. An ideal stopover for cyclists with The Celtic Trail cycle route passing the bottom of the drive. The Lodge is a great base for all outdoor activities: boat trips around Ramsey Island, coasteering, kayaking, surfing or just lazing on the beach. The lodge sleeps 23 in 5 separate rooms, all en suite with great showers. There is a modern fully equipped kitchen/diner with sea view patio & picnic tables and with a panoramic view of the Preseli mountains to Strumble Head and the North Bishop with glorious sunsets over the Irish sea. There is also a sitting room for cosy evenings, on-site washing/drying room and ample off road parking. Dogs welcome by prior arrangement. Smoking outdoors. Visit Wales graded 4 star.

DETAILS

- **Open** - All year, check in from 4pm, check out 10.30 am. All day access.
- **Number of beds** - 23: 3x4, 1x5, 1x6.
- **Booking** - Advised in high season. 50% deposit.
- **Price per night** - Adult £20. Under 16 £15. Group rates available
- **Public Transport** - Trains at Fishguard (9m) and Haverfordwest (17m). Fishguard/Rosslare ferry. National Express: Haverfordwest. 413 Bus: St Davids-Fishguard 50yds from Lodge. Seasonal coastal shuttle service for walkers.
- **Directions** - GR Landranger 157, SM 827 317. A40 from Haverfordwest, left at Letterston (B4331) to Mathry. Left onto A487 to St Davids, right in Croesgoch for Llanrhian, at crossroads right for Trefin. Lodge is on right after ½ mile.

CONTACT: Carolyn Rees
Tel: 01348 837859
Caerhafod@aol.com www.caerhafod.co.uk
Llanrhian, St Davids, Haverfordwest, Pembrokeshire, SA62 5BD

HAMILTON
BACKPACKERS

Hamilton Lodge Fishguard, a cosy Hostel with free WiFi, close to the
Pembrokeshire Coastal Path. Perfect for hikers, cyclists or family groups. The
Lodge is comfortable and friendly, sleeping nine in total - with an en suite double
room (king size bed) and two dormitories (1 x 3 beds, 1 x 4 beds). All rooms
centrally heated and recently redecorated (2016). Fully equipped kitchen, dining
area and lounge. Charming, secluded private garden and covered patio with
seating. Free light breakfast provided. Parking close by. One minutes' walk from
centre of town and close to a number of great pubs. There is a fully stocked
Co-Op supermarket within 5 minutes' walk. Smoking is permitted in the garden.
No curfew. Dog friendly - owner "Q" has a very friendly and laid back labrador.
Groups of up to 18 are welcome in collaboration with James John Hamilton
House hostel next door. (See page 338)

DETAILS

■ **Open** - All year.
■ **Number of beds** - 9 (+10): 1 x 4, 1 x 3 and 1 x 2. (Plus 10 next door)
■ **Booking** - Booking advised to confirm beds. 50% deposit required from groups.
■ **Price per night** - £20 to £21 pp in dorms, from £24.50 in double en suite.
■ **Public Transport** - Fishgaurd has train station (Fishguard & Goodwick) and
ferries to Rosslare in Ireland. Port is 1 mile away (approx taxi fare £7). National
Express coaches at Haverfordwest (15 miles). Local buses call 01239 613756.
■ **Directions** - From Haverfordwest (A40) to Fishguard Square (A487), straight
across roundabout then take first right (Hamilton Street), Hostel is 150m on left. From
Cardigan A487, through Lower Town, up steep hill, turn left 100m after Globe Pub.
From Ferry port 1 mile to Fishguard Town Centre (Square), turn left, then first right.

CONTACT: Quentin Maclaurin
Tel: 01348 874797 / 07505562939
hamiltonbackpackers@hotmail.com www.hamiltonbackpackers.co.uk
23 Hamilton Street, Fishguard, Pembrokeshire, SA65 9HL

JAMES JOHN
HAMILTON HOUSE

James John Hamilton House is a brand new conversion of the first free school in Fishguard, built in 1850 by James John Hamilton. The house sleeps 10 people in four private rooms. Upstairs is a large open plan lounge with exposed beams, comfy sofas and dinning table. Next to this is a self catering kitchen and a double bedroom. The three other three bedrooms, a twin, a double and a four person family room are downstairs and are all en suite. There is a patio with picnic table and across the garden is Hamilton House Backpackers. where rooms are available for a further 9 people (see page 336). There is free parking for one car, with a town car park only 40m away. Dogs welcome. Close to the town centre with a choice of pubs. Fishguard is a natural harbour surrounded by the sweeping sands of Cardigan Bay. The Pembrokeshire Coastal Path passes through the town and communities of grey seals and dolphins are regularly seen in its harbours.

DETAILS

■ **Open** - All year.
■ **Number of beds** - 10 (+9): 1 x twin, 2 x double, 1 x 4 (double & bunk bed) plus 9 beds next door.
■ **Booking** - Please book by phone or email.
■ **Price per night** - From £20 to £28 per person.
■ **Public Transport** - Fishguard has excellent new train links and operates a regular ferry service to Rosslare in Ireland. For local buses in Pembrokeshire phone Richard Bros 01239 613756.
■ **Directions** - Look for entrance to old school building behind Hamilton Backpackers on Hamilton Street (See directions on page 336).

CONTACT: Steve Roberts
Tel: 01348 874288
stephenism@hotmail.com www.jamesjohnhamilton.co.uk
19a Hamilton St, Fishguard SA65 9HL

Piggery Poke is a 16 bed, 4 star hostel on the public footpath that loops from the Wales Coast Path between Mwnt and Aberporth. Local cycle routes link the road at the top of the entrance drive to long distance cycle routes Lôn Teifi (within 4 miles) and the Celtic Trail (see Sustrans Route 82). Piggery Poke is a new conversion of an old building and has 3 dormitories sleeping up to 8, 5 and 3, each with en suite facilities. The dining room seats 16 at one sitting. There is a drying room on the ground floor and wireless broadband is available by arrangement. There is a large garden area with sea views and barbeque, there is also a cycle store. Courtesy collection and delivery service is usually available from points within 15 miles along the coast for walkers or cyclists and/ or their cycles/luggage. Ample parking is provided.

DETAILS

- **Open** - All year round, 7.30am to 10am and 4pm to 10pm, at the latest
- **Number of beds** - 16: 1 x 8, 1 x 5, 1 x 3
- **Booking** - Book by phone or via our website.
- **Price per night** - £25 per person.
- **Public Transport** - Trains at Aberystwyth and Carmarthen. From Aberystwyth station take the X50 bus to Blaenannerch or 550 bus to Felinwynt, via Aberporth. From Carmarthen station take the 460 or 461 bus to Cardigan (Finch Square) then change to the 550 bus to Aberystwyth via Aberporth, alighting at Felinwynt.
- **Directions** - Piggery Poke hostel is part of Cardigan Coastal Cottages, at Ffrwdwenith Isaf, Felinwynt, half-way between Mwnt and Aberporth, 4 miles along the coast north of Cardigan. Lat: 52.13108, Long: -4.58939. Map X222837, Y251268.

CONTACT: Paul or Angela
Tel: 01239 811777
hostel@piggerypoke.co.uk www.piggerypoke.co.uk
Ffrwdwenith Isaf, Felinwynt, Cardigan, SA43 1RW

MAES-Y-MOR

Maes-y-Mor offers superior accommodation at a budget price. A 4 star double room apartment and new 4 star boutique self-catering house which sleeps 7 are also available. Ideally situated near the town centre, around the corner from the beach and 5mins' walk to train and bus stations. Accommodation at the hostel is room-only. There is a large kitchen/diner with fridge-freezer, hob oven, microwave and toaster enabling guests to prepare their own food. Bedrooms have TV, tea/coffee making facilities and beds of a superior quality to ensure a good night's sleep. Free WiFi internet and towels are provided. There is a car parking area at rear and secure shed for bikes. Aberystwyth is an ideal base for exploring Wales. Visit Devil's Bridge with its dramatic waterfalls, the Vale of Rheidol narrow gauge railway, the National Library of Wales, the castle and the harbour. Aberystwyth is a university town with plenty of night life. Personal and helpful service. Warm Welcome to all Croeso Cynnes i Bawb.

DETAILS

- **Open** - All year, 8am to 10pm.
- **Number of beds** - 19 : 7 x 2 (twin), 1 x 2 (double), 1 x 3 (family en-suite)
- **Booking** - Booking advisable.
- **Price per night** - Twin and double rooms from £50. Single room from £30. Discount for larger groups.
- **Public Transport** - Bus and train stations are within approximately 400 mts.
- **Directions** - From bus and train stations follow Terrace Road in a straight line towards beach. Turn right at Tourist Board shop, then Maes-y-Mor is about 30 mts along, next to the cinema.

CONTACT: Mererid or Alaw
Tel: 01970 639 270. Mobile:07966502715
maesymor@hotmail.co.uk www.maesymor.co.uk
25 Bath Street, Aberystwyth, Ceredigion, SY23 2NN

This budget bunkhouse is nestled in the Teifi valley, perfect for exploring the local area.

Bedding is included and facilities include a self-catering kitchen and a lounge, with terraced garden and BBQ area.

Twenty five minutes' drive will get you to the stunning Ceredigion coastline.

There are many village pubs and restaurants within walking distance.

Shaggy Sheep are expert in organising adventure activity holidays ideal for hen & stag weekends, corporate team building, youth groups, couples and families.

Get in touch to find out more.

DETAILS

- **Open** - Jan-Dec, 24hrs.
- **Number of beds** - 22 (5x4, 1x2)
- **Booking** - book by email or through the website
- **Price per night** - email with numbers and stay length for a quote
- **Public Transport** - No
- **Directions** - Take A484 from Carmarthen to Saron. Turn right at Rhos. Through Pentrecwrt to Llandysul, turn right at Half Moon pub, see us on the left or follow Sat Nav to SA44 4AJ.

CONTACT: Chris
Tel: 01559 363911
bookings@shaggysheepwales.co.uk www.shaggysheepwales.com/
Old Commerce House, Pontwelly, Llandysul, Carmarthen SA44 4AJ

THE LONG BARN

WALES

Penrhiw is a working organic farm in beautiful countryside with views over the Teifi Valley. The stunning Ceredigion Coast and the Cambrian Mountains are an easy drive away and the busy small town of Llandysul (1.5 miles) has all essential supplies. The Long Barn is a traditional stone barn providing comfortable, warm, self catering bunkhouse accommodation for 31 people. The Cowshed provides self catering accommodation for 6. The Annex has a double bed and single bed with kitchenette. The Cwtsh has a double bed and a sofa bed. Each unit can be hired separately or combined for larger groups.

The farm's location is ideal for exploring, studying or simply admiring the Welsh countryside. Activities enjoyed by guests in the surrounding area include fishing, swimming, climbing, abseiling, canoeing, farm walks and cycling. The accommodation is available all year, having adequate heating with lovely warm log fires, roof insulation and double glazing throughout.

DETAILS

■ **Open** - All year, all day.
■ **Number of beds** - 43: Long Barn 31: 1x15,1x14,1x2. Cowshed 6:1x6. Annex: 3: 1x3 (dbl+single). Cwtsh: 3: 1x3 (dbl+sofa bed)
■ **Booking** - Essential, deposit required
■ **Price per night** - £15pp . Discount for groups and mid week bookings.
■ **Public Transport** - Trains and National Express at Carmarthen (16 miles). Local bus service at Landysul (1.5 miles) details/booking 0871 2002233 www.bwcabus.info
■ **Directions** - OS map 146, GR 437 417. In Llandysul, at the top of the main street, take right hand lane. Turn sharp right down hill. After 100 yds turn sharp left. Another ½ mile turn first right. Continue for 1 mile and Long Barn is on your right.

CONTACT: Tom or Eva
Tel: 01559 363200 Mob 07733 026874
cowcher@thelongbarn.co.uk www.thelongbarn.co.uk
Penrhiw, Capel Dewi, Llandysul, Ceredigion, SA44 4PG

GILFACH WEN
BARN

Gilfach Wen Barn has been converted to provide competitively priced homely self-catering accommodation for individuals, extended families or groups on a working farm in South West Wales. Graded as a 4 star bunkhouse it sleeps up to 32 in 7 bedrooms and has a large kitchen/dining room, lounge, drying room and undercover BBQ area. There is a downstairs bedroom and shower room for disabled. The facilities are walker, cyclist and equestrian friendly. The barn is WiFi enabled, fully equipped and Brechfa village with its shop and pub is within walking distance (1 mile). Adjacent to Brechfa Forest, the Cothi Valley and Llanllwni Mountain, Gilfach Wen Barn is a perfect venue for a holiday or weekend away – you need never leave the valley. This is a stunningly beautiful area close to Brecon Beacons National Park, in the foothills of the Cambrian Mountains but only a short drive to the beach, Pembrokeshire or Gower. Virtual tour available on the barn's website.

DETAILS

- **Open** - All year, all day.
- **Number of beds** - 32: 3x6, 1x5, 1x4,1x3,1x2 in 10 double beds and 12 singles.
- **Booking** - Advance booking required.
- **Price per night** - From £17.50pp. During school holidays and at weekends minimum numbers apply for advance bookings. Last minute bookings at weekend may be available at £20pp for individuals and small groups.
- **Public Transport** - Trains and coaches at Carmarthen. Daily bus from Carmarthen to Brechfa passes gate. Bus is a request stop service. You can ask to be dropped off and can catch the bus at the bottom of the drive.
- **Directions** - GR SN 513 292 On the B4310 between Horeb and Brechfa.

CONTACT: Jillie
Tel: 07780 476737
info@brechfa-bunkhouse.com www.brechfa-bunkhouse.com
Gilfach Wen, Brechfa, Carmarthenshire, SA32 7QL

TYN CORNEL
TYNCORNEL HOSTEL

Ty'n Cornel Hostel is an isolated former farmhouse in the hills, with a cosy open fire. Favoured by walkers, cyclists, bird watchers and lovers of solitude it is in the beautiful Doethie valley on the Cambrian Way long distance footpath.

There are comfortable wooden bunk beds and good self-catering facilities. You can enjoy the wild open moorlands of the Elenydd uplands and you can walk the old drovers road to Dolgoch Hostel (see page 348). Other attractions include the Cors Caron National Nature Reserve, the Red Kite Centre and museum in Tregaron, Teifi Pools, Llyn Brianne reservoir, Dolaucothi Roman gold mines, Strata Florida Abbey and the National Trust's Llanerchaeron country house.

DETAILS

- **Open** - All year. Reception 5pm -11pm, 7am -10am.
- **Number of beds** - 16: 2x8.
- **Booking** - Booking advisable, essential mid November to mid March. Ring hostel managers on 01980 629259 or email tyncornel.bookings@btinternet.com.
- **Price per night** - £12 per adult, £9 (under 18s). Block bookings negotiable. Campers £8.
- **Public Transport** - Trains: Aberystwyth 28m, Llanwrtyd Wells 16m, Cynghordy 12m. Coach: X40 (Cardiff – Aberystwyth) Lampeter 15m. Bus: 585 (Lampeter – Tregaron) Llanddewi-Brefi 7m.
- **Directions** - Road from Llanddewi-Brefi, near Tregaron, follow hostel signs SE 7m (last mile track). Bridle path S up Doethie valley on the Cambrian Way (Llandovery 15 m) or byway 2m NW from Soar y Mynydd chapel.

CONTACT: Janet or Richard
Tel: 01980 629259
gill.keen@dolgoch.org www.elenydd-hostels.co.uk
Llanddewi Brefi, Tregaron, Ceredigion, SY25 6PH

DOLGOCH
HOSTEL

Come and experience the peace of this unique location in the remote Tywi valley. A stay in this 17th century farmhouse will take you into an era before electricity, with a log burner for heat. Dolgoch is a traditional simple hostel owned by the Elenydd Wilderness Trust. It has hot showers, a self catering kitchen/dining room and 20 beds in 3 dormitories and has been refurbished to include new toilets, solar powered showers and less able accommodation. Private rooms are available and the access track has been upgraded. The Lôn Las Cymru (Welsh National Cycle Route) and the Cambrian Way pass nearby and there are many other mountain tracks to explore on foot, by mountain bike or pony. The hostel is ideal for bird-watchers and lovers of solitude and is close to an old drovers' track which leads over the scenic Cambrian mountains for 5 miles to the equally remote and simple Ty'n Cornel Hostel (see page 346). Why not stay a night in each hostel and follow in the treads of the old drovers?

DETAILS

- **Open** - All year 24 hours. Reception 5pm -11pm, 8am -10am.
- **Number of beds** - 20: (in 3 rooms). Private rooms available.
- **Booking** - Booking information on yha.org.uk or from Gillian Keen
- **Price per night** - £12 per adult, £9 (under 18). Campers £8.
- **Public Transport** - Train to Aberystwyth, Carmarthen or Llanwrtyd Wells. Bus X40: Cardiff/Carmarthen to Lampeter/Aberystwyth. Bus 585: Lampeter/Aberystwyth to Tregaron. Postbus 287: Llandovery to Rhandirmwyn.
- **Directions** - SN 806 562. You can walk to Dolgoch over the hills from Tregaron or take the winding Abergwesyn mountain road. The hostel is ¾ mile south of the bridge, along an unsurfaced track.

CONTACT: YHA Booking Office or Gillian Keen
Tel: 01440 730 226
dolgoch@yha.org.uk www.elenydd-hostels.co.uk
Dolgoch, Tregaron, Ceredigion, SY25 6NR

STONECROFT
LODGE

Stonecroft Lodge self-catering guest house is situated in Llanwrtyd Wells, 'the smallest town in Britain'. Surrounded by the green fields, mountains and glorious countryside of mid Wales, Llanwrtyd is in renowned red kite country and is a great centre for mountain biking, walking, pony trekking etc.

The town hosts many annual events such as the Man v Horse Marathon, World Bog Snorkelling Championships and the Mid Wales Beer Festival.

The hostel offers a warm welcome and a comfortable stay. It has private and shared rooms with fully made-up beds. There is a fully equipped kitchen, a lounge with TV and video, free laundry and drying facilities, central heating, a large riverside garden and ample parking. The hostel adjoins our Good Beer Guide pub, Stonecroft Inn (where great food is available), and is truly your 'home away from home', offering the best of everything for your stay.

DETAILS

- **Open** - All year, all day - phone on arrival.
- **Number of beds** - 27: 1 x 1 : 3 x 4 : 1 x 6 : 4 x (dbl + 1 sgl)
- **Booking** - Welcome, 50% deposit.
- **Price per night** - £16. Discounts for 3+ nights. Phone for exclusive-use rates.
- **Public Transport** - Llanwrtyd Wells station on the Heart of Wales line is a few minutes' walk from the hostel.
- **Directions** - GR 878 468. From Llanwrtyd town centre (A483) take Dolecoed Road towards Abergwesyn. Hostel is 100 yds on left. Check in at Stonecroft Inn.

CONTACT: Jane Brown
Tel: 01591 610332
party@stonecroft.co.uk www.stonecroft.co.uk
Dolecoed Road, Llanwrtyd Wells, Powys, LD5 4RA

Stay at the 16th century New Inn on the River Wye and discover the forgotten countryside of mid Wales. The New Inn has a bunkhouse ideal for parties of walkers and cyclists as well as double, twin and family B&B rooms. The bunkhouse has its own entrance and a large lobby which can be used for boots and waterproofs. Secure storage is available for cycles and motor-cycles. The bunkhouse is self-contained with toilets and showers.

There are no self-catering facilities but the inn specialises in serving imaginative home-cooked locally grown food. A Welsh breakfast of home-made sausages and dry cured bacon is available for £5.50. Explore the surrounding countryside, inhabited by red kites, or relax in the secluded beer garden. There is plenty of parking and a large function room for parties

DETAILS

- **Open** - All year, all day. Pub closed 3pm - 5pm some days.
- **Number of beds** - Bunkhouse 10: 1x6, 1x4; B&B 11: family rooms, double & twin
- **Booking** - Book by phone or email.
- **Price per night** - £12 pp (Bunkhouse), £60 sole use of 6 bed room, £40 sole use of 4 bed room. Breakfast £5.50pp. En suite B&B in inn £70 double/twin. Family rooms also available from £100.
- **Public Transport** - Trains at Llandrindod Wells (5 miles). Infrequent bus service.
- **Directions** - Newbridge-on-Wye is on the A470 between Builth Wells and Rhayader. Travelling north on the A470 take a right turn in Newbridge and the New Inn is on the right.

CONTACT: Debbie and Dave
Tel: 01597 860211
dave@pigsfolly.orangehome.co.uk www.pigsfolly.co.uk/bunkhouse.htm
New Inn, Newbridge-on-Wye, Llandrindod Wells, Powys, LD1 6HY

LLYSDINAM
FIELD CENTRE

Llysdinam Field Centre offers affordable accommodation in Mid Wales surrounded by beautiful countryside and close to the market town of Llandrindod Wells. The Wye Valley Walk and the Builth Wells to Rhayader cycle route pass close by. The Elan Valley (12 miles), the Royal Welsh Showground (6 miles) and the Brecon Beacons National Park are within easy reach. The bunkhouse with its adjoining kitchen and dining room comfortably sleeps 24. The kitchen facilities can be used for self-catering or healthy, tasty vegetarian meals can be provided. There is also a small self-catering flat for up to 6 people. All facilities are basic but comfortable, ideal for activities, workshops, conferences and study visits. An extra meeting room is available for hire. The Centre has a long history and ongoing future in ecological research. It also focuses on sustainability and education projects with a range of partners including artists, biologists and architects. Sorry no hen or stag parties.

DETAILS

■ **Open** - All year, all day access once booked in.
■ **Number of beds** - 30: Bunkhouse 24: 1x24. Flat 6:1x4,1x2
■ **Booking** - Non-returnable deposit £50 for all bookings. Email or use online form.
■ **Price per night** - £12 pp. Breakfast £3.50, Packed lunch £5, Evening meal £10.
■ **Public Transport** - X47 Bus from Llandrindod Wells stops at Newbridge-on-Wye, 20 mins' walk from accommodation. Trains are at Builth Wells and Llandrindod Wells
■ **Directions** - Turn off the A470 in Newbridge-on-Wye onto the B4358 towards Beulah. Immediately after river bridge take the first right, signposted Llysdinam. After 0.6km take the second left turn (no cattle grid). Look for Field Centre 200m on left.

CONTACT: Dorienne Robinson
Tel: 07514 358330
enquiries@llysdinamfieldcentre.co.uk www.llysdinamfieldcentre.co.uk
Newbridge-on-Wye, Llandrindod Wells, Powys, LD1 6NB

Set in the beautiful Mid Wales countryside on the Glyndwrs Way the bunkhouse is an ideal location for exploring or unwinding. Built to the highest standards, with 4 star tourist board rating, it provides high quality accommodation for groups or individuals. It can also be booked for conferences and seminars. There is a well equipped kitchen and a large communal area with fabulous elevated views over the Mid Wales countryside. The bunk beds are large with comfortable mattresses. Pillows and pillowcases are included, sheets and duvets can be hired for £3 per set. Attractions close by include sailing, golf course, outdoor pursuit centre, shooting range, motorbike school and the picturesque market town of Llanidloes (0.5 mile) with many places to eat and drink. You will need to bring your own soap and towels. Boots and dirty footwear must be kept in the drying room so please bring footwear for indoors. Taxis for walkers and cyclists to / from routes available.

DETAILS

■ **Open** - All year, 24 hours. Arrival and departure times by arrangement.
■ **Number of beds** - 27 in 2 dormitories and 1 family room.
■ **Booking** - Booking is required (with non-refundable deposit) by phone, email or booking form on plasnewyddbunkhouse.co.uk.
■ **Price per night** - Sole use £403 per night. Individuals £20 pp.
■ **Public Transport** - Caersws train station (7 miles), Llanidloes bus station (0.5 mile). Pick ups can be arranged from these points if required.
■ **Directions** - From Llanidloes take the Gorn Road and Plasnewydd is signposted on the left hand side after about half a mile.

CONTACT: Susan
Tel: 01686 412431 / 07975 913049
susanvaughan67@aol.co.uk www.plasnewyddbunkhouse.co.uk
Gorn Rd, Llanidloes, Powys, SY18 6LA

BEILI NEUADD
BUNKHOUSE

Beili Neuadd Bunkhouse is a converted 18th century stone barn beautifully positioned in quiet, secluded countryside with delightful views, its own paddocks, stream, pools and woodland. The centrally heated barn sleeps 16 in 3 en suite bunkrooms and includes a fully equipped kitchen/dining room and drying room. The bunks have full sized mattresses, bed linen is included and towels can be hired. Accommodation is also available in an adjacent chalet, there is B&B in the main house and space to camp in the paddock. The paddock has picnic tables and a BBQ and there is ample parking in the yard. The barn is 2.5 miles from the small market town of Rhayader - the gateway to the Elan Valley reservoirs, 'the Lakeland of Wales'. A wide range of activities are possible including cycling, mountain biking, fishing, pony trekking, canoeing, bird watching and walking. Perfect for celebrations and get togethers.

DETAILS

- **Open** - All year, all day access.
- **Number of beds** - 16: 2x6,1x4. Chalet: 1 double, 2 singles. B&B: 3 double rooms
- **Booking** - Booking preferred (with deposit).
- **Price per night** - : £19 per person, sole occupancy £275. Chalet £20pp or £60 full occupancy (4 people). B&B £50pp £80 for two.
- **Public Transport** - Nearest trains at Llandrindod Wells -12 miles. Some buses from Rhayader. Taxi from Rhayader about £4. Assistance with transport available.
- **Directions** - OS Explorer 200/OS147 GR 994698. Take the A44 east bound from Rhayader town centre (clock). After 0.4 miles turn left on unclassified road signposted Abbey Cwm-hir with Beili Neuadd sign. Take 1st left after 1.5 miles. Beili Neuadd is 2nd farm on right after 0.4 miles.

CONTACT: David and Alison Parker
Tel: 01597 810211
info@beilineuadd.co.uk www.beilineuadd.co.uk
Beili Neuadd, Rhayader, Powys, LD6 5NS

MID WALES
BUNKHOUSE

Mid Wales bunkhouse is affordable, warm and comfortable, accommodating individuals or groups in outstanding rural surroundings close to the Elan Valley, Wye Valley, Trans Cambrian Trail, Glyndwrs Way and Cycle Routes 8 and 81. Lots of circular walks and rides from the door and the Cambrian mountains to the west make the location ideal for walkers, mountain bikers, cyclists, riders, bird watchers, fishermen, trekkers and more. Fully equipped for self-catering or meals available if arranged in advance. Outside covered veranda and secluded garden with barbeque and pizza oven. Access to River Marteg where otters and many bird species have been spotted. Covered cycle storage. B&B for horses by arrangement. Camping and tipi available with special rates for combined bookings. An ideal base for DofE, scout groups, walking/cycling clubs etc.

DETAILS

- **Open** - All year, 24 hours. Arrivals after 3pm (advise if after 7pm) , depart by 11am.
- **Number of beds** - 20
- **Booking** - At short notice please phone to check availability. Otherwise book online, email or phone with deposit.
- **Price per night** - £15pp, £75 for private 6-bed room. Sole use of dormitory area (sleeps 14) £170 per night, sole use of entire bunkhouse (20 people) £240 per night.
- **Public Transport** - Trains at Llandrindod Wells/Newtown. NE coach to Llanidloes. Buses from Llandrindod to Rhayader and limited service to St. Harmon and Pant Y Dwr. We can collect from Llandrindod, Llanidloes or Newtown by arrangement.
- **Directions** - From Rhayader take A44/A470 towards Llangurig then B4518 towards St Harmon. At the Mid Wales Inn turn right, After a mile turn right, Bunkhouse on right in half a mile. SatNav use is not advised. GR SN998750.

CONTACT: John or Steph
Tel: 01597 870081
enquiries@bunkhousemidwales.co.uk www.bunkhousemidwales.co.uk
Woodhouse Farm, St Harmon, Rhayader, LD6 5LY

PLAS DOLAU
COUNTRY HOUSE HOSTEL

Plas Dolau is set in 25 acres of quiet countryside just 3 miles from the popular coastal town of Aberystwyth. Ideal for exploring West Wales, walking, cycling, riding, fishing and golf etc. and central for day trips to Snowdonia and Pembrokeshire. The warm country mansion (WTB 4 star hostel) has mainly dormitory style accommodation for up to 45 people. An adjoining Swedish style farmhouse (WTB 3 star guest house) can take another 15. Plas Dolau includes meeting rooms, dining rooms, games room, outdoor areas and walks. Various options for accommodation, provision of food, cooking facilities, etc are available. Ideally suited for youth groups, field courses, retreats, house parties and many other groups or individuals. WiFi is available to all from the guest house. Please feel free to phone to discuss your requirements:

DETAILS

- **Open** - All year, 24 hours.
- **Number of beds** - 45: + cots etc. Plus 16 in farmhouse.
- **Booking** - Recommended.
- **Price per night** - From £20 (including basic breakfast) to £35 (private room, en suite with full breakfast). From £650 per night for the whole mansion
- **Public Transport** - Nearest train station is in Aberystwyth. Taxi from the station will cost £6-7. National Express coaches and local buses (525 and 526) will set down at the end of the hostel drive.
- **Directions** - GR 623 813, OS map 135. On the A44, 3 miles from Aberystwyth (1 mile east of railway bridge, 0.6 miles west of A4159 turning to Bow Street). Roadside sign: "Plas Dolau B&B Y Gelli".

CONTACT: Pat Twigg
Tel: 01970 617834
pat@plasdolau.co.uk www.plasdolau.co.uk
Lovesgrove, Aberystwyth, Ceredigion, SY23 3HP

TOAD HALL

Toad Hall is a small hostel beside the River Dovey, close to Snowdonia National Park. It is not far from the centre of the lively town of Machynlleth, which has an alternative feel and an annual comedy festival. NCN Cycle route 8 and Glyndwrs Way route pass through Machynlleth. Cader Idris mountain is 6 miles away. Toad Hall Hostel has a four bed-roomed self contained accommodation unit above the family home. There is a mixture of double, twin and bunk beds and bedding is supplied for a small cost. The small self-catering kitchen has seating for 4 and there is a basic shower room. There is a large games room with seating around an open fire which is available until 9pm at night. The hostel is a centrally heated older building providing simple accommodation. There is a flat garden for camping or bike/canoe storage and a workshop for bike repairs. Under 18s and well behaved dogs welcome by agreement. Book in advance.

DETAILS

- **Open** - Not always open, please phone to find out and always pre-book. Please vacate rooms from 12 -3 pm for cleaning. No arrivals after 11pm.
- **Number of beds** - 10: 1x4 (family), 1x2 (twin), 1x2 (dbl), 1x2
- **Booking** - Advance booking necessary - phone on the day if necessary. Payment in advance. Email is a good way to book as the phone is not always manned.
- **Price per night** - £16 pp + £2 per stay for bedding. Reductions for groups.
- **Public Transport** - 200m to train station (services to the Midlands, North Wales and Aberystwyth). 100m to Lloyds coaches depot and local bus stop
- **Directions** - Toad Hall is situated directly behind the car park of the Tuffins/Texaco petrol station. Tuffins/Texico is on the main road in Machynlleth very close to the railway station.

CONTACT: Will
Tel: 01654 700597 / 07866 362507 (mobile) or Eva 07807 849216
willcoyn@hotmail.com
Toad Hall, Doll St, Machynlleth, Powys, SY20 8BH

BRAICH GOCH
BUNKHOUSE & INN

The Braich Goch is a 16th century coaching inn situated 3 miles from Cadair Idris. There are stunning views of the Dulas Valley and Dyfi Forest. The Braich has been specifically set up with outdoor enthusiasts in mind. Facilities include drying room, secure bike storage and large well equipped self-catering kitchen. There are 6 bedrooms, 4 en suite and a further two bathrooms. WiFi. See a 360 degree virtual tour on our website. The location is ideal for walking, mountain biking, cycling, climbing and canoeing at all levels as well as bird watching or simply chilling out. The Cli-machx Trail & Dyfi Forest mountain bike trails are on the doorstep. The Braich is also a pub with pool table, darts and other games to keep you entertained in the evening! In the area are King Arthur's Labyrinth and Corris Craft Centre, Centre for Alternative Technology, Coed-y-Brenin Forest Park, Nant yr Arian and the coast. Wales Tourist Board 4 stars. Walkers & Cyclists Welcome Awards.

DETAILS

- **Open** - All year, all hours by arrangement.
- **Number of beds** - 26: 5 x 4, 1 x 6
- **Booking** - Essential for groups. 20% deposit, balance 4 weeks before arrival.
- **Price per night** - Sole occupancy (26 beds) 2 or more nights, £468pn. Sole occupancy 1 night, £494. Small group/individuals 2 or more nights, £18.50 pppn. Small group/individuals 1 night, £19 pp.
- **Public Transport** - Nearest train station to Corris is Machynlleth. Bus stop outside the 'Braich Goch' Inn. Taxis can be hired from Machynlleth.
- **Directions** - GR 754 075 On A487 between Machynlleth and Dolgellau at Corris turning. 2.5 miles north of Centre for Alternative Technology.

CONTACT: Ann or Andy
Tel: 01654 761229 Mobile: 07881 626734
annbottrill123@btconnect.com www.braichgoch.co.uk
Corris, Machynlleth, Powys, SY20 9RD

CORRIS
HOSTEL

Perfect for group activity and family gatherings, Corris Hostel offers a very special atmosphere that disengages the stresses of the outside world. The award winning hostel is renowned as a spiritual haven with its caring, easy going atmosphere, friendly staff, meditation areas, cosy wood fires and collection of inspiring books, games and artefacts.

Outdoors the terraced landscaped gardens provide a serene, inspirational environment for even the largest groups. An added bonus is the barbecue and camp fire areas. Nestled in the foothills of Cadair Idris, the hostel enjoys splendid views over the Dyfi Valley in the Snowdonia National Park. Down river are the Dyfi Biosphere nature reserves and miles of golden beaches at Aberdyfi, while the lofty Cadair Idris nestles in the next valley. Close by is the Centre for Alternative Technology and a range of environmental activities.

DETAILS

- **Open** - All year, all day access.
- **Number of beds** - 42/44
- **Booking** - Phone to check.
- **Price per night** - Adult £16 child £13. Breakfast £4.25. Private rooms extra.
- **Public Transport** - Transport: Buses 30, T2, 34 and X28 pass Machynlleth train station on the Cambrian Coast line with connection to Aberystwyth and Birmingham.
- **Directions** - GR 753 080. We are in the mountain village of Corris 6 miles north of Machynlleth. At Braich Goch turn off A487 into Corris. At Slaters Arms pub turn left, hostel is 150m uphill just beyond a small private car park. Guests' cars can be parked in private car park.

CONTACT: Michael or Debbie or Jackie
Tel: 01654 761686
mail@corrishostel.co.uk www.corrishostel.co.uk
Old School, Corris, Machynlleth, Powys, SY20 9TQ

TY'N Y BERTH
MOUNTAIN CENTRE

Ty'n y Berth is a former school at the foot of Cadair Idris on the southern edge of the Snowdonia National Park. Surrounded by mountains, valleys and crystal clear rivers, yet only 12 miles from the coast, it's a great location for outdoor activities and family holidays. The spacious accommodation sleeps up to 43 including a separate unit for 8 which can also be hired on its own. The main room is divided into dining and lounge areas. There is a commercial kitchen, recently renovated, with large oven, dishwasher, hob and microwave, plenty of toilets & showers, drying room, pay phone, lockable storage for boats & bikes and parking for 10 cars. Corris is within walking distance and has two pubs: the Slaters Arms, which does bar meals, and the Braich Goch Inn. Courses are also available in climbing, mountain walking, abseiling, gorge scrambling, mine exploration, ropes courses, orienteering, and team building. Accommodation for a further 36 is available at the Bryn Coedwig Centre (also run by Wide Horizons), four miles from Ty'n Y Berth in Aberllefenni.

           GROUPS ONLY

DETAILS

- **Open** - All year, all day.
- **Number of beds** - 43: 35:1x8,1x9 3x6, 2x2, 2x1 + 2 occasional beds. Rugog:8
- **Booking** - Book by phone/fax or email.
- **Price per night** - £378+vat, sole use self catering. Rugog unit £110+vat.
- **Public Transport** - Trains run from London to Machynlleth with a change at Birmingham New Street.
- **Directions** - On entering Corris Uchaf from north on A487 you will enter a 30 mph speed limit. Ty'n y Berth is the old school on the right, just inside the 30mph signs.

CONTACT: Jane
Tel: 01654 761678
info@corris-bunkhouse.co.uk   www.corris-bunkhouse.co.uk
Corris Uchaf, Machynlleth, Powys, SY20 9RH

With 4 miles of stunning beach just 20 metres from the front door, Borth Youth Hostel is the perfect location of a beach holiday.

This characterful Edwardian house has 9 bedrooms with sea views.

A great base for visits to the Centre for Alternative Technology, Aberystwyth or the beautiful Dyfi Biosphere. A short drive away from Snowdonia National Park. For those after an adrenalin filled break why not try mountain biking or surfing?

With two classrooms also available Borth YHA is perfect for those school trips too. The hostel has free WiFi, a games and TV room, bike storage and drying room. Meals and a licensed bar are available.

Photo © Copyright Martin Thirkettle.

DETAILS

- **Open** - All year check in 5 - 10.30pm check out 8am - 12 noon
- **Number of beds** - 60
- **Booking** - online via YHA website or by phone
- **Price per night** - from £18 pp
- **Public Transport** - train station at Borth- trains to and from Aberystwyth.
- **Directions** - on main B4353 which goes through the centre of Borth hugging the coast. 1/2 mile north of the station.

CONTACT: John Taylor
Tel: 01970 871498
john@borthyouthhostel.co.uk
Ceredigion, Wales, SY24 5JS

HYB BUNKHOUSE
DOLGELLAU

HyB Bunkhouse is on Heol y Bont (Bridge St) in Dolgellau (Lon Las Sustrans 82), mid Wales, at the foot of Cader Idris. Centrally located above Medi gifts, with free parking at rear for up to four cars. Near pubs, shops and restaurants, HyB backs onto the Mawddach trail near the river Wnion. It is 10 minutes' drive to Coed y Brenin mountain biking centre. This quirky listed building has original features such as oak floors, beams and panelling and consists of four bunk rooms, sleeping 16 in total. Each room has a mini-kitchen for basic self-catering with fridge, hob, toaster and kettle. One room is en suite and there are also two other bathrooms. Bring your own bedding or rent on request. The entrance is at the rear of the building. Sharp left at the corner of the public toilets on the Marian car park, and sharp second right through double wooden gate into private car park. The key pad entry is on single yellow door. Strictly no stag parties. No communal lounge.

DETAILS

■ **Open** - All year except Xmas and New Year.
■ **Number of beds** - 16: 4 x4.
■ **Booking** - Please phone or email during office hours 10am - 4.30pm.
■ **Price per night** - £20 per person. Limited bedding sets available @£5.
■ **Public Transport** - Buses stop at Eldon square (1 minute walk) and link with train stations at Machynlleth and Barmouth for connections to Midlands and London.
■ **Directions** - HyB is above Medi - the last shop before the main bridge on the one way system out of Eldon square. By car turn into Y Marian car park and take a sharp left behind the public loos into HyB car park through the double wooden gates.

CONTACT: Nia
Tel: 01341 421755
post@medi-gifts.com
2-3 Heol y Bont (Bridge St), Dolgellau, Gwynedd, LL40 1AU

Some places you will stay at for a short while, but they will stay with you for ever. The Bunkorama at Gwastad Agnes is such a place. This converted stone stable provides comfortable and well equipped accommodation for cyclists, backpackers, climbers and explorers. At the end of a day's expedition you can sit at the Bunkorama, cuppa in your hands and trace your route across from Cader Idris. You can gaze out across Cardigan Bay and wonder why you had never discovered Gwastad Agnes before. You certainly won't forget it. The Bunkorama provides accommodation for individuals or groups in Snowdonia close to the Cambrian Way, Cycle route 8 and the Ardudwy Way.

For mountain goats the rock climbing of the Barmouth Slabs is a 5 minute walk and for mountain bikers you are only 20 minutes by car to Coed y Brenin, the UK's first dedicated mountain bike centre.

DETAILS

- **Open** - all year round.
- **Number of beds** - 2 rooms each sleeping 4. Plus sofa bed in lounge
- **Booking** - on-line, phone, email, post or on site
- **Price per night** - £15 pp + £5 per stay if bedding needed and towel available £2 per stay
- **Public Transport** - Bus and train to Barmouth approx 40 mins' walk to hostel.
- **Directions** - From the A496 out of Barmouth turn left up Panorama Road and after approximately 1 mile turn sharp left after small car park on right. The hostel is second entrance on left after about 200 metres. Follow Bunkorama signs up Panorama Road

CONTACT: Graham
Tel: 01341 281134 or 07738467196
thebunkorama@gmail.com www.bunkorama.co.uk
Gwastad Agnes Off Panorama Road, Barmouth, Gwynedd, LL42 1DX

BUNKHOUSE
AT THE WORKHOUSE

The newly refurbished and well equipped bunkhouse at Y Dolydd Llanfyllin Workhouse offers a unique holiday experience. Stay in one of the last remaining Victorian workhouses still open to the public. Set in 6.5 acres of beautifully peaceful grounds, Y Dolydd is a registered charity developing the bunkhouse, history centre and venue, owned and managed by the community. The Bunkhouse is available March to October for individuals, families or groups. It is near to Welshpool, Oswestry and Shrewsbury. Close to the Berwyn Mountains National Nature Reserve it has access to a range of outdoor and adventure activities including scrambling, water sports, walking and cycling. Nearby attractions include Lake Vyrnwy and Pistyll Rhaeadr waterfall, the tallest single drop waterfall in the UK. Y Dolydd is also a venue and is available for exclusive hire for your wedding, private party, festival, conference or meeting. The History Centre is open daily 10am - 5pm, is free to enter and is well worth a visit to learn more about the building and the people who lived and worked in it.

DETAILS

- **Open** - March - October inclusive.
- **Number of beds** - 24: 1x4, 1x8, 1x12
- **Booking** - via phone or email.
- **Price per night** - £15 including linen/duvets/pillows. Groups discounts may apply.
- **Public Transport** - Trains: Shrewsbury & Welshpool. Buses to Welshpool. The Tanat Valley Bus runs a request stop service from Welshpool which drops at the gate.
- **Directions** - Do not use Satnav. Llanfyllin is on A490 Oswestry to Welshpool road. The Workhouse is the large Victorian building on the right just before you enter town.

CONTACT: Tree Marshall
Tel: 07534 354 082
bunkhouse@the-workhouse.com www.the-workhouse.org.uk/
Y Dolydd, Workhouse, Llanfyllin, SY22 5LD

BALA
BACKPACKERS

For outdoor adventures within the Snowdonia National Park, Bala Backpackers offers good value 'hostel-style' accommodation, including; 30+comfy SINGLE BEDS in bedrooms of 3,4 or 5, with two washrooms of cubicle-showers, wet-room, 3 private TWIN ROOMS and 3 new EN SUITES. The 19th century character buildings are located in a quiet, sunny, chapel square, in the bustling market town of Bala, mid North Wales. It is clean, safe and nice for the price, with a fully-fitted self-catering guest kitchen. Catering is available on demand, or try the new ECO-Caffé for lunch 12-4pm. Bala boasts a five-mile-long lake, a white-water river for raft rides, and nestles beneath three 900 metre peaks. The lakeside, river and leisure pursuits are 5 mins' walk away. Plan your activities or just soak up the atmosphere in town, where new tourism attractions include Mary Jones World, Gorwellion Gardens, Lottery Play Park and the Sailing Club.

DETAILS

- **Open** - All year by arrangement, 8.30-20.30. Front door locked 00.30 – 6.00am.
- **Number of beds** - 45: 2x3, 3x4, 3x5 + 3 twin rooms + 3 en suites
- **Booking** - On-line or by answerphone or email.
- **Price per night** - 1 night £21, 2 nights £39, 3 nights £49, weekly £89. Twin room: £49 or en suites from £59. Double holiday-let: £220/4 nights. Hostel sheet-bag hire £3/week or bring sheets/sack & pillowcase .
- **Public Transport** - Trains: Wrexham (30 miles) or Barmouth (30miles). Bus no 94 every 2 hours daily from Wrexham and Barmouth.
- **Directions** -. GR 926 358. Bala is on A494. Turn in the middle of Bala High Street, opposite the White Lion Royal Hotel, down Tegid Street to see HOSTEL Sign. Unload outside Hostel, but park round corner, in FREE overnight pay & display.

CONTACT: Stella Welch
Tel: 01678 521700
info@Bala-Backpackers.co.uk   www.Bala-Backpackers.co.uk
32 Tegid Street, Bala, LL23 7EL

BALA
BUNK HOUSE

The bunkhouse is a converted 200-year-old Welsh stone building, set back from the road in over an acre of picturesque grounds with private parking.

Modernised to provide accommodation for outdoor activity groups, it is light, airy and comfortable with storage heating. There is a large lounge/dining area and bunk rooms for 2, 4 and 8 plus annexe for 6. Separate ladies' and gentlemen's toilets have washing areas and hot showers. Fully equipped self-catering kitchen. Also there is a self-contained bunkroom sleeping 6, with small kitchenette, shower and toilet/washing area which is ideal for smaller groups and families. Sheets, pillows & pillowcases are provided - bring a sleeping bag.

There is a splendid view of the Berwyn Hills; together with the Aran and Arenig hills they provide superb walking. Bala Lake and the National White Water Centre are brilliant for water sports. Good pubs, restaurants and shops in Bala.

DETAILS

- **Open** - All year, no restrictions.
- **Number of beds** - 26 : 1x2, 1x4, 1x6, 1x8, 1x6 self-contained
- **Booking** - Book if possible, ring or write with 20% deposit. Weekends are busy.
- **Price per night** - Single night £17 pp, two or more nights £16pp per night
- **Public Transport** - Trains at Wrexham (30 miles). National Express at Corwen (10 miles). Local buses call at Bala (1.6 miles from hostel). Call hostel for a taxi.
- **Directions** - GR 950 372. From England take M6, M54, A5 through Llangollen then A494 for Bala. We are on the A494 1.5 miles before Bala.

CONTACT: Guy and Jane Williams
Tel: 01678 520738
thehappyunion@btinternet.com www.balabunkhouse.co.uk
Tomen Y Castell, Llanfor, Bala, Gwynedd, LL23 7HD

Llangollen Hostel offers clean and comfortable twin and double rooms, en suite family rooms, private four-bed and six-bed en suite rooms, and a great value six-bed dorm. Prepare your meals in our fully fitted kitchen/dining room, then relax in our cosy lounge by the log fire. We have a book exchange, free WiFi, plenty of games, laundry facilities, a drying room, and bicycle/canoe storage. Perfect location for walking, climbing, canoeing and mountain biking in the Vale of Llangollen. Families will love visiting the steam railway, horse drawn canal boats and Pontcysyllte Aqueduct - a World Heritage Site. The town offers a great choice of restaurants/pubs and is home to a fringe music and arts festival and the International Eisteddfod. Llandegla, Chester, Wrexham and Offa's Dyke Path are all nearby. You are assured of a happy and comfortable stay, freedom to come and go as you please, and above all, a warm welcome.

DETAILS

- **Open** - All year, all day.
- **Number of beds** - 32.
- **Booking** - Internet, email or phone.
- **Price per night** - From £18pp dorm. £20pp for a private 3,4,5 or 6 bed room. £45 twin/double or £50 en suite. Family of 4 £60, £10 per extra child
- **Public Transport** - Nearest train station is Ruabon with regular trains to Chester and Shrewsbury. Buses from Ruabon to Llangollen operate throughout the day and take 15 mins. Daily National Express from London.
- **Directions** - From the A5 heading west, the hostel is located 50 yards past the main set of traffic lights on the right. Parking is at the rear of the hostel on Market Street – at the main traffic lights, turn right then first left.

CONTACT: Arlo Dennis
Tel: 01978 861773
info@llangollenhostel.co.uk www.llangollenhostel.co.uk
Berwyn Street, Llangollen, LL20 8NB

Tyddyn Bychan is an 18th century traditional Welsh farmhouse and barns set in private grounds and surrounded on all sides by farmland. Situated in an excellent central location, for mountain biking, road cycling, canoeing, walking, climbing, fishing and numerous watersports including whitewater rafting.

The main bunkhouse sleeps 18 in two en suite rooms. All the bunks are handmade and of a very high standard. The smaller bunkhouse sleeps 9 in two en suite rooms and has its own kitchen, conservatory and lounge. All bedding is included.

Delicious homemade food is available if booked in advance. The bunkhouses are ideal for self-catering with very well equipped kitchen/dining rooms. There is a good parking area well away from the road.

DETAILS

- **Open** - All year, all day.
- **Number of beds** - 28: 1x10; 1x8; 1x6; 1x3
- **Booking** - Booking is essential
- **Price per night** - £15 pp including bedding.
- **Public Transport** - Nearest train station is at Betws-y-Coed. Nearest National Express service at Llandudno. Phone 01492 575412 for details.
- **Directions** - GR 931 504. Turn off A5 at Cerrigydrudion. Take B4501 out of village for Llyn Brenig, take the turning on left for Cefn Brith. After about 2 miles you will see a phone box on left, chapel on right and the road widens for a layby. The gate for Tyddyn is on the left directly opposite junction on the right.

CONTACT: Lynda
Tel: 01490 420680 Mob: 07523 995741
lynda@tyddynbychan.co.uk www.tyddynbychan.co.uk
Cefn Brith, Cerrigydrudion, Conwy, LL21 9TS

This converted Grade II listed stone farm building offers the perfect base for enjoying the Snowdonia National Park. In a rural setting on the 8,000 hectares Ysbyty Estate it has easy access to the A5 and is only six miles from Betws-y-Coed. The 400 year old building offers group accommodation with lots of character, substantial dining and social space and a large private car park. The large enclosed garden at the rear of the bunkhouse has picnic benches and a barbecue area. There is excellent access to outdoor activities in the surrounding area including walks from the door of the bunkhouse so you can forget your car for a few days. Local attractions include the Tree Top Adventure Course at Betws-y-Coed, Zip World at Penrhyn Quarry, Bethesda, Zip World and Bounce Below at Llechwedd Slate Caverns, Blaenau Ffestiniog, the Plas y Brenin National Mountain Centre at Capel Curig, shops, leisure centre, swimming pool at Llanrwst and the seaside resort of Llandudno. No pets.

DETAILS

- **Open** - All year, 24 hours.
- **Number of beds** - 18: 2 x dormitories + 1x1 single bedroom.
- **Booking** - Early booking recommended (March to October is very busy).
- **Price per night** - Short breaks: 2 nights from £380 .
- **Public Transport** - Trains at Betws-y-Coed (6 miles), Llandudno Junction (20 miles) and Llanrwst (10 miles); National Express bus station at Llandudno. Some local buses to Betws-y-Coed, but we advise bringing your own transport.
- **Directions** - Situated 6 miles SE of Betws-y-Coed near the junction of the A5 and the B4407 (signposted Ysbyty Ifan and Ffestiniog). GR855511 (OS sheet 116).

CONTACT: National Trust Cottages Group Accommodation Team
Tel: 0344 3351296
group.accom@nationaltrust.org.uk · www.nationaltrustholidays.org.uk
National Trust Ysbyty Estate Office, Dinas, Betws-y-Coed, Conwy, LL24 0HF

CELLB

Stay in Blaenau Ffestiniog's historic Edwardian police house, recently converted to provide comfortable dorm rooms as well as a cinema & restaurant. A small self-catering kitchen is available with inside or outside seating or you can grab a drink or eat in the restaurant and bar. Safe storage for bikes and climbing gear is available making this the perfect base for an adventurous holiday in Snowdonia. Right in the centre of Snowdonia, Blaenau Ffestiniog is the perfect base for climbers, mountain bikers, and walkers or those looking for great food, culture and attractions. For adrenaline junkies Zip World & Bounce Below are near by and there are great mountain bike trails at Coed y Brenin, Gwydr Forest, Penmachno and around Trawsfynydd Lake, including some family trails. If you are not an adrenaline junkie there is still plenty to do. Explore Llechwedd Slate Caverns, travel on the famous Ffestiniog and Welsh Highland narrow gauge railway, castles and beaches galore and the Portmeirion village.

DETAILS

- **Open** - Open all year, all day
- **Number of beds** - 11: 1x6, 1x3, 1x2
- **Booking** - individuals and small groups book on-line. Contact hostel for sole use.
- **Price per night** - From £20. Sole use of the hostel starts at: £396 for the weekend (Friday – Sunday) £1,386 for the week.
- **Public Transport** - Bus 1B from Porthmadog. Trains from Llandudno Junction and Porthmadog (Ffestiniog Railway narrow gauge). Station/buses 5 mins' walk.
- **Directions** - From A470 Blaenau Ffestiniog centre, turn onto Park Square and follow the road. CellB is the old police building on the left. There is parking behind.

CONTACT: Reception
Tel: 01766832001
prisoner@cellb.org cellb.org/
Park Square, Blaenau Ffestiniog LL41 3AD

TREKS
BUNKHOUSE

Treks Bunkhouse, 900 feet above sea level, is high in the mountains near the Welsh-speaking village of Blaenau Ffestiniog. It is ideal for people who enjoy the rugged beauty of Snowdonia and a short airy walk to the pub of an evening. A modern conversion of a golf club house, graded 4 star by VisitWales, Treks is set in a wild area on the outskirts of the village and provides year round accommodation for individuals and groups. There is a self-catering kitchen and five bedrooms sleeping between 1 and 6 people, ideal for groups, families or groups of families. Beds are fully made up with sheet and duvets and towels are available to hire for a small charge. The is a large lock up ideal for canoes and bikes. There are many tourist attractions available within a short drive: Llechwedd Slate Caverns, Bounce Below, Zip World Titan, Antur Stiniog, Ffestiniog Railway, Go Below Adventures, Coed y Brenin Mountain Bike Centre, Portmeirion Italian Village, Bala White Water Rafting and Harlech Castle.

DETAILS

- **Open** - All year, check in 14:00 - 20:00
- **Number of beds** - 16: 1x6, 1x4, 1x3, 1x2, 1x1
- **Booking** - Online, by phone or email.
- **Price per night** - £16 to £20 per person.
- **Public Transport** - Express Motor's Bus 35 from Dolgellau (4 times a day), bus 1B from Porthmadog (hourly). Trains from Llandudno Juction and Ffestiniog Railway narrow gauge trains from Porthmadog. Station/buses 20 mins' walk from bunkhouse.
- **Directions** - Two thirds of a mile from the centre of Ffestiniog on the B4391 towards Bala. Look for a cattle grid and small lane on the right with catle gird.

CONTACT: Dyfed
Tel: 07796 172 318
treksbunkhouse@gmail.com www.treksbunkhouse.co.uk
Y Cefn, Ffestiniog, Gwynedd, LL41 4PS

MAENTWROG
BUNKHOUSE

Maentwrog bunkhouse is a newly renovated 200 year old cowshed situated on a working beef and sheep farm.

It has a fully equipped kitchen, underfloor heating, TV/DVD player, BBQ area, laundry facilities, power washer and lockup available for bikes.

Local activities range from hill walking (Moelwyn and Cnicht are 10 minutes away), white water rafting, Coed y Brenin cycling centre, Blaenau Ffestiniog down hill cycle track, RopeWorks, canyoning, Ffestiniog narrow gauge railway and several beautiful beaches are all within 15 to 20 minutes' drive as well as the Welsh costal path passing at the end of the lane.

Please contact direct for any other information

DETAILS

- **Open** - All Year.
- **Number of beds** - 4
- **Booking** - booking essential
- **Price per night** - £18 pppn bring sleeping bags or hire bed linen @£3 pp
- **Public Transport** - Public bus to bottom of lane 400m walk. Arriva Wales train to Penrhyndeudraeth
- **Directions** - Turn into Maentwrog village.then follow the A496 towards Harlech for 1 mile with lay-by on right, take immediate left up small lane for 400m, first farmhouse on right

CONTACT: Mrs Eurliw M Jones
Tel: 01766590231
emj2@hotmail.co.uk www.bunkhousesnowdonia.com
Felen Rhyd Fach, Maentwrog, Blaenau Ffestiniog, Gwynedd, LL41 4HY

SNOWDON LODGE
GROUP HOSTEL

Stay in the birthplace of Lawrence of Arabia! Snowdon Lodge hostel provides comfortable self-catering style group accommodation in a large grade 2 listed character building. The property is located in the picturesque village of Tremadog. Snowdon Lodge is perfect for a family reunion or simply as a base for a group of friends to explore this beautiful part of Snowdonia and the nearby Lleyn Peninsula. The hostel has 10 rooms of different sizes (twins, doubles and small dormitories). Bathroom and shower facilities are shared. There is a large fully equipped self-catering kitchen, a dining room seating 40, two lounge/TV rooms with real log fires in winter, a drying room and a very large private car park leading to extensive woodland walks. Snowdon Lodge is ideally positioned just 6 miles from Mount Snowdon, yet only 2 miles from beautiful beaches such as Black Rock Sands. The famous Italianate village of Portmeirion is also only 4 miles away. Within a mile are the Ffestiniog and Welsh Highland railways and the famous Tremadog rocks for climbers. Sorry, no stag or hen parties.

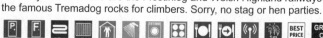   **BEST PRICE** **GROUPS ONLY**

DETAILS

- **Open** - January – December, all day access.
- **Number of beds** - 35: 2 x 6 (family), 1 x 5, 1 x 6 , 3 x twin, 3 x double
- **Booking** - Essential.
- **Price per night** - Sole use £600 per night. Minimum 2 nights, bank holidays minimum 3 nights. Longer stays could attract discounted prices, please ask.
- **Public Transport** - Half mile from Porthmadog train station and 250 yards from National Express coach stop.
- **Directions** - 800m from Porthmadog just off A487 at the start of Tremadog village.

CONTACT: Carl or Anja
Tel: 01766 515354
info@tudorlodge.co.uk www.snowdonlodge.co.uk
Lawrence House, Church Street, Tremadog, Nr Porthmadog, Gwynedd, Snowdonia, LL49 9PS

LLEDR HOUSE

Lledr House nestles in the heart of Snowdonia National Park. A former YHA, this newly refurbished hostel is delightfully situated in its own woodlands in the beautiful Lledr Valley just outside the picturesque village of Dolwyddelan. Guests come back year after year, having delighted in the huge improvements, including luxury mattresses, modern bathrooms, well equipped kitchen, free WiFi and an extended car park also suitable for motorbikes. Whether you are a lone traveller, large family, DofE or a group of friends, Lledr House offers clean, cheap, comfortable accommodation. All bedding is provided in private single, twin and family rooms and one nine-bed dorm. There is also a luxury self-contained cedar log cabin, sleeping 5, in the grounds. Enjoy the riverside garden, patio, BBQ and views of Moel Siabod. Woodland walks, cycle trails and forest surround the hostel. Betws-y-Coed, stunning Llyn Elsi and Tree Tops high rope course just 4 miles away. Pub and Spar shop within walking distance.

DETAILS

- **Open** - Open March to November inc. Check in from 5pm till 10.30pm.
- **Number of beds** - 36: House 31: 1x9, 2x4,1x6, 3x2, 2x1. Cabin 5: 1x5
- **Booking** - Book by phone/email with credit card. First night's deposit for groups.
- **Price per night** - From £18pp. Sole use £550, £600 at bank holidays. Cabin from £100 (minimum of 2 night bookings in cabin).
- **Public Transport** - Pont-y-Pant station on the Conwy Valley Line is ¾ mile away.
- **Directions** - On the A5 from Llangollen to Bangor turn left just before Betws-y-Coed onto the A470 (signed Dolgellau). The hostel is 4 miles on right side of road. Walking from Pont-y-Pant station, turn left and left again after stone road bridge.

CONTACT: Brian or Melanie Quilter
Tel: 01690 750202 Mobile: 07915 397705 or 07915 397660
Lledrhouse@aol.com www.ukyh.com
Pont-y-Pant, Dolwyddelan, North Wales, LL25 0DQ

PLAS CURIG
HOSTEL

This five star hostel has been stylishly refurbished since its previous existence as Capel Curig YHA and provides luxurious comfort in stunning surroundings. With views of Snowdon, the hostel is in the village of Capel Curig, the heart of Snowdonia National Park, and only 10 mins' drive from the mountain. The only five star hostel in North Wales, Plas Curig welcomes individuals, couples, families and groups. Dorms sleep 4 to 8 people in bunks and family rooms, doubles and twins are also available. Each bunk has a comfy mattress, curtains for privacy, light, socket and is ready made with hypo-allergenic bedding. There is a well equipped self-catering kitchen and dining facilities. The TV room, lobby, lounge and library have free WiFi and there are private shower rooms with WC and basins. There is a drying room, outside storage for bikes/canoes and car parking. Well behaved dogs welcome in private rooms. A luxury 6 person holiday let is available on site. Pubs and cafés close by. Snowdonia has it all!.

DETAILS

- **Open** - All year. Check in between 5-10pm.
- **Number of beds** - 59: 1x8, 2x6, 4x4, 1x 4/5, 2x 3/4, 2x 2/3,1xdouble, 1xtwin
- **Booking** - Book online with card.
- **Price per night** - Dorms from £20.00. Family rooms from £90 per room. Doubles & twins from £50 per room. Dogs £5. Exclusive hire of hostel from £1000 per night.
- **Public Transport** - Trains at Betws-y-Coed (5 miles). Buses: Snowdon Sherpa 97A Portmadog to Betws-y-coed, S2 Pen-y-Pass to Betws-y-Coed and S6 from Bethesda (with connections to Bangor) all run past the hostel.
- **Directions** - On the A5 in the centre of Capel Curig village.

CONTACT:
Tel: 01690 720 225
info@snowdoniahostel.co.uk www.snowdoniahostel.co.uk
Plas Curig, Capel Curig,Betws-y-Coed,North Wales, LL24 0EL

CABAN CYSGU
GERLAN BUNKHOUSE

Caban Cysgu offers comfortable, purpose-built accommodation at the foot of the Carneddau in the Welsh-speaking village of Gerlan. A warm welcome is guaranteed at this community run bunkhouse. An ideal location for walking in Snowdonia, providing a great base for the 'Fourteen 3000ft Peaks' long-distance challenge. For the adrenalin junky, it's just a 5 minute drive to Zip World; the longest and fastest zip line in Europe, "The Nearest Thing to Flying!!" Brilliantly located for mountain biking with plenty of off-road trails nearby. And for road cyclists the bunkhouse is ideal for exploring Snowdonia, whilst for leisurely rides the hostel is within a mile of Sustrans route 'Lôn Las Ogwen'.

Rock-climbing at Idwal is close at hand, as well as Ysgolion Duon for the dedicated winter climbers. The nearby Afon Ogwen provides a popular venue for canoeists. For more leisurely pursuits, try visiting Coed Meurig, Penrhyn Castle or the Greenwood Centre. Shops, pubs and cafés in Bethesda are within walking distance.

DETAILS

- **Open** - All year, all day.
- **Number of beds** - 16 : 1x5, 1x2, 1x1, 1x8
- **Booking** - Not essential, but recommended.
- **Price per night** - From £14 - £16
- **Public Transport** - Bangor train station is 6 miles. Catch a bus from Bangor bus station to Gerlan (66), or Bethesda (fare £1.40). Taxi from Bangor approx. £15.
- **Directions** - GR 632665. A5 southbound, turn left in Bethesda centre just before Spar. Bear right, up hill over 2 cross-roads. Hostel is 300m at the old school on left.

CONTACT: Dewi Emyln, Manager
Tel: 01248 605573 Mob: 07464676753
dewi@cabancysgu-gerlan.co.uk www.cabancysgu-gerlan.co.uk
Ffordd Gerlan, Gerlan, Bethesda, Bangor, LL57 3ST

CONWY VALLEY
BACKPACKERS BARN

Conwy Valley Backpackers is situated on a peaceful working farm with organic status in the heart of the beautiful Conwy Valley, with excellent access to Snowdonia. Centrally heated with fully equipped self-catering kitchen, log fires, hot showers and a fire alarm system. There are three separate dorms sleeping 4, 6 and 10, two of which have their own toilet facility. Secure bike/canoe storage, grazing for horses and tourist information are available. Beside the barn is a small stream and guests may picnic and BBQ on the river bank. An ideal space for restoration, relaxation and retreat. Bring a sleeping bag or hire bed linen (£3). Continental breakfast (£3.50) and packed lunch (£6) are available by arrangement. Local activities range from fishing and hiking to white water rafting and mountain biking. Surf Snowdonia is within walking distance and Zip World a short drive away. There are great pubs and eating places within walking distance. Groups and individuals are welcome. Sorry - no dogs.

DETAILS

- **Open** - All year, all day.
- **Number of beds** - 20 in dorms of 4, 6 & 10
- **Booking** - Not essential but recommended
- **Price per night** - From £20pp. Sole use from £275. £3pp bed linen hire.
- **Public Transport** - Train stations and coaches at Llandudno Junction and Conwy. Local bus 19 or 19a runs every 20 minutes from Conwy and Llandudno Junction, ask driver to drop you at Pyllau Gloewon farm gate.
- **Directions** - GR 769 697. Six miles south of Conwy on the B5106, look for Backpackers sign just before entering Tal-y-Bont.

CONTACT: Claudia
Tel: 01492 660504 Mob: 07956 851425
info@conwyvalleybarn.com www.conwyvalleybarn.com
Pyllau Gloewon Farm, Tal-y-Bont, Conwy, Gwynedd, LL32 8YX

Conwy Valley
BACKPACKERS
BARN
www.conwyvalleybarn.com
01492-660504

B&B

J.W. LEES

YE OLDE
BULL INN

BULL ST

LLANDUDNO
HOSTEL

James and Melissa would like to invite you to their charming Victorian 4 star boutique hostel. We are a friendly hostel where individuals, families and groups (including schools) are welcome all year. Some of the guests' comments: "friendliest hostel we've ever stayed in", "Wow isn't it clean", "these bathrooms are fabulous, as good as any hotel". Come and try us, we love to meet new people and look forward to getting to know you. Set in the heart of the Victorian seaside resort town of Llandudno, an ideal place to shop or explore the many and varied local attractions. Excellent blue flag beaches, dry slope skiing, toboggan run, ten pin bowling, bronze age copper mine, traditional pier and many museums, fishing trips, etc. Llandudno is within easy travelling distance of Snowdon, Bodnant Gardens and local castles. We are able to book local attractions for groups and secure some discounts.

DETAILS

- **Open** - All year (telephone in winter prior to arrival). All day.
- **Number of beds** - 46: 2x8, 2x6, 4x2, 1x4, 1 x family.
- **Booking** - Essential April to July.
- **Price per night** - From £23 per person, £55 per private twin room, £60 per private twin en suite. Group and family rates on request. Special offers autumn/winter.
- **Public Transport** - Trains at Llandudno. Turn right as you exit station, cross road, turn left down Vaughan Street (towards the beach), left into Charlton Street.
- **Directions** - From the A55 take A470 and follow signs to Llandudno town centre, straight through all roundabouts, after Asda turn 3rd left into Vaughan Street (signed train station), then 1st right into Charlton Street. Hostel is No 14.

CONTACT: James
Tel: 01492 877430
info@llandudnohostel.co.uk www.llandudnohostel.co.uk
14 Charlton Street, Llandudno, LL30 2AA

PLATTS FARM
BUNKHOUSE

Platt's Farm Camp-site and Bunkhouse is situated within a range of Victorian farm buildings dating back to 1858, in the charming village of Llanfairfechan. Ideally situated close to the A55, the Bunkhouse sits at the start/end of the 14 Welsh 3000 peaks walks in the Snowdonia National Park, within a 10 minute walk of the Wales coastal path and on the No.5 cycle route. The bunkhouse has 3 star Visit Wales grading. It has 2 bunk rooms sleeping a total of 10 people.

The kitchen is equipped with a four ring cooker, microwave, kettle, fridge/freezer, toaster, TV, table to seat 10 and electric fire. Heating is by electric storage heaters and all heating and lighting are included in the price. Pans, crockery, cutlery, and bedding is provided. Ample off road parking and adjacent covered area for BBQs. 11 camping pitches with covered picnic areas also available. Shops, pubs and cafés are within 5 minutes' walk.

DETAILS

- **Open** - All year, check out before 11am, check in after 2pm.
- **Number of beds** - 10
- **Booking** - Deposit required. Non refundable balance is payable 2 weeks before arrival. Most major credit or debit cards and PayPal accepted.
- **Price per night** - £15.00 per person per night. Exclusive use £150 per night.
- **Public Transport** - By train to Llanfairfechan station. Bus from Llandudno or Bangor stops right by the entrance. National cycle route No 5 passes the entrance.
- **Directions** - A55 westbound Exit 15, remain on this road. The entrance to Platt's Farm is a sharp turn on the right just after the traffic lights and bus stop. A55 eastbound Exit 14, follow the road over the A55 then turn left on to Aber Road.

CONTACT: Sam Davies
Tel: 0(44)1248680105
sam@plattsfarm.com www.plattsfarm.com
Platts Farm Bunkhouse, Aber Road, Llanfairfechan, Conwy, LL33 0HL

Totters is situated in the heart of the historic castle town of Caernarfon. Sheltered by the castle wall, it is only 30 metres from the shores of the Menai Straits and enjoys some fantastic sunsets. The town not only offers the visitor a huge selection of pubs and restaurants to choose from, but also acts as the perfect base for trips into the Snowdonia National Park. There is very good public transport in and out of the National Park. The hostel is a 200-year-old, five floored town house, which is fully heated with all the comforts of home. Facilities include a common room with TV and games, book exchange, dining room and a secure left luggage facility. There are five bedrooms which sleep either 4 or 6 and can be arranged as mixed or single sex dorms. The Penthouse room, a huge double en suite room with views over the Straits, can be a double or a family room. Across the road there is a self-catering town house which sleeps 6. See website for more details of all our accommodation.

DETAILS

- **Open** - All year, all day access. Book in by 10pm.
- **Number of beds** - 28 : 3 x 6, 2 x 4, 1 x 2 (en suite), 1 x 2 (twin)
- **Booking** - Booking is essential for groups in June, July, August and September.
- **Price per night** - £18.50pp in a dorm. £50 for a double/twin en suite. £44 for a twin. Discounts for groups.
- **Public Transport** - Bangor train station is 9 miles from the hostel. Catch a bus from outside the station to Caernarfon. National Express coaches drop off in Caernarfon 200m from the hostel.
- **Directions** - Coming by road: follow signs for town centre, turn right 200m after the big Celtic Royal hotel, keep going and Totters is the last house on the left.

CONTACT: Bob/Henryette
Tel: 01286 672963 Mob: 07979 830470
totters.hostel@googlemail.com www.totters.co.uk
Plas Porth Yr Aur, 2 High Street, Caernarfon, Gwynedd, LL55 1RN

ARETE
OUTDOOR CENTRE
WALES

The Arete Outdoor Centre in Snowdonia National Park, offers excellent access to the stunning coastline, meandering rivers, awesome mountains and large lakes of North Wales and Anglesey. With comfortable, affordable, bunkhouse style accommodation and large kitchens for easy catering this is a great base for groups of friends or family. The area is passionate about its language, music and history and is rich with magnificent castles, steam railways, heritage and festivals, so there's plenty to do. The team are happy to help with advice on how best to spend your stay and a range of exciting outdoor activities are available through the centre's well qualified and experienced staff. Catering for over 100 people is available. Several social rooms allow space for down-time, the games room having pool and table tennis tables. Large storage for bikes, kayaks and surfboards and individual cloakrooms for outdoor kit. Car parking available and a large field for activities. Local eating out at Glyntwrog Inn is just 200m away.

DETAILS

- **Open** - All year, all day.
- **Number of beds** - 100+ in 22 rooms split into three blocks of 20, 58 and 30+
- **Booking** - via email: info@aretecentre.co.uk or phone 01286 672136.
- **Price per night** - Catered from £30pp, self-catering from £15 pp. Sole use deals.
- **Public Transport** - Anglesey Airport. Train to Llanfairpwll or Bangor. Buses to Caernafon and local buses from Bangor and Caernarfon,
- **Directions** - Sat navs use LL55 4AP. From A55 at jct 11 follow signs to Llanberis and then Llanrug. Turn left just before the Glyntwrog pub the Centre is 200m on your right. Pickups from Bangor station can be arranged or use taxi or local bus.

CONTACT:
Tel: 01286 672136
info@aretecentre.co.uk www.aretecentre.co.uk
Arete Outdoor Education Centre, Llanrug, Caernarfon, Gwynedd, LL55 4AP

PENTRE BACH
BUNKHOUSE

Pentre Bach Bunkhouse provides dog friendly alpine style accommodation, outdoor activities and a camp-site. The Bunkhouse is heated with electric radiators and has two floors. The ground floor has tables with benches and a cooking area with gas burners, microwaves, fridge and freezer. Upstairs are alpine sleeping platforms with mattresses for 16. Drying room and toilets with washing facilities and showers, shared with the camp-site, are just across the yard. Based between Waunfawr and Betws Garmon, Pentre Bach is surrounded by the superb scenery of Moel Eilio and Mynydd Mawr and has views towards Mount Snowdon. There are great walks from the bunkhouse or take a short car journey to the Nantlle ridge and the main footpaths up Snowdon. Bach Ventures provides guided walks, kayaking, climbing, gorge-scrambling and coasteering. Large or small groups and individuals all welcome. Local pub is CAMRA Pub of the year in the area. Great beer and good food.

DETAILS

- **Open** - 9am-10pm for Enquiries. Arrive from 4pm, leave by 11am.
- **Number of beds** - 16: 1x16.
- **Booking** - One night's deposit required with balance payable before arrival. Short notice bookings accepted by phone or email with deposit/balance payable on arrival.
- **Price per night** - £12 per person (inc gas / electric / showers). Sole use bookings negotiable according to group size.
- **Public Transport** - Train station at Bangor. S4 bus from Caernarfon to Beddgelert stops at the bottom of the drive on request.
- **Directions** - GR 531 579. At Pentre Bach just south of Waunfawr on the Caernarfon to Beddgelert road (A4085). Look for Pentre Bach Bunkhouse sign.

CONTACT: Karen Neil
Tel: 01286 650643(5-10pm) or 07798733939(9-5pm)
info@bachventures.co.uk www.pentrebachbunkhouse.co.uk
Pentre Bach, Waunfawr, Caernarfon, Gwynedd, LL54 7AJ

CWM PENNANT
WALES **HOSTEL/TRAINING CENTRE**

Cwm Pennant Hostel is a 56 bed independent hostel offering relaxed accommodation for individuals, families and groups. It also offers adventure activities for groups provided by Outdoor UK Ltd and catering is available to groups and individuals. The hostel is set within stunning grounds in the Snowdonia National Park and has fantastic views of the Cwm Pennant valley and Moel Hebog. It is 5 miles from Porthmadog. Cwm Pennant Hostel has a lounge, drying room, games/training room and self-catering kitchen. Home cooked food is available on request. Guests have access to complimentary tea and coffee. A range of additional facilities are available including a power washer for mountain bikes, on-site parking and secure storage for bikes, kayaks and canoes. The area is ideal for hill walking, rock climbing and canoeing.

DETAILS

- **Open** - February to December for advanced booking, 7:30-12noon; 4.30-10pm.
- **Number of beds** - 56: 4 x 4, 1 x 6, 1 x 8, 1 x 10, 1 x 16.
- **Booking** - Advance booking recommended, a deposit of 20% is required.
- **Price per night** - £18.50 (adult), £15 (under 16), under 3's free. From £1,495 sole use two night weekend. Breakfast from £4 to £7, discounts for advanced booking. Packed lunches from £4.95. Evening meals on request from £8.95 for two-courses.
- **Public Transport** - Porthmadog train station is 5 miles away. Take the number 1 bus towards Caernarfon and get off at the Cwm Pennant turning on the A487. From here follow the brown hostel signs - 1 mile walk to the hostel.
- **Directions** - From Porthmadog take the A487 towards Caernarfon. Take second turning on the right after passing through Penmorfa village and follow the brown hosel signs.

CONTACT:
Tel: 01766 530888 or 01706 877320
bookings@cwmpennanthostel.com www.cwmpennanthostel.com
Golan, Garndolbenmaen, Gwynedd, LL51 9AQ

ABERSOCH
SGUBOR UNNOS

Croeso/Welcome! Sgubor Unnos provides luxury bunkhouse accommodation on a Welsh speaking, traditionally run, family farm in the village of Llangian, one mile from Abersoch. Abersoch is famous for its watersports and there are great surfing beaches at Hell's Mouth and Porth Ceiriad. Centrally located, the bunkhouse is the ideal base for outdoor activities including walking the newly opened Llyn Coast Path, surfing, cycling, golf, fishing and sailing. A few miles from Llangian, at the tip of the Peninsula lies Bardsey Island where 20,000 saints are buried! Why not pay them a visit? Trips around the island can be arranged. The modern bunkhouse offers three bedrooms ideal for individuals or groups. There is a fully equipped kitchen/lounge, disabled facilities, covered BBQ area, secure storage and private parking and free WiFi. There is a traditional village shop and phone box 500m away. For details on area see website. Photos taken by Tony Jones www.llynlight.co.uk

DETAILS

- **Open** - All year, all day.
- **Number of beds** - 14: 2 x 4, 1 x 6
- **Booking** - Not essential but recommended.
- **Price per night** - £20 (adult), £10 (under 10 years), including a light breakfast and bed linen. Discount for more than 2 nights.
- **Public Transport** - Nearest train station is Pwllheli (7 miles). Good local bus and taxi service to Llangian. Public transport details on website.
- **Directions** - GR 296 288 On entering Abersoch from Pwllheli, take the right hand turning up the hill signed to Llangian (follow brown signs). On left on leaving village.

CONTACT: Phil or Meinir
Tel: 01758 713527
enquiries@tanrallt.com www.tanrallt.com
Fferm Tanrallt Farm, Llangian, Abersoch, Gwynedd, LL53 7LN

ABERDARON FARM
BUNKHOUSE

Aberdaron Farm Bunkhouse is two miles from Aberdaron village with its white-painted fishermen's houses, sandy beach and water's edge church. The Bunkhouse has underfloor central heating and 3 bunk rooms sleeping 8, 4 (en suite) and 3 (en suite) in a bunk and camp bed. There is a large social room with dining tables, chairs, beanbags, TV, Nintento Wii and board games. The small basic kitchen has a hob, microwave, George Foreman cooking machine, kettle and toaster. A self service breakfast of cereal, bread, tea and coffee is provided. Bring sleeping bags or hire duvet and pillow for £3. There is a drying room with washing machine & tumble dryer and toilet & shower blocks. Whistling Sands is only 1.5 miles away and Bardsey Island (Ynys Enlli) lies across The Sound two miles off the tip of the Llyn Peninsula. The Island has been a place of pilgrimage since early Christianity and a boat from Aberdaron to Bardsey is a great place to see the seals. Pets allowed (with notice). Bike hire available. Holiday cottages and camping are also available on the farm.

DETAILS

- **Open** - All year, all day (arrive after 4pm and leave by 11am).
- **Number of beds** - 15: 1x8, 1x4 (en suite), 1x3 (en suite)
- **Booking** - Deposit of 50% paid by credit or debit card, remainder to be paid 4 weeks prior to arrival. Booking held for 5 days without deposit.
- **Price per night** - £16pp, £18 pp (en suite) inc breakfast. Enquire for sole use of room or bunkhouse and family room prices. Minimum of 3 days on bank holidays.
- **Public Transport** - Arriva bus17, Pwllheli to Aberdaron, 6 times a day (not Sun).
- **Directions** - Follow signs for Anelog, the first one is just after entering Aberdaron.

CONTACT: Gillian Jones
Tel: 01758 760345 Mob: 0779 414 7195
enquiries@aberdaronfarmholidays.co.uk www.aberdaronfarmholidays.co.uk
Y Gweithdy, Anelog, Aberdaron, Pwllheli, LL53 8BT

ANGLESEY
OUTDOOR CENTRE

Anglesey Outdoor Centre is an ideal base for groups, individuals or families to explore and enjoy the outdoor playground and mild climate of Anglesey. There are opportunities for adrenalin adventures to gentle relaxation - from coasteering, sea kayaking, climbing, and windsurfing to beach activities, gentle walks and bird watching. Anglesey Outdoors is just a mile from Porthdafarach Beach and the coast path, and only 2km from Sustrans Cycle Route 8. The Centre has four self contained areas each with their own self-catering and bathroom facilities. These can be hired individually or together, ideal for all group sizes and budgets. There are dorms, private and family rooms. Bedding is provided or you can bring your own sleeping bags in the Gogarth dorms. Full catering available and an on-site bar/bistro. The Centre is set in 14 acres of grounds providing plenty of space for groups and individuals. Gear store, ample parking, drying room and free WiFi. Yurts and Cabans also available.

DETAILS

- **Open** - All year, 24 hour access.
- **Number of beds** - 68; Main Centre 33:1x7,4x5,1x4,1x2. Maris Annexe 10:5x2. Ty Pen Annexe 8:1x4,2x2. Gogarth Dorms 16:1x7,1x7,1x2. Some extra beds available.
- **Booking** - Essential during the peak season and recommended at other times.
- **Price per night** - £9pp (Gogarth Dorms) to £18pp (en suite twin). Ask for sole use.
- **Public Transport** - 2km from trains and ferry at Holyhead. Regular buses ½ mile.
- **Directions** - Arriving at the last roundabout on the A55, take the third exit toward Trearddur Bay. Immediately take the first left turning onto Porthdafarch Rd. Follow for approx 1.5miles. Signed on left hand side for Anglesey Outdoors & Paddlers Return.

CONTACT: Penny Hurndall
Tel: 01407 769351
angleseyoutdoors@gmail.com www.angleseyoutdoors.com
Porthdafarch Road, Holyhead, Anglesey, LL65 2LP

Wonderfully situated at the south end of Holy Island, Anglesey, in a 7 acre Area of Outstanding Natural Beauty, and 300m from a beach. The Centre is an excellent base for so much in the outdoors and is immediately adjacent to the Anglesey Coastal Path - good walking on a varied and accessible coast. All around there are prehistoric remains, spectacular geology, a wide range of habitats and species of marine life and plants, and excellent bird watching opportunities. For kayakers there are classic sea tours, overfalls, playwaves, surf and rockhopping. Climbers have Gogarth nearby and Rhoscolyn offering all grades in an attractive setting. Divers can beach launch for wrecks and fish. The Centre has two self-contained units and camping with toilets and showers. Careful energy use is encouraged, with composting and recycling. Nearby Holyhead has rail links and ferries to Ireland. Walking distance to pub.

DETAILS

- **Open** - All year, 24 hour access.
- **Number of beds** - 20: 2x2, 1x4, 2x6. 16: 1x3, 2x4,1x5.
- **Booking** - Essential
- **Price per night** - £375 for exclusive use, £21.00 per person.
- **Public Transport** - Trains at Holyhead (10km) (London direct 4.5 hrs) or Valley (5km). National Express at Valley (6km). Bus 23/25 Holyhead - Rhoscolyn (1km) or 4/44 Holyhead - Four Mile Bridge (3km). Ferry: Holyhead - Dublin or Dun Laoghaire.
- **Directions** - GR SH 278 752. From A5 traffic lights at Y Fali/Valley take B4545 Trearddur. After 2km at Four Mile Bridge fork left at sign to Rhoscolyn 2miles. After 2km sharp left at camping symbols. After 800m fork right at large white gatepost.

CONTACT: Jacqui Short
Tel: 01407 860469
enquiries@outdooralternative.co.uk www.outdooralternative.co.uk/
Cerrig-yr-Adar, Rhoscolyn, Holyhead, Anglesey, LL65 2NQ

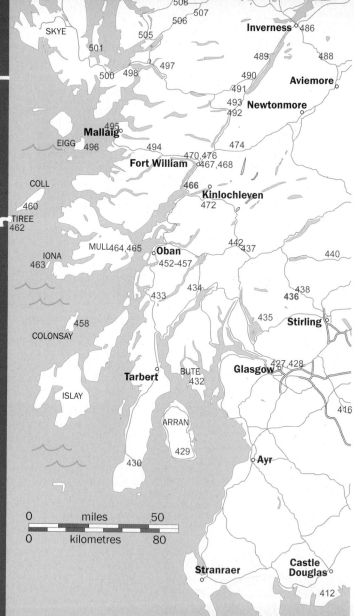

South Scotland

SKYE
501
500 498 497
505
506 507
508

Inverness 486
489
488
490 Aviemore
491
493 Newtonmore
492

Mallaig 495
EIGG 496
494
474
470,476
Fort William 467,468

466
Kinlochleven
472

COLL
460
TIREE
462

MULL 464,465
Oban
452-457

IONA
463

442 437
440

433 434
438
436
435 Stirling

COLONSAY
458

Tarbert
BUTE
432
Glasgow 427,428

416

ISLAY
ARRAN
429
430

Ayr

0   miles   50
0   kilometres   80

Stranraer
Castle
Douglas
412

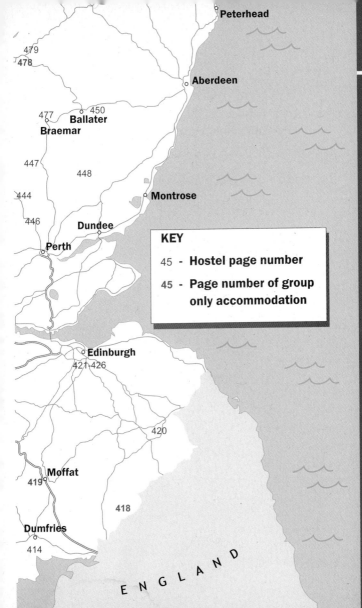

South Scotland

Peterhead

479
478

Aberdeen

477 450
Ballater
Braemar

447

448

444

446

Montrose

Dundee

Perth

KEY

45 - **Hostel page number**

45 - **Page number of group only accommodation**

Edinburgh
421-426

420

Moffat
419

418

Dumfries
414

ENGLAND

KEY

45 - **Hostel page number**

45 - **Page number of group only accommodation**

0   miles   50

0   kilometres   80

Durness   519

503

Stornoway

504

LEWIS

513

HARRIS   502

Ullapool

510   512

509

Gairloch

NORTH UIST

508

507

506

Portree

SKYE   501

505

489

SOUTH UIST

497

490

491

493

492

500   498

BARRA

Mallaig   495

474

496

EIGG

494

470,476

Fort William   467,468

COLL

466

Kinlochleven

460

472

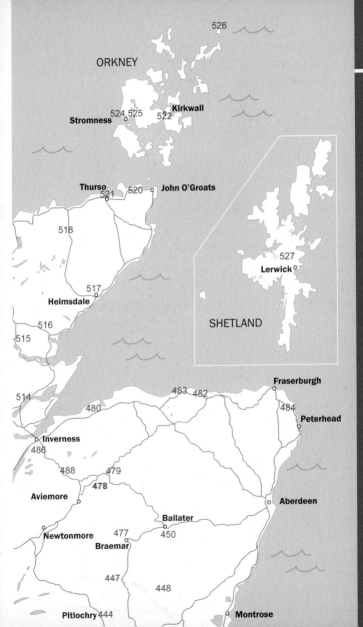

ORKNEY

526

Kirkwall

Stromness 524 525 522

Thurso 521 520 John O'Groats

518

527

Lerwick

SHETLAND

517

Helmsdale

516

515

514

Fraserburgh

483 482

480

484

Peterhead

Inverness

486

488 479

478

Aviemore

Aberdeen

Ballater

Newtonmore 477 450

Braemar

447

448

Pitlochry 444

Montrose

North Scotland

CASTLE CREAVIE
HAY BARN HOSTEL

Castle Creavie Haybarn has been converted to a comfortable family friendly independent hostel sleeping 4. Quietly set on a working farm it is surrounded by spectacularly beautiful Galloway countryside. Hugely spacious open plan design, oak floors, with 4 comfortable beds, dining area, wood burning stove, separate kitchen with basic cooking facilities, fridge, washroom and W.C. Also available on site are: hot showers, washing/drying facilities, bike wash and safe store, farmhouse breakfast (pre booked) £7.50 pp. Ideal base for walkers and cyclists with 7Stanes and NCN Route 7 (3 miles away). Guests are welcome to enjoy the farm footpaths and observe the daily life on this working sheep farm. Available seasonally: fresh baked bread, cakes and honey, home reared pork and lamb, sausage, bacon and fresh farm eggs. Castle Creavie is named after two Iron Age forts, and is 4 miles from the popular harbour town of Kirkcudbright which has a good range of pubs, cafés, and restaurants. Galloway is famed for its many castles, abbeys, first class walks and long sandy beaches.

DETAILS

- **Open** - All year, all day.
- **Number of beds** - 4: 1x4.
- **Booking** - Book by phone and online. Deposit required by post or PayPal.
- **Price per night** - £15pp with beds made up. £60.00 for sole private use.
- **Public Transport** - 4 miles from Kirkcudbright citylink services.
- **Directions** - From the A75 take the A711 to Kirkcudbright. In the town centre turn left at the Royal Hotel onto the B727 (Gelston), pass the cemetery and at the next road junction go straight on (Auchencairn / Dundrennan). Follow for approx 4 miles.

CONTACT: Charlie and Elaine Wannop
Tel: 01557 500238
elaine@castlecreavie.co.uk www.castlecreavie.co.uk
Castle Creavie, Kirkcudbright, Dumfries and Galloway, DG6 4QE

MARTHROWN
SCOTLAND OF MABIE BUNKHOUSE

Marthrown is set in the heart of Mabie Forest, about 6 miles south of Dumfries. It has a traditional sauna, a wood burning spring water hot tub, a large BBQ, garden areas, a challenge course and plenty of room for groups.

The forest has a variety mountain bike routes, ranging in length and difficulty and the 7Stanes mountain bike trails are nearby. Although we are a self-catering hostel group meals are available to order. Marthrown is suitable for all age groups. Facilities include secure store for bikes and equipment and a large dining area suitable for meetings. For something a little different why not try staying in the Roundhouse or Yurt? Are you looking for a completely different type of Scottish wedding venue to tie the knot? The Bunkhouse, Roundhouse and Yurt are also available for forest and outdoor weddings, see website.

DETAILS

- **Open** - All year, 24 hours - late arrival by arrangement.
- **Number of beds** - 26: 1x8:1x7:1x6:1x5 + Roundhouse, Yurt, Tipi and camping.
- **Booking** - Booking essential.
- **Price per night** - £16 to £19.50.
- **Public Transport** - From Dumfries (White Sands) take the Stagecoach bus service 372 to Mabie Forest. It is best to arrive in daylight. 1.5 mile walk from road.
- **Directions** - From Dumfries take A710 (west) to Mabie Forest passing through the village of Islesteps. Turn right signposted Mabie Forest and Mabie House Hotel. Follow tarmac road over speed bumps to the end of the hotel and forest rangers office, through courtyard and onto forest track, Marthown is signposted and is exactly one mile into the forest.

CONTACT: Mike or Pam Hazlehurst
Tel: 01387 247900
pamhazlehurst@hotmail.com www.marthrownofmabie.com
Mabie Forest, Dumfries, DG2 8HB

WEE ROW
HOSTEL

Located in the heart of New Lanark World Heritage Site 'Wee Row', provides a unique hostel experience nestled in the spectacular South Lanarkshire Valley in southern Scotland. Only one hour drive from Glasgow and Edinburgh, Wee Row is the perfect base to explore these popular cities but you don't have to go far to find plenty to do.

The award winning New Lanark Visitor Centre is on the doorstep. Here you can step back in time and rediscover life of this working mill village. The hostel sleeps 62 guests in 18 private rooms all with en suites and has terrific views over the River Clyde and surrounding countryside.

There is a modern fully equipped self-catering kitchen; comfortable dining area and TV lounge. WiFi is complimentary throughout the public areas. Facilities include bike storage and there is a laundry and drying room. Traditional cooked breakfasts are available and an evening dinner menu is also available.

DETAILS

- **Open** - All year.
- **Number of beds** - 62: 6x2, 1x3, 3x3, 8x4 +Studio appt
- **Booking** - www.newlanarkhostel.co.uk
- **Price per night** - From £19.50 per person
- **Public Transport** - Buses and train to Lanark. 30 min walk to hostel.
- **Directions** - M75 Jct11 A70 toward Lanark. Follow brown tourist signs to New Lanark. (New Lanark Road) take sharp right on to Rosedale Street

CONTACT: Reception
Tel: 01555 666 710
weerowhostel@newlanark.org www.newlanarkhostel.co.uk
Wee Row Hostel, Wee Row, New Lanark, Lanark, Lanarkshire, ML11 9DJ

WELCOME TO
Wee Row Hostel

ENTRANCE THIS WAY

WHITHAUGH PARK

SCOTLAND

Whithaugh Park is nestled in the beautiful landscape of the Scottish Borders, sharing its 110 acre slice of Scottish countryside with red squirrels, deer and a variety of other wildlife. A collection of 30 alpine lodges, provides flexible accommodation for groups of 2 to 192. With smaller family-style lodges or 'clusters' for groups of 10 to 65. Each cluster has its own kitchen, dining area and meeting room. The site's sports hall can double as a dining room for larger groups. Self-cater or take a catered package.

On site is a 20m swimming pool, sports fields and low ropes course, as well as a wide selection of optional instructed activities such as canoeing, climbing and archery. Newcastleton village is a short walk away, where there are local shops, several cafés, restaurants and pubs. The fantastic scenery around Whithaugh Park can be explored on foot or by bike, as the 7stanes mountain bike trails and several road-cycling routes pass through the village. The Lakes, Hadrian's Wall and Kielder Forest & Water Park are all within easy reach.

DETAILS

- **Open** - All Year, all day
- **Number of beds** - 192: 20 lodges with 6-13 beds
- **Booking** - by email or telephone
- **Price per night** - Prices start from just £105 for two nights for a family of four.
- **Public Transport** - Train: Carlisle, bus to Newcastleton from Carlisle and Hawick
- **Directions** - From B6257 south of Newcastleton take turning for Whithaugh and 7stanes trail. Take first left signposted Whithaugh Park.

CONTACT: Reception
Tel: 013873 75394
whithaugh@rockuk.org www.rockuk.org/centres/whithaugh-park
Newcastleton, Scottish Borders, TD9 0TY

GROUP ACCOMMODATION SCOTLAND

The Well Road Centre is a large Victorian house set in its own grounds in the charming spa town of Moffat. The centre is ideal for youth groups, adult groups, conferences, residential workshops, sports events, multiple family gatherings and outdoor activity clubs. All rooms are fully carpeted and centrally heated. The Centre has two spacious meeting rooms, a large bright self-catering kitchen fully equipped for 65, a games hall for indoor activities, a table tennis room and a snooker room. There are 13 bedrooms of various sizes, two of them with en suite facilities. Two separate toilet/shower areas for mixed groups. Bring your own sleeping bags or duvets. Ample parking for cars, minibuses and equipment trailers and the nearby park can be used for sports activities. Moffat is in the Southern Uplands, an hour from Edinburgh and Glasgow. An ideal area for golfers, bird watchers, walkers and cyclists, it is central to the "7Stanes" mountain bike venues. All groups have sole use.

 GROUPS ONLY

DETAILS

- **Open** - All year, all day.
- **Number of beds** - 70: in 13 rooms (2 en suite).
- **Booking** - Check availability and send £100 deposit to secure booking.
- **Price per night** - From £750 for two nights for up to 30 people. £25 per person for 31 people or more.
- **Public Transport** - Trains at Lockerbie (16m). Citylink bus to Glasgow/Edinburgh.
- **Directions** - From A74 take Moffat turning and enter the High Street (town square). Turning to the right around the shops on the south side of the square, follow Holm St to the T-junction. Turn left into Burnside, following up and right into Well Rd.

CONTACT: Ben Larmour
Tel: 01683 221040
Ben8363@aol.com www.wellroadcentre.com
Well Road Centre, Well Road, Moffat, DG10 9BT

KIRK YETHOLM
SCOTLAND FRIENDS OF NATURE HOUSE

Kirk Yetholm Friends of Nature House, nestling below the picturesque village green, is a former village school that has been offering hostel style accommodation for over 70 years. Located at the start / end of the Pennine Way it is a classic stop and is also ideal for those doing the St. Cuthbert's Way and for cyclists on the Borderloop Cycle Route or Sustrans Route 84. A great base for local day hikes, particularly suited to individuals, families and small groups. Recently upgraded, the house offers a friendly and peaceful retreat after a day exploring the stunning countryside and local heritage. There is a comfortable lounge, a well equipped kitchen, seating for 18 in the dining area and secure bike storage. Evening meals and breakfast are available in adjacent Border Hotel. Well stocked village shop and other eateries 10 min's walk away. FoN is one of Europe's oldest environmental groups with 600K members and 800 houses across Europe. Under 16's should be accompanied by an adult sharing the same dorm.

DETAILS

- **Open** - All year (Nov-Feb incl. groups only). Reception 5pm-11pm & 8am-10am.
- **Number of beds** - 22: 1x7, 1x5, 1x4, 2x2 (twin), 1x2 (bunk).
- **Booking** - Book via website, email or phone. Verbal bookings held until 6pm daily.
- **Price per night** - From £18, under 18's from £15. Discounts for IFN / SYHA / HI.
- **Public Transport** - Kelso to Kirk Yetholm approx every 2hrs. Stops within 100m of building. Connections onwards from Kelso to all parts of country and to rail station
- **Directions** - OS Grid Ref: NT 826 282. Geo-Coord: 55.533378 -2.277233. 7 miles from Kelso on Pennine Way. Located 100m below the village green at Kirk Yetholm.

CONTACT: Manager
Tel: 01573 420639
kirkyetholm@thefriendsofnature.org.uk www.thefriendsofnature.org.uk
Friends of Nature House, Waukford, Kirk Yetholm, Kelso, Roxburghshire, TD5 8PG

Euro Hostel Edinburgh Halls is the perfect place to base your summer visit to Edinburgh. Available from 9th June to 3rd September 2017 you can have an apartment to yourself or share with others for a great budget stay.

Located in the heart of the Old Town close to the Royal Mile Euro Hostel Edinburgh Halls is perfect for backpackers, shoppers, groups or those visiting the famous Edinburgh Festival. Single, twin, double and triple private bedrooms are available or you can rent a whole apartment for up to 10 guests.

All apartments are equipped with kitchen/dining areas and shared bathrooms.

DETAILS

- **Open** - Check-in is available from 3pm and check-out is by 11am
- **Number of beds** - 310
- **Booking** - 12% non-refundable deposit
- **Price per night** - From £20
- **Public Transport** - National Trains: Waverley Station (12 min walk). National buses at St Andrews Bus Station.
- **Directions** - From Waverley Station. Take Market St exit. Turn left under the bridge, veer right up Jeffrey St. Cross over the High Street onto St Mary's Street. Down hill, over Cowgate. Turn into St John's Hill and reception is at Darroch Court located on your left hand side. From St Andrews bus station head to Princes Street and Waverley Train Station and then follow directions to EuroHostel Edinburgh above.

CONTACT: Reception
Tel: +44 (0) 8454 900 461
edinburgh@eurohostels.co.uk www.eurohostels.co.uk/edinburgh/
Darroch Court, St John's Hill Edinburgh EH8 9UQ

HAGGIS
HOSTELS

Occupying a recently renovated Georgian building dating from 1862, Haggis Hostels, is situated in the heart of Edinburgh just 50 metres from Princes Street. The hostel offers self-catering facilities and fully equipped rooms with privacy curtains, reading lights and international sockets. There is adjustable heating in every room. The communal kitchen is high spec and features two of every appliance, ideal for groups of up to 34. Being so centralised in the Scottish capital, Haggis Hostels has everything on its doorstep whether you're heading to the theatre, concert hall, pub or club. There is something for everyone. Friendly staff will help you plan your excursions around Edinburgh and provide you with all the information you need to make your stay enjoyable. The hostel offers free breakfast, high speed free WiFi, luxury bedding and towels, a laundry service, secure storage and a communal kitchen with dining area. For more information please download the free smartphone app or visit the website

DETAILS

- **Open** - All year, 24 hour reception.
- **Number of beds** - 34.
- **Booking** - Online on our website, phone or email.
- **Price per night** - Standard mixed room from £18. Female or male only room from £22. Family room for £80. Breakfast and taxes included in all prices.
- **Public Transport** - Buses to St Andrew Square bus station. Air link shuttle service to Edinburgh's Waverley train station direct from Edinburgh Airport. Trains to Edinburgh's Waverley train station. Tram service to St Andrew's Square.
- **Directions** - At the east end of Princes Street, follow the road around to the left and you will find us on the right.

CONTACT:
Tel: 0131 557 0036
info@haggishostels.co.uk www.haggishostels.co.uk
Haggis Hostels 5/3 West Register Street, Edinburgh, EH2 2AA.

ROYAL MILE
BACKPACKERS

Royal Mile Backpackers is a small and lively hostel with its own special character! Perfectly located on the Royal Mile, the most famous street in Edinburgh, Royal Mile Backpackers is the ideal place to stay for the independent traveller.

Our comfortable beds and cosy common areas will make you feel at home and our friendly staff are always on hand to help you make the most of your time in Edinburgh.

DETAILS

■ **Open** - All year, all day. Reception 7am – 3am (24hrs during August).
■ **Number of beds** - 48
■ **Booking** - Booking not always essential, 1st night's payment required for booking.
■ **Price per night** - From £14 per person. ID required for check in.
■ **Public Transport** - Only a 5/10 minute walk from both Edinburgh bus station and Waverley train station. A taxi costs between £3-£5 from each. The airport bus also stops out side the train station on the last stop so is very easy to get to the hostel.
■ **Directions** - From main bus station turn left onto Princes Street then take first right onto Northbridge. At top turn left onto the High St. on the Royal Mile. From train station take the Princes Street exit (up Waverley Steps), at top go right then right again up Northbridge, then left at cross roads, hostel is on the left above the Oxfam shop. From airport take bus no.100 to city centre, get off at Waverley Bridge. Walk away from Princes St. towards the roundabout, go over roundabout onto Cockburn Street. At the top of Cockburn Street turn left onto the High St. on the Royal Mile. Cross traffic lights at Northbridge and hostel is on left above Oxfam.

CONTACT: Receptionist
Tel: 0131 557 6120
royalmile@scotlandstophostels.com www.scotlandstophostels.com
105 High Street, Edinburgh, EH1 1SG

CASTLE ROCK
HOSTEL

In a wonderful location, facing south with a sunny aspect and panoramic views over the city, Castle Rock Hostel is just steps away from the city centre with the historic Royal Mile, the busy pubs and late-late nightlife of the Grassmarket and Cowgate and of course the Castle.

Most of the rooms have no traffic noise, there are loads of great facilities, 24 hour reception and no curfew. With its beautiful and dramatic skyline Edinburgh is truly one of the world's great cities. The cobbled streets of the Old Town lead past mysterious gothic buildings up to the magnificent castle. Below the castle's rocky pinnacle lies the New Town's 200 year old Georgian splendour.

DETAILS

- **Open** - All year, all day.
- **Number of beds** - 302
- **Booking** - Booking not always essential. First night's payment needed to book.
- **Price per night** - From £14 per person. ID required for check in.
- **Public Transport** - 5/10 minute walk from Edinburgh bus stn and Waverley train stn. (taxis £3-£5). Airport bus goes to train station so it's easy to get to the hostel.
- **Directions** - 10 minutes' walk from Waverley train station – turn left out of the station and continue to small roundabout. Cross over and continue up Cockburn Street to the top. Turn right onto the Royal Mile and follow uphill towards the Castle. Take the left fork at the Hub (church) and the hostel is situated 200 yards on the left side of Johnston Terrace next to two red telephone boxes. By Car – follow signs for city centre towards the Castle turning onto Royal Mile uphill towards the Castle then left fork at the Hub onto Johnston Terrace.

CONTACT: Receptionist
Tel: 0131 225 9666
castlerock@scotlandstophostels.com www.castlerockedinburgh.com
15 Johnston Terrace, Edinburgh, EH1 2PW

HIGH STREET
HOSTEL

The High Street Hostel has become a hugely popular destination for world travellers since opening in 1985 and is one of Europe's best regarded and most atmospheric hostels.

Located just off the historic Royal Mile in a 400 year old building it is the perfect base for exploring all the city's attractions – and of course its wonderful nightlife.

Providing excellence in location, ambience and facilities, the hostel is highly recommended by more than ten of the world's top backpacker travel guides.

DETAILS

- **Open** - All year, all day.
- **Number of beds** - 156.
- **Booking** - Booking in advance not always crucial, 1 night's payment for booking.
- **Price per night** - From £14 per person. ID required for check in.
- **Public Transport** - Only a 5/10 minute walk from Edinburgh bus station or Waverley train station. Taxis cost between £3-£5 from each. The airport bus also stops outside the train station on the last stop so it is very easy to get to the hostel.
- **Directions** - From the bus station (St Andrews Square) turn left onto Princes Street then first right onto Northbridge. At top turn left onto the High Street on the Royal Mile and hostel is on Blackfriars St. on right. From railway station main exit turn left onto Waverley Bridge then right at the mini rounbdaout and straight ahead up the Mound, at the junction go left, then at cross roads left again going down the Royal Mile. Cross at the traffic lights at Northbridge and Blackfriars St is second on the right. From airport take bus 100 to last stop, Waverley Bridge and follow as above.

CONTACT: Reception
Tel: 0131 557 3984
highstreet@scotlandstophostels.com www.highstreethostel.com
8 Blackfriars Street, Edinburgh, EH1 1NE

EURO HOSTEL
GLASGOW
SCOTLAND

A smarter alternative to a hotel in the city, with a prime location, five mins' walk from Glasgow Central Station, friendly staff, lively bar and clean comfortable private and shared en suite rooms. Perfect for clubbing, shopping and discovering the city's cultural heritage, vibrant nightlife and live music scene. Or for visiting family, coast to coast cycle rides, attending sporting events or just a good sleep to break a long journey. The VIP suites are ideal for school groups, sports clubs and groups of friends celebrating special occasions. The hostel's Mint and Lime bar serves 'all you can eat buffet breakfast' for £5, meal deals and weekly drink promos with 15% bar discount card available. It is the perfect place to sit back and relax with other guests or enjoy the Sky Sports screen, an ideal pre-club venue. The 24 hour reception will help you with discounted sightseeing, free nightclubs, upgrades and discounted car parking. The hostel has a self-catering kitchen, dining area, laundry and free superfast WiFi. Close to O2 Academy, Hampden. Hydro, SECC, Classic Grand and Clyde auditorium.

DETAILS

- **Open** - All year, late and early check outs available.
- **Number of beds** - 444 rooms: single, doubles, 2, 4, 8 and 14 person all en suite
- **Booking** - Book online with 12% deposit, Full balance within 28 days for groups.
- **Price per night** - Beds from £10, Rooms from £20. VIP suites from £14pp. Breakfast £5. Ask about group discounts. See special offers on Euro Hostels website.
- **Public Transport** - Central railway station 2 mins, Queen Street railway station 7 mins, Buchanan Bus Station 10 mins, Glasgow Airport 8 miles.
- **Directions** - The hostel is on the corner of Jamaica Street and Clyde Street.

CONTACT: Reception
Tel: 0141 222 2828
glasgow@euro-hostels.co.uk www.euro-hostels.co.uk
318 Clyde Street, Glasgow, G1 4NR

TARTAN
LODGE

The perfect location - within walking distance of Merchant City and Glasgow City Centre and also to thriving Dennistoun. Old world charm and contemporary elegance are interwoven in this hostel, set within a former 19th century church and Masonic Lodge on Alexandra Parade, Glasgow. Tartan Lodge provides affordable accommodation for budget and business travellers, comprising a selection of double bedrooms and twin rooms all with en suite bathrooms and LCD Tvs. Additionally, there are shared dormitories for budget travellers and backpackers, with a choice of eight, six, four and three bed dormitories for male and female only offering bespoke bunk bed design. Dorm room facilities include a double plug socket, shelf and underneath storage for each bunk. All dorms are en suite and also have family facilities. Towels can be hired for £2 (plus £5 deposit), or purchase a padlock for your bunk for £2. A reading light for each bunk is available from reception.

DETAILS

- **Open** - All year. Check in from 2pm. Check out by 11am
- **Number of beds** - 93: 5xdouble, 2xtwin, 1xtriple. Dorms: 2x3, 8x4, 1x4 female, 2x6, 1x6 female, 2x8
- **Booking** - on line. Early/late check in available for extra charge.
- **Price per night** - Dorms from £18pp, Private rooms from £50 per room
- **Public Transport** - Bus First38 from Glasgow Central and Glasgow Queen Street stations
- **Directions** - From M8 take the exit toward A803/Kirkintilloch, turn left onto Castle St, turn left at the 1st cross street onto Alexandra Parade/A8. Hostel is on the left before the petrol station.

CONTACT: Reception
Tel: 0141 554 5970
info@tartanlodge.co.uk www.tartanlodge.co.uk
235 Alexandra Parade, Glasgow, G31 3AW

Kilmory Haven provides ideal group accommodation in a tranquil, rural setting. The Isle of Arran is one of the most accessible Scottish islands, only one hour by ferry from the mainland. It offers the visitor hill-walking, mountaineering, golf, fishing, cycling, pony trekking and a bewildering choice of extreme sports. The bunkhouse is affordable, modern, comfortable and able to sleep up to 23. All the bed linen is supplied, so there's no need to bring anything except your towels and food! Sole use is available (please contact for details) There is a great, contemporary kitchen & dining area with all you'll need. Attached to the bunkhouse is the village hall which can provide extra rooms and an auditorium at extra cost. Ideal for educational groups, weddings, music workshop groups, clubs or any group needing extra facilities. Kilmory Haven welcomes your family, club, group, school or stag & hen parties. Also adjoining the bunkhouse is the 1934 Club (Bar) which is open at the weekend. Phone or email with your queries. Registered Scottish Charity SC028200.

DETAILS

- **Open** - All year, 24 hours.
- **Number of beds** - 23: 2 x 8 (dorm) 1 x 4 (en suite) 1 x 3 (en suite)
- **Booking** - Book ahead, 50% deposit.
- **Price per night** - £16 per person for groups of 15+. £21 pp for smaller groups.
- **Public Transport** - Buses stop on demand directly outside the hall and bunkhouse. These buses meet all the ferries that arrive and depart from the main ferry terminal at Brodick.
- **Directions** - Bunkhouse attached to Kilmory Public Hall located in village centre.

CONTACT: Manager
Tel: 01770 870345
kilmory.hall@btinternet.com www.kilmoryhall.com
Kilmory Haven, Kilmory, Isle of Arran, KA27 8PQ

The Campbeltown Backpackers is housed in the Old Schoolhouse, a Grade B listed building. Offering easy access to the facilities of Campbeltown including swimming pool, gym, the "wee toon" cinema and Springbank, Kilkerran and Glen Scotia distillery tours, it is a good stop along the Kintyre Way which gives walkers spectacular views of the surrounding islands. The area also enjoys very good wind surfing, surfing, mountain bike routes and other major cycle trails.

Kintyre is full of cultural and historical interest being the place where St Columba came ashore from Northern Ireland bringing Christianity to Scotland. Robert the Bruce spent time in Kintyre on his way to Rathlin, whilst the beach at Saddell was the location for Paul McCartney and Wings' video for "Mull of Kintyre". For wildlife lovers the Kintyre Peninsula is a great place to see otters, seals and even golden eagles as well as red, roe and sika deer.

DETAILS

- **Open** - All year, out by 10.30am on day of departure.
- **Number of beds** - 16 1x6, 1x10
- **Booking** - By email, only phone if you require a booking within 4 days
- **Price per night** - £18 per person/£20 for casual guests
- **Public Transport** - 5 buses a day from Glasgow (926). Passenger and cycle ferry links to Northern Ireland and Troon. The islands of Gigha, Islay, Jura and Arran are all served by ferries. Two flights per day to and from Glasgow International Airport
- **Directions** - Adjacent to the Heritage Centre on the B842 towards Machrihanish. 10 minute walk from the bus

CONTACT: Alan
Tel: 01586 551188
info@campbeltownbackpackers.co.uk www.campbeltownbackpackers.co.uk
Kintyre Amenity Trust, Big Kiln, Campbeltown, Argyll, PA28 6JF

WELCOME

Campbeltown
BACKPACKERS
Tel: 01586 551188

Bute Backpackers, a friendly independent hostel with panoramic views of Rothesay seafront, has 40 beds with a mixture of single, twin, double and family rooms. The main house has a sea front sun lounge with woodburner and open fire. The self-catering kitchen is equipped to the highest standard and there is a large seafront dining room with catering facilities. Some of the rooms are en suite and there are separate male and female showers and toilets on each level. There is also a separate self-contained cottage dorm with its own fully equipped kitchen and bathroom. Other facilities include Sky TV, internet, WiFi access, drying room and laundry. There is a private car park for twelve cars and secure bike racks. There are regular live music sessions which include open mic for any budding musos to join the fun. VisitScotland rated as 4 star.

DETAILS

- **Open** - All year, 24hr access, no curfew. Reception 10am - 10pm.
- **Number of beds** - 40: Main house 32 in 14 rooms; Cottage 8.
- **Booking** - Deposit only required for group bookings.
- **Price per night** - From £20pp. £22.50pp in twin room. £25 private single.
- **Public Transport** - Take train to Wemyes Bay Station and Ferry Port (40 mins from Glasgow Central). Then ferry to Rothesay, Isle of Bute. Hostel 900m from ferry or take a taxi (taxi rank adjacent to port) which costs approximately £2.50.
- **Directions** - Turn right as you leave ferry and walk straight ahead for 200m past the discovery centre and putting green. Continue straight ahead for another 250m and Bute Backpackers is on your left. By car turn right on to main road. Continue for 300m to the mini roundabout . Head straight on for a further 300m and the hostel and access to the private car park is adjacent to the main road on your left.

CONTACT: Reception
Tel: 01700 501876
butebackpackers@hotmail.com www.butebackpackers.co.uk
The Pier View, 36 Argyle Street, Rothesay, Isle of Bute, PA20 0AX

With 16 en suite rooms and great views of Loch Awe, Torran Bay Hostel is the perfect base for a fantastic Highlands holiday. Free fishing from Torran Farm land is included, or why not venture out on the loch? Boat and canoe launching is available along with a large parking area. Boat hire can be arranged through the hostel. Just 30 miles from Oban, 13 miles from Lochgilphead and close to the Crinnan canal, Torran Bay is located at the south end of Loch Awe which is 25 miles long. Excellent for fishing for brown trout, pike, arctic char, perch and roach or just a day relaxing on the loch with TBFL boat hire. Other activities include walking, on Torran Farm land and beyond, hiking, cycling, bird watching and golf. The hostel can accommodate up to 40 guests, with rooms arranged in different combinations. It has two well equipped kitchens for self-catering and the local Indian/Chinese takeaway delivers to the hostel. Prices includes continental breakfast and all rooms have TV, DVD and WiFi

DETAILS

■ **Open** - All year round, all day.
■ **Number of beds** - 34: 10 x 2 or double, 2 x double and single, 1 x 4 , 2 x 3
■ **Booking** - booking 4 rooms or more, full payment required 14 days before arrival
■ **Price per night** - from £45 to £72 per room. inc continental breakfast and parking. Group bookings welcome. Please note. prices per room not per person.
■ **Public Transport** - Buses Lochgilphead to Ford, Monday, Wednesday and Saturday
■ **Directions** - From Glasgow take A82 to Tarbet then take the A83 to Lochgilphead, Lochgilphead to Kilmartin A816. 1 mile past Kilmartin follow signs to Ford B840. From Ford take Dalavich road for 1 mile. Hostel on the right.

CONTACT: Joachim or Sheila Brolly
Tel: 01546 810 133 or 01546 810 270
torranbayhostel@mail.com www.torran-bay.co.uk
Torran Farm, Ford, Lochgilphead. PA31 8RH

INVERARAY
HOSTEL

Inveraray Hostel is a purpose-built wooden building in extensive grounds. An excellent self-catering kitchen, plus dining and sitting areas, provide a friendly ambience where the staff encourage guests to interact. Small 2 or 4 bed dorms make the hostel equally suitable for solo travellers, couples, families and small groups. Bed linen is provided and towels are available for hire. A large car park, bike shed and drying room are available.

Inveraray is a small planned town in the southern Highlands of Scotland with a range of shops, restaurants, 2 pubs and cash machines. Attractions include a magnificent C18th castle set in wooded grounds and gardens, and a jail where you can experience the lifestyle of former inmates! There are local forest walks and a modest climb to a viewpoint with a fantastic view down the loch. From Inveraray you can drive to access points for several Munros and the famous "Cobbler". Well-located for cyclists, walkers, motor bikers and those touring Scotland by car.

DETAILS

- **Open** - March to October. Sole-use October to March. Reception 4pm-9pm.
- **Number of beds** - 28: 4 x 4, 6 x 2, all bunk beds
- **Booking** - On website. Larger groups and families book by email.
- **Price per night** - From £17pp.Families please enquire. Breakfast £3.50 May-Sept.
- **Public Transport** - Bus 926 or 976 from Glasgow (about 6 per day, 7 days). Bus 976 from Oban (3 per day, 7 days). Bus 926 from Campbeltown.
- **Directions** - From A83 at Inveraray take A819, hostel 200m on left.

CONTACT: Manager
Tel: 01499 302 454
info@inverarayhostel.co.uk www.inverarayhostel.co.uk
Dalmally Road, Inveraray, Argyll, PA32 8XD

Set on the banks of Loch Lomond on the West Highland Way, Balmaha Bunkhouse offers quality assured accommodation for up to 14 at an affordable price. Continental breakfast, bedding, WiFi, tea and coffee are included and there is a self-catering kitchen. The bunkhouse is ideal for hen, stag and family get togethers, corporate away-days, meetings, conferences or as a base to explore the wider area. There is a private self-catering chalet called The Roost sleeping 4 people in a double bed and one set of bunks and bed & breakfast in the main house with en suite rooms and breathtaking views over the loch. The accommodation is situated on the shores of Loch Lomond, just 5 minutes' paddling to the first of the islands (Inchcailloch), from where you can explore other islands with ancient graveyards with the burial place of Rob Roy`s cousin and scenic landscapes. Kayaks and canadian canoes can be hired on site. Welcome to the romantic, adventurous and beautiful experience of Loch Lomond.

DETAILS

- **Open** - Open until 10th June 2017. Arrive 2pm-7pm, leave before 10am.
- **Number of beds** - Bunkhouse 14: 1x6,1x4 (family),1x2 (double/twin),1x2 (twin); The Roost 4: 1x4; B&B: 1xDbl, 1x2(bunks)
- **Booking** - No bookings are being taken after 10/6/2017. Groups of 6+ Jan & Feb.
- **Price per night** - £20pp. Sole use of bunkhouse £280. Chalet £80. Dog (in bunkhouse only) £5, B&B £35. No credit/debit cards.
- **Public Transport** - Train from Glasgow Queen Street to Balloch then 309 Bus.
- **Directions** - Opposite the bay and the telephone box. Bus stop 100m from hostel

CONTACT: Jock and Gwen Cousin
Tel: 01360 870 218   Mob: 07921 293285
jock@balmahahouse.co.uk www.balmahahouse.co.uk
Balmaha, Loch Lomond, Stirlingshire, G63 0JQ

TROSSACHS
TRYST

Now specialising in group bookings with exclusive use of the Lodge. Trossachs Tryst was purpose-built on its own 3 acre site, set amidst beautiful scenery on the edge of the Trossachs National Park. The 4 star hostel, just outside the beautiful tourist town of Callander, is finished to a high standard offering great accommodation at an even better price. Trossachs Tryst has proved extremely popular with all kinds of groups from musicians and family reunions through to yoga and corporate events. The rooms are all en suite including 2 x 8 bed, 2 x 4 bed and 1 x 6 bed with the 4 bed rooms making ideal family or twin rooms. There is a spacious living room with wonderful views of the surrounding hills, separate dining area plus a well equipped kitchen. The garden is very large with flat lawn, patio and picnic tables for al fresco dining around the lodge. We also have a laundry and drying room. There is an on-site cycling centre as well as an abundance of outdoor activities such as hill walking, pony trekking, Go-ape, Segway treks, water sports, fishing and sailing.

DETAILS
- **Open** - All year (Sept to June, whole hostel bookings only). Reception 8am - 9pm.
- **Number of beds** - 30
- **Booking** - Groups must book with deposit.
- **Price per night** - £500 per night for exclusive use of the hostel (approx £16 per person). Price includes linen and tea/coffee. Discounts for longer bookings.
- **Public Transport** - Trains: Stirling (15 miles). Citylink coach: Callander(1.5 miles).
- **Directions** - GR 606 072. The hostel is situated one mile up Invertrossachs Rd from its junction with the A81 (Glasgow Rd) in Callander.

CONTACT: Emma Close
Tel: 01877 331200 Mob: 07885 691751
emma@fabb.org.uk www.trossachstryst.com
Invertrossachs Road, Callander, Stirling, FK17 8HW

STRATHFILLAN
WIGWAMS
SCOTLAND

On a working farm within the Loch Lomond and Trossachs National Park this is an ideal location for a single night, weekend or a week's let for families or groups. An ideal base for hill walking with Munros, the West Highland Way, canoeing, fishing, and skiing nearby. The Wigwams are comfortably equipped with mattresses, electric lights and heating, some are en suite. Large wigwams sleep 4/5 on benches and there is a small wigwam sleeping 4 with mattresses on the floor. Each has its own car park, picnic bench and campfire. Beaver is a deluxe wigwam sleeping 5 with kitchen, toilet, shower & TV. Also available are self catering lodges, some with separate bedrooms, lounge, kitchen, shower and toilet. There is space for camping and caravans. Kirkton Farmhouse sleeps groups up to 12 and there is a yurt sleeping 5. Logs,kindling and peat available in the shop, also home made sausages to cook on your camp fire. Site has toilet /shower block, hot and cold water and a fully equipped kitchen.

DETAILS

- **Open** - All year.
- **Number of beds** - 133: Wigwams: 1x4, 18x5 Lodges: 1x8, 1x6, 1x5, 1x4, Farmhouse:12
- **Booking** - Book by phone or email.
- **Price per night** - Small wigwam £40 for 2. Large wigwam £48 for 2. Yurt £70 for 2. £10/extra adult, £8/extra child. From £230 per week. Lodges from £280-500/week. Short breaks in lodges from £70/night. Bedding and towels £3/set.
- **Public Transport** - Train and buses at Tyndrum 2 miles away.
- **Directions** - Situated on Scottish Agricultural College's research farm on the A82 three miles north of Crianlarich, thirty minutes south of Glencoe Ski-Centre.

CONTACT:
Tel: 01838 400251

wigwam@sac.ac.uk www.wigwamholidays.com/Strathfillan_Wigwam_Village
Auchtertyre, Tyndrum, Crianlarich, Perthshire FK20 8RU

CALLANDER
HOSTEL

Situated within the town of Callander at the start of the Loch Lomond and Trossachs National Park, Callander Hostel is a great location for tourists and outdoor enthusiasts alike. With outstanding views over Ben Ledi this Visit Scotland 5 star Hostel has recently been refurbished to a high standard. The comfortable beds, en suite rooms and fully equipped self-catering kitchen will ensure that you have all you need for the perfect retreat. The bunk beds have a utility board with reading lights, plug sockets and USB charging facilities. The hostel has a bright, spacious lounge with comfy sofas, WiFi and a wood burning stove. The gardens have a childrens play area, BBQ pods and seating to enjoy the stunning views. Callander is known as the Gateway to the Highlands and has walking and cycling routes, golf, fishing, sailing, horse riding and canoeing. Callander Hostel is an inspiration from the Callander Youth Project. Check out the hostel's website to find out more.

DETAILS

- **Open** - All year, all day. Open 24 hours.
- **Number of beds** - 28: 2 x 8 bed dorms, 1 x 6, 1 x twin/double, 1 x family room (4)
- **Booking** - Debit/credit card secures booking
- **Price per night** - £18.50 per person in dorm, £60 per twin/double en suite room.
- **Public Transport** - There is a bus from Stirling to Callander. Easy walk from bus stop to the hostel. Exit the bus at Ancaster Square, turn left and walk down the street to the "Golf Shop", then turn left on to Bridgend.
- **Directions** - From A84 in Callander turn onto Bridgend and cross the bridge. Callander Hostel is on the right hand side just over the bridge.

CONTACT: Patricia
Tel: 01877 331465
bookings@callanderhostel.co.uk www.callanderhostel.co.uk
6 Bridgend, Callander, FK17 8AH

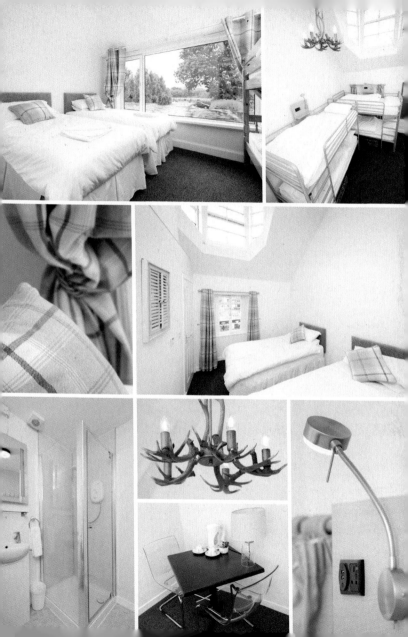

COMRIE
CROFT

Welcome to Scotland's hiking and mountain biking holiday destination. Stay in the 4* homely hostel, dine in the on site cafe (seasonal) and explore the biking and hiking trails. You can book the whole hostel for the exclusive use of your group. Biking facilities on site include a bike park, graded, grin enducing, down hill tracks, family-friendly valley routes, and a bike shop for hire and repairs. For hiking there are four way-marked trails on site, a path to the village of Comrie and access to glens and mountains beyond. Comrie is a lively and vibrant village with shops, pubs, riverside walks and many local events throughout the year including the famous Flambeaux parade at Hogmanay. Visit Combruith House at the heart of Comrie. Just over an hour's drive from Edinburgh or Glasgow, the Croft is great for any kind of getaway on wheels or legs. You can even get married there! Comrie Croft holds a 'Gold' award in the Green Tourism Business Scheme. Guests arriving without a car get a 10% discount.

DETAILS

- **Open** - All year. All day.
- **Number of beds** - 56 + 46 + 14 (3 units)
- **Booking** - Recommended
- **Price per night** - Individuals from £18, U18's free. Exclusive use price on enquiry.
- **Public Transport** - Train stations: Dunblane, Stirling, or Perth. Our own bus stop is served by no. 15 from Perth (approx. every hour). Summer only Citylink service to Oban and Fort William. Ring of Breadalbane hop-on hop-off service from Easter to October (see breadalbane.org)
- **Directions** - Signposted from A85 between Crieff (5miles) and Comrie (2miles).

CONTACT:
Tel: 01764 670140
info@comriecroft.com   www.comriecroft.com
Comrie Croft, By Crieff/Comrie, Perthshire, PH7 4JZ

BY THE WAY
HOSTEL AND CAMPSITE

By The Way Hostel and Campsite can be found in the Loch Lomond National Park halfway between Arrochar's peaks and the grandeur of Glencoe. The site is aimed primarily at outdoor enthusiasts and with great walking (the West Highland Way passes by the hostel), climbing, and white water rafting. There is lots to be enthusiastic about, Munro-baggers can find 50 Munros within 20 miles. Accommodation options range from camping (with an indoor cooking/dining area and campers' drying room), basic trekker huts/cabins (own cooking utensils required) and a purpose built four star hostel with twin and double rooms as well as dormitory accommodation, great self-catering facilities and drying room. For more comfort still there's a three bedroom chalet and two bedroom chalet. By The Way is in Tyndrum with the village pub, shops, café and Tourist Information Centre nearby. The Glasgow to Fort William road is 250m from the site (far from the madding traffic noise) and both the Glasgow Oban and Glasgow Fort William trains stop in Tyndrum.

DETAILS

- **Open** - All year. Camping from April to end September. 8am - 10am & 2pm - 8pm.
- **Number of beds** - 26 in hostel; 36 in huts; 50 camping.
- **Booking** - Always phone in advance. Deposit (Visa/Access) guarantees bed.
- **Price per night** - Hostel dorms from £20.00pp. Huts vary in price. Camping £8pp.
- **Public Transport** - Intercity coach and rail service pick-up points in Tyndrum to Edinburgh, Glasgow, Fort William and Oban. Sleeper service to London.
- **Directions** - GR NN 327 302. Travelling on A82 follow sign in village for Tyndrum Lower Station. Hostel is immediately before station.

CONTACT: Kirsty Burnett
Tel: 01838 400333
info@TyndrumByTheWay.com www.TyndrumByTheWay.com
Lower Station Road, Tyndrum, FK20 8RY

PITLOCHRY
SCOTLAND BACKPACKERS HOTEL

Located right in the centre of beautiful Pitlochry, this friendly and comfortable hostel is an old Victorian hotel literally bursting with character and providing dorms and private rooms (with en suite). Comfy beds come with fitted sheets, duvets and 2 fluffy pillows and private rooms have fresh towels included. If you are visiting Pitlochry to enjoy the vast array of outdoor activities or simply want to get away from it all and relax, the hostel has everything you need to ensure you make the most of your time in this beautiful Perthshire town. Overlooking the street below, the bright spacious lounge has comfy sofas and as much free tea, coffee and hot chocolate as you can drink. It also has free WiFi, loads of local information, some games and musical instruments and a free pool table. A separate movie lounge has comfy sofas and loads of films to chose from. A great place to meet like minded people and although you might think you're only staying one night, you'll end up staying three or four - it's that kind of place!

DETAILS

- **Open** - March to November. Open 7.30am-1pm and 5pm-10pm (please check at reception as times may vary).
- **Number of beds** - 79.
- **Booking** - Booking in advance not always essential, first night's payment required.
- **Price per night** - From £15pp for dorms. Private rooms from £20 pp
- **Public Transport** - Buses stop on Atholl Road and the hostel is only 1min walk. The train station exits onto Atholl Road also, only 5 mins' walk.
- **Directions** - Take the A924 Atholl road from the A9, the hostel is on the right if coming from the south and left if coming from the north. A customer car park behind the building is accessed from Birnham Place (just past/before the hostel).

CONTACT: Receptionist
Tel: 01796 470044
info@pitlochrybackpackershotel.com www.pitlochrybackpackershotel.com
134 Atholl Road, Pitlochry, PH16 5AB

In the centre of Birnam just 10 minutes' walk from Dunkeld, this refurbished Victorian manse has 7 bedrooms and offers a mix of self-catering hostel and bed & breakfast accommodation. Tucked away in the forests of Perthshire the village of Birnam is a perfect base to discover the mountains, waters, rich culture and heritage of Big Tree Country. GTBS Gold award winning Jessie Mac's has private doubles, bunk rooms and family rooms, all en suite, offering a warm welcome and a good night's rest. The ground floor double room has wheelchair access. LGBT friendly and well behaved dogs are welcome by arrangement. An hour by car from Edinburgh and Glasgow with good public transport links. A great choice whether you're looking for an affordable hostel room to share with friends or prefer a private room to yourselves.

DETAILS

■ **Open** - Check in between 4 & 6.30 pm. Check out by 10.30am.
■ **Number of beds** - 21: 4x2, 2x4, 1x5
■ **Booking** - Book via website, email or phone
■ **Price per night** - Dorm £20pp +continental breakfast £25, +cooked breakfast £28. Private double £28pp (based on 2 sharing), £33, £36. Child £9 in shared room. Infants free. Group rates available.
■ **Public Transport** - Direct buses from Edinburgh/Inverness and connections from Glasgow. Direct trains from Edinburgh and Glasgow. Non car users are treated to a mug of tea/coffee, a bun and a fluffy towel on arrival!.
■ **Directions** - Take Birnam/Dunkeld turning off the A9, Jessie Macs is in the centre of Birnam on the main "Perth Road"

CONTACT: Dot Mechan
Tel: 01350 727 324
info@jessiemacs.co.uk www.jessiemacs.co.uk
Murthly Terrace, Birnam, Dunkeld PH8 0BG

GULABIN
LODGE

Gulabin Lodge is beautifully situated in the heart of Glenshee at the foot of Beinn Gulabin and is the nearest accommodation to the Glenshee ski slopes. The lodge offers excellent accommodation for individuals, families and groups, has under-floor heating throughout and two cosy lounges with log fires for those colder months. All rooms have been tastefully decorated with some rooms having mezzanine platforms which are ideal for families. Based on site at the lodge there are many activities available for all ages and abilities including a Ski School and equipment hire facility for the winter months. The lodge is an ideal base for schools groups and for activities such as climbing, walking or mountain biking. Mountain bike hire and guided trips are also available. Meals can be provided for groups and also transport to and from airports and rail stations. Registered 4 Star VisitScotland Activity Accommodation provider. AALS Registered L9768/R1801.

DETAILS

- **Open** - All year, 24 hours.
- **Number of beds** - 37: 9 rooms available.
- **Booking** - Booking advisable.
- **Price per night** - From £20pp self catering. Family rooms, twins, 4 person and 6 person rooms. Full board available. Sole use available. Separate 12 bed also available
- **Public Transport** - Train and bus stations at Pitlochry (22 miles), Blairgowrie (20 miles), Glasgow (100 miles), Edinburgh (70 miles). Post bus calls half a mile away.
- **Directions** - Gulabin Lodge is on the A93 road at Spittal of Glenshee - 20 miles north of Blairgowrie and 19 miles south of Braemar. Transport can be arranged.

CONTACT: Darren and Tereza
Tel: 01250 885255 Mobile: 07799 847014
info@gulabinlodge.co.uk www.gulabinoutdoors.co.uk
Spittal of Glenshee, By Blairgowrie, PH10 7QE

PROSEN
HOSTEL

Glenprosen is the most intimate of the Angus Glens on the southernmost edge of the Cairngorms National Park. Two Munros, the Mayar and Driesh link Glenprosen to the Cairngorms plateau. The Minister's Path leads over to Glen Clova, whilst a footbridge and path along the prettiest stretch of the river Prosen connect to Glenisla and the Cateran Trail in Perthshire. Prosen Hostel was converted from the old primary school to provide accommodation for those using the upgraded East Cairngorms footpath network. Converted to the latest and greenest specification, the living room has a wood burning stove, internet connection, and raised area for admiring the view (and red squirrels) through the school's huge windows. A drying room and laundry facilities complete the cosy welcome. It sleeps a total of 18 in 4 bunkrooms, sleeping 4, 4 and 6 and a family room sleeping 4. The nearby village hall is available to rent for ceilidhs, music sessions, parties and celebrations. STB 4 star.

DETAILS

- **Open** - All year, all day.
- **Number of beds** - 18:1x6, 3x4
- **Booking** - Book by phone or email.
- **Price per night** - £18 - £20 per person. Minimum periods & prices apply for Christmas and New Year.
- **Public Transport** - Trains Dundee; No public transport beyond Kirriemuir.
- **Directions** - From Kirriemuir follow B955 signed to Prosen, Clova and Cairngorms National Park. At Dykehead fork left. Carry on for 7 miles until public road ends at telephone kiosk. Turn acute right and follow tarmac 200m uphill to hostel.

CONTACT: Hector or Robert
Tel: 01575 540238/302
ihg@prosenhostel.co.uk www.prosenhostel.co.uk
Prosen Hostel, Balnaboth, Kirriemuir, Angus, DD8 4SA

HABITAT
@BALLATER

Habitat hostel is a five star self-catering hostel situated in the centre of Ballater, near Balmoral, on the east side of the Cairngorms National Park. The bunk and private rooms, all en suite, offer great accommodation for groups, families and independent travellers. Either book the whole hostel, a room or just a bed. No minimum stay. Large open plan kitchen/dining/communal area with wood burning stove. Drying room and cycle storage available. Excellent facilities, comfortable beds and a friendly welcome. A great location in the east Cairngorms; amazing walking, climbing and cycling nearby; on the bus route between Aberdeen and Braemar; Lochnagar and Loch Muick less than 10 miles away; Balmoral only a 15 min drive; Muir Of Dinnet Nature Reserve (MacGregor's Cave) and Cambus O May Forest just up the road; a mound of castles nearby; close to Lecht and Glenshee ski resort. The village has restaurants & cafés, bike hire and shops including a butchers, a deli and Co-op.

DETAILS

- **Open** - All year. Reception open 8-10am & 5-10pm. Hostel is closed 10am-5pm.
- **Number of beds** - 25: 1 x 8, 1 x 6, 1 x 2, 3 x family room (double & bunk)
- **Booking** - Recommended, especially for groups. Availability shown on website.
- **Price per night** - From £20pp(dorms) £31(private). Book all for a 25% discount.
- **Public Transport** - Airport/Trains in Aberdeen. Bus (201/202/203 Stagecoach) from Aberdeen bus/train station to Ballater (every 30-60mins, journey takes 2-2.5hrs).
- **Directions** - Driving: From Aberdeen enter Ballater on A93, before road splits turn right on track. From Braemar drive through village, turn left with A93 & left on track. Walk: 5mins walk from Co-op - walk past church, left on Albert Road, right on track.

CONTACT: Dominique & Daniel Drewe-Martin
Tel: 013397 53752
info@habitat-at-ballater.com www.habitat-at-ballater.com
Bridge Square, Ballater, Aberdeenshire, AB35 5QJ

BACKPACKERS PLUS
OBAN
SCOTLAND

Many people's favourite hostel thanks to its friendly atmosphere and beautiful seaside town setting. Excellent facilities include free WiFi throughout, free breakfast, free all-day hot drinks, clean spacious rooms, secure bike storage, laundry service, cool communal areas with lots of character, strong hot showers, comfortable beds, and a well-equipped self-catering kitchen. There's a pool table and other games and lots of information from the knowledgeable staff about the area. Oban has spectacular views across to the islands and the bustle of fishing boats, ferries, yachts and seabirds make the waterfront a lovely place to be. Easy ferry access to the many beautiful Scottish Isles. Ancient standing stones, medieval castles, hairy coos and whisky distilleries are all nearby. The best fish and chips in Scotland are within 200 metres. Choose between custom made spacious bunk beds (including your own personal reading light, double power socket and locker), or a little extra privacy in one of our comfortable single, twin, double or family rooms. Experience backpacking with a Plus!

DETAILS
- **Open** - All year, reception 7am-10pm, occasionally closed in middle of the day.
- **Number of beds** - 50-60 dorm beds, family, double, twin rooms, some en suite.
- **Booking** - recommended but not essential. Deposit = 1st night's board required.
- **Price per night** - dorms from £12 pp, private rooms from £18 pp
- **Public Transport** - From Citylink bus and train station walk along the waterfront, up George Street, past the Taj Mahal restaurant. Hostel is straight ahead on the left.
- **Directions** - From A85 turn left at the Kings Knoll Hotel onto Deanery Brae. Sharp right onto Breadalbane Street. Hostel is at the bottom of the street on the right.

CONTACT: Receptionist
Tel: 01631 567189
info@backpackersplus.com   www.backpackersplus.com
The Old Church, Breadalbane St, Oban, Argyll, PA34 5PH

OBAN BACKPACKERS

Whether you're passing through Oban on the way to the Islands, or staying for a couple of days and exploring historic and beautiful Argyll, the original Oban Backpackers is a great place to stay, meet like minded people and probably end up staying longer than planned. Situated in the heart of the town Oban Backpackers is perfectly located to enable you to experience all Oban has to offer without burning a hole in your wallet. Completely refurbished in May 2013 the hostel offers dormitory accommodation with wide, comfortable, bunks, made up with fitted sheets, duvets and pillows. Powerful showers with loads of hot water add to the comfort and if required, towels can be hired from reception. The fully equipped kitchen has everything you will need to cook up your favourite meals and there is plenty of storage and fridge space available. The big cosy lounge with a real fire, pool table, free hot drinks, WiFi, musical instruments, games and book swap makes it a great place to stay and unwind.

DETAILS

- **Open** - March - November. 7am - 10pm.
- **Number of beds** - 54: 1x12, 1x10, 1x8, 4x6
- **Booking** - Online or by phone, first night's fee as deposit
- **Price per night** - From £15. Whole hostel bookings-email for quote
- **Public Transport** - 10 minute walk to Oban train station and Citylink buses
- **Directions** - From A85 turn left onto Deanery Brae take the sharp right onto Breadalbane Street. Oban Backpackers is on the left. From bus and train - walk along the waterfront keeping sea on left. Continue straight up George Street, bare right to Bredalbane Street. The hostel is on the right.

CONTACT: Reception
Tel: 01631 562 107
info@obanbackpackers.com www.obanbackpackers.com
Breadalbane Street, Oban, PA34 5NZ

CORRAN
HOUSE

Corran House is part of a Victorian terrace with magnificent seascapes across the bay to the Isle of Kerrera and the hills of Mull. There is a warm welcome for visitors and reasonably priced accommodation for singles, couples, families and groups. The house has a large self-catering kitchen, spacious TV lounge, comfortable, commodious, well appointed guest rooms and 4 bed dormitories with generous size beds. Most rooms have en suite facilities. Corran House is well situated for exploring Argyll and visiting the inner Hebrides. It is only a short walk along the sea front to the bus, train and ferry terminals. Downstairs is MarkieDans bar with Oban's best patio beer garden with spectacular views. The pub offers great highland hospitality, tasty meals, live entertainment, widescreen TV, a pool table and the best range of malt whiskies on the west coast. Guests receive a 10% discount if they dine at MarkieDans. Live music every weekend with fantastic bands - see our website for details.

DETAILS

- **Open** - All year. Reception 10am-11pm. Check in after 3pm.
- **Number of beds** - 62 in total - 26 bunks- 5x4 1x6. Plus guest rooms: 16
- **Booking** - Book early and in advance. Early/late arrival with notice.
- **Price per night** - Bunk rooms £18 or £20 en suite. Guest rooms from £27.50 - £40pp if 2 sharing. Single rooms from £45. Always book direct for the best rate.
- **Public Transport** - Oban train, bus and ferry terminals are 900m from the house.
- **Directions** - Corran House overlooks Oban Bay to the west of the town centre. From the Tourist Information and all the Oban transport terminals, with the sea on your left, walk along George Street past the Columba Hotel into Corran Esplanade. Follow the seafront for 300m. Corran House is on your right above Markie Dans Bar.

CONTACT:
Tel: 01631 566040
enquiries@corranhouseoban.co.uk www.corranhouseoban.co.uk
1 Victoria Crescent, Corran Esplanade, Oban, Argyll, PA34 5PN

COLONSAY
SCOTLAND BACKPACKERS LODGE

Colonsay Backpackers Lodge is located on a peaceful and idyllic Inner Hebridean island to the south of Mull which boasts magnificent sandy beaches, ancient forests and beautiful lochs. The place is teeming with wildlife which includes dolphins, seals, otters and many rare species of bird. There are ancient standing stones and a 14th century priory with exceptional carved Celtic tombstones. The famous Colonsay House gardens and café are open to visitors three times a week. The pub, café, shop and village hall, where there are regular ceilidhs, are all within three miles. Fresh lobster and crab can be bought from fishing boats in the harbour and the best oysters in the world are grown on Colonsay. Play a round of golf or treat yourself to a meal in the hotel. The lodge is a refurbished former gamekeeper's house with bothies. Centrally heated, it has 2 twin, 3 twin bunk and 2 three bedded rooms. It has a large dining/cooking/sitting area and a sitting room with log fire. Bed linen, towels and WiFi provided.

DETAILS

- **Open** - All year, 24 hours.
- **Number of beds** - 16: 5 x 2; 2 x 3
- **Booking** - Payment required 24 hours in advance.
- **Price per night** - £25pp twin, £19.50pp bothy
- **Public Transport** - Train and coach to Oban. Caledonian MacBrayne ferry to Colonsay takes 2.5 hours. Flights Hebridean Air from Connel
- **Directions** - Ferry departs Oban 6 times per week April to October; Sun, Mon, Wed, Thurs, Fri, Sat (rest of year Mon, Wed, Fri, Sat). Flights Tues, Thurs from Connel Airport, nr Oban. Transport from the harbour can be arranged if required.

CONTACT: The Manager
Tel: 01951 200312
cottages@colonsayholidays.co.uk www.colonsayestate.co.uk
Colonsay Estate Cottages, Isle of Colonsay, Argyll, PA61 7YP

COLL
BUNKHOUSE

Coll Bunkhouse provides five star hostel accommodation in the Inner Hebrides. The beautiful Isle of Coll offers so much, whether you are into walking, stargazing, wildlife-spotting, diving, cycling, sailing or kayaking, you can do it all.

The bunkhouse is bright and airy, with 16 beds in two dorms of 6 and one family room for 4 which can also be booked as a twin room. Ideal for small groups or independent travellers. The building is brand new, with a fully equipped kitchen and modern facilities throughout. Whether you're looking for an island adventure or a quiet place to relax, a warm welcome awaits.

DETAILS

- **Open** - All year, 24 hours.
- **Number of beds** - 16: 2x6, 1x4
- **Booking** - Not always essential but highly recommended. Full payment is required at time of booking, or a deposit for a group booking.
- **Price per night** - £21pp (dorm). Private rooms £80 (quad), £65 (triple), £50 (twin). Discounts for group bookings (exclusive use) of two nights or more from 5% to 50%
- **Public Transport** - Ferry from Oban takes 2.40 hours. Sailings every day in summer and five times a week in winter. Flights from Oban four times a week. Bikes are free on the ferry and can be booked onto trains to Oban. Free car parks in Oban.
- **Directions** - Coll Bunkhouse is situated in the centre of the village of Arinagour, very close to the local shop and the hotel/bar. From the ferry walk along Main Street continuing onto Shore Street. The bunkhouse is on your left hand side, next door to An Cridhe, the new community centre. From the airport take the road to Arinagour and the bunkhouse will be on your right hand side as you enter the village.

CONTACT: Jane
Tel: 01879 230217
jane@developmentcoll.org.uk www.collbunkhouse.com
Arinagour, Isle of Coll, Argyll, PA78 6SY

MILLHOUSE
HOSTEL

Tiree is an idyllic Hebridean island, perfect for outdoor pursuits, wildlife enthusiasts, and those wanting to experience the tranquillity of stunning white beaches and crystal clear seas.

A warm welcome and excellent facilities await you at Millhouse. There are bikes for hire to explore the island, visit the lighthouse museum, 'ping' the ringing stone, find the standing stones, wonder at the Machair flowers or watch the seals. Watersports take place on adjacent Loch Bhasapol, and the secluded Cornaig beach is a ten minute walk away.

There is a resident RSPB warden on the island and a bird hide near the hostel. For walkers, Millhouse is on the Tiree Pilgrimage route linking the ancient chapels and monuments around the island. 4 star hostel with free WiFi.

DETAILS

■ **Open** - Mar-Oct, open in winter by arrangement. Open all day. Check in 4pm Check out 10am.
■ **Number of beds** - Hostel 16 : 2 x 2/3, 2 x 5.
■ **Booking** - Advisable, please check vacancies before boarding the ferry
■ **Price per night** - Dorm from £24pp. Twin from £28pp. Family room £72-£120 per room.
■ **Public Transport** - Caledonian MacBrayne ferry from Oban to Tiree or Flybe flight from Glasgow. Local ring and ride bus 01879 220419.
■ **Directions** - From end of ferry road turn right at T junction and continue for 5 miles to Millhouse Hostel.

CONTACT: David Naylor
Tel: 01879 220892
mail@tireemillhouse.co.uk www.tireemillhouse.co.uk
Cornaigmore, Isle of Tiree, Argyll, PA77 6XA

'BEST ECO-HOSTEL IN SCOTLAND' (GTBS). Tucked into the rocky outcrops at the north end of the island, Iona Hostel has spectacular views to Staffa and the Treshnish Isles, and beyond Rhum to the Black Cuillins of Skye. The hostel is situated on the working croft of Lagandorain (the hollow of the otter).

This land has been worked for countless generations, creating the familiar Hebridean patchwork of wildflower meadow, crops and grazing land, home to an amazing variety of plants and birds. It offers quiet sanctuary for those that seek it, within easy reach of island activities.

Whether travelling on your own, with friends, or as part of one of our many visiting groups, Iona Hostel offers you a warm welcome - with the best views this side of heaven. 4 star STB. Green Tourism Gold Award. We regret no dogs.

DETAILS

- **Open** - All year, closed 11am-1pm for cleaning - no curfew.
- **Number of beds** - 21: 1x2, 2x4, 1x5, 1x6.
- **Booking** - Strongly advised
- **Price per night** - £21.00 adult / £17.50 under 10's (bedding included).
- **Public Transport** - Caledonian Macbrayne ferry service from Oban or Mull 08705 650000. For buses on Mull 01546 604695. Taxi service on Iona 0781 0325990.
- **Directions** - You cannot bring your car onto Iona, but there is free parking in Fionnphort on Mull at the Columba Centre. Iona Hostel is the last building at the north end of the island, 2 km from the pier and up beyond the abbey.

CONTACT: John MacLean
Tel: 01681 700781
info@ionahostel.co.uk www.ionahostel.co.uk
Iona Hostel, Iona, Argyll, PA76 6SW

CRAIGNURE
BUNKHOUSE

Craignure Bunkhouse is an eco-sensitive hostel in an atmospheric setting, close to Craignure Pier where the ferry arrives from Oban. Next to the bunkhouse is The Craignure Inn, a popular traditional inn offering food, drink and a welcoming atmosphere. Craignure is the hub for the island bus services and tourist information. The bunkhouse has a biomass boiler and solar powered heating. There are two rooms of 6 beds and two rooms of 4 beds, each with an en suite shower. Each bunk has a locker, a reading light and USB port. The Convivial is a large communal room, with well equipped kitchen, ample dining space, plenty of books/games and a large Freesat television surrounded by comfortable couches and chairs. Free WiFi throughout the building. Bed linen is provided and towels can be hired. Laundry, equipment/bike store and drying room are available. Mull has great beaches. A visit to Duart Castle, a sea trip to Staffa, ferry trip to Iona, or shopping trip to Tobermory are all recommended.

BEST PRICE

DETAILS

- **Open** - All year, closed 11am-4pm for cleaning.
- **Number of beds** - 20: 2x4, 2x6
- **Booking** - Booking through website or phone.
- **Price per night** - £22 per person per night. 4 berth rooms, £80 per night. 6 berth rooms, £120 per night. Whole hostel, £380 per night, by prior arrangement.
- **Public Transport** - Ferries from Oban dock at Craignure Pier. Coaches and trains run frequently from Glasgow to Oban. Craignure is the hub for the island buses.
- **Directions** - From Craignure pier, turn left and look out for the Craignure Inn 350 metres down the road. The bunkhouse is next door.

CONTACT: Ross or Chris
Tel: 01680 812043   Mob:07900 692973
info@craignure-bunkhouse.co.uk   www.craignure-bunkhouse.co.uk/
Craignure Bunkhouse, Craignure, Isle Of Mull, Argyll And Bute, PA65 6AY

SHIELING
HOLIDAYS

SCOTLAND

Right on the sea, with views to Ben Nevis. There are otters on site, and you may see porpoises, dolphins and eagles. Your accommodation is in shared Shielings, unique carpeted cottage tents, made on Mull, which are clean, bright and spacious and have real beds for 2, 4, or 6 people. Or you can hire a Shieling to yourself or stay in a self catering cottage. There are super showers, and a communal Shieling with woodburning stove, TV, payphone and launderette. Free WiFi. Campfire. Bike hire.

Stroll to the ferry, pub, café, shops, and swimming pool. Walk to Duart Castle, home of the Clan Maclean. Catch the bus for Tobermory for Iona (where Columba brought Christianity to Scotland) and for Staffa (home of puffins, and inspiration for Mendelssohn's overture 'Fingal's Cave'). A perfect base for all Mull. You don't need a car.

DETAILS

- **Open** - April to October, 24 hours (reception 8am - 10pm).
- **Number of beds** - 18: 6 x 2, 1 x 6.
- **Booking** - Please email a booking enquiry from our website.
- **Price per night** - £14.00 pp. Under 15s £10. Bedding £4 pp.
- **Public Transport** - From Glasgow, rail or bus (0871 266 3333) at 12.00, ferry (01680 812343) at 16.00 from Oban, arrive Mull 16.50; back by 09.30 ferry, arrive Glasgow by 1600. Please check times before travel.
- **Directions** - Grid Ref 724 369. From ferry, left on the A849 to Iona. After 400 metres, left opposite church past old pier to reception by the sea - 800 metres in all.

CONTACT: David Gracie
Tel: 01680 812496
sales@shielingholidays.co.uk www.shielingholidays.co.uk
Craignure, Mull, Argyll, PA65 6AY

CORRAN BUNKHOUSE

Corran Bunkhouse 4 star accommodation is situated in a stunning lochside location surrounded by mountains in the magnificent Highlands of Scotland, 8 miles south of Fort William and 7 miles north of Glencoe. The Corran Bunkhouse is made up of two fully equipped self-catering bunkhouses which between them can offer comfortable accommodation for up to 32 people. One bunkhouse sleeps 12 and the other sleeps 20 making Corran Bunkhouse an ideal base for small and large groups. Individual travellers are welcome and the room sizes make the bunkhouse ideal for family groups. All bedrooms have a TV and en suite facilities. There are fully equipped kitchen/dining areas, drying room, central heating, laundry facilities, private parking and a steam room situated in the smaller bunkhouse. Children and pets welcome. Group discounts. Come and enjoy the many outdoor activities available in the area such as climbing, walking, canoeing, kayaking, cycling and mountain biking.

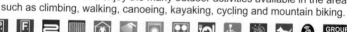

DETAILS

■ **Open** - All year.
■ **Number of beds** - 32: 8x2 1x3 2x4 1x5
■ **Booking** - Advisable but not necessary - major credit cards accepted.
■ **Price per night** - £20pp, £18pp for group bookings. £24 for single occupancy. Prices include all bedding. (Prices under review 2017 - VAT registration in progress).
■ **Public Transport** - Trains at Fort William (8 mile bus or taxi ride to hostel). Regular buses toward Fort William from the south and from Inverness stop 100m from hostel (ask for Corran Ferry). Check the Citylink web site for bus details.
■ **Directions** - On the Onich side of the Corran Ferry 8 miles south of Fort William. Turn onto A861 Corran Ferry Road from A82. Bunkhouse on the left before slipway.

CONTACT: Alan & Halina
Tel: 01855 821000
info@corranbunkhouse.co.uk www.corranbunkhouse.co.uk
Corran Ferry Approach Road, Onich, Fort William, PH33 6SE

BANK STREET
LODGE
SCOTLAND

Bank Street Lodge is situated 100 metres from Fort William High Street which has numerous shops, pubs, restaurants and banks. There is a fully equipped kitchen with cooker, fridge, microwave, cutlery and crockery provided. The common room lounge has a TV, it also provides tables and chairs for eating self prepared meals, and a snack vending machine.

All bedding is provided. Some rooms are en suite (twins, doubles and family). WiFi is also now available in our lounge/TV room. The Stables Restaurant, at the front of the building, serves fine food for lunches and dinners (also breakfast from May to September) - treat yourself! Fort William is an ideal base from which to enjoy walking, climbing, cycling or mountain biking. The world-renowned Nevis Range Mountain Bike Trails and Ski Centre are only a short distance from the town centre. Three star STB rating.

DETAILS

- **Open** - All year (closed for 3 days at Xmas), 24 hour reception. Entry from 1.00pm, depart by 10.00am.
- **Number of beds** - 43: 6 x 4, 4 x 3, 1 x 7
- **Booking** - Booking advised. Deposit required for long stays or groups.
- **Price per night** - From £18 to £22.00 per person. Group rates available
- **Public Transport** - Train and bus stations at Fort William, 500 metres from Lodge.
- **Directions** - Head for town centre via the underpass, turn left after Tesco supermarket on Bank Street, then head up the hill for 150 metres. Hostel is above the Stables Restaurant. Car parking is available.

CONTACT: Reception
Tel: 01397 700070
bankstreetlodge@btconnect.com www.bankstreetlodge.co.uk
Bank Street, Fort William, PH33 6AY

FORT WILLIAM
BACKPACKERS

Deep in the Highlands, surrounded by spectacular mountain scenery lies Fort William, a mecca for those with a spirit of adventure. You can start (or end) the 'West Highland Way' in Fort William, hike or bike along mountain trails, go for a boat trip on the sea loch or just take it easy amidst the wonderful scenery. Even in winter Fort William stays busy with skiing, snow-boarding, mountaineering and ice-climbing. Nestling on a hillside above the town, with wonderful views, this characterful and comfy hostel provides everything you'll need after a day in the hills. In the evening put your feet up in the elegant lounge in front of a real fire or stroll down to the choice of local pubs. Ben Nevis, Britain's highest mountain, is just around the corner and below it is Glen Nevis, perhaps Scotland's prettiest glen, with wonderful waterfalls and ancient pine forest. Dramatic and eerie, Glencoe awaits a few miles away for an excellent day trip.

DETAILS

- **Open** - All year, all day. Reception 7am-noon and 5pm-10.30pm (times may vary).
- **Number of beds** - 38
- **Booking** - First night's payment required to confirm booking.
- **Price per night** - From £17 per person. ID required for check-in.
- **Public Transport** - Train and bus stations are only 5/10 minute walk from hostel.
- **Directions** - From north on the A82 go right at roundabout towards town centre. Turn left onto Victoria Road, then left at fork onto Alma Road. From south on the A82 go straight over first roundabout. At second roundabout go right onto Belford Road following Inverness signs, then turn right up Victoria Road then into Alma Road at left fork. From stations walk past supermarket, turn left before the underpass, heading onto the Belford Road. The hostel is just a bit further up, on Alma Road, on the right.

CONTACT: Receptionist
Tel: 01397 700 711
info@fortwilliambackpackers.com www.fortwilliambackpackers.com
Alma Road, Fort William, PH33 6HB

SMIDDY
BUNKHOUSE

Find a friendly welcome at this comfortable, mountain hostel with a loch-side location overlooking the Caledonian Canal 4 miles from Fort William & Ben Nevis. The pine clad interior has a cosy, friendly atmosphere with stunning mountains and water on the doorstep with the meeting of the West Highland Way and Great Glen Way only yards away. Hot showers. Fully equipped kitchens always available. (local shop open until 11pm daily). 2 efficient drying / laundry rooms. All bedding provided. Free WiFi. Fully heated for all year round use. Lockable bike & canoe stores. Ample off road parking. Outdoor information, daily weather & snow reports. Advice/instruction/guiding with resident mountain and water based instructors for: winter and summer walking/climbing; river, loch and sea kayaking; dinghy sailing. Hire of kayaks/open canoes, dinghy and other equipment. AALS licensed & DofE Approved Activity Provider for expeditions. Group and family accommodation. Meeting / lecture room available.

DETAILS

- **Open** - All year, all day (with key).
- **Number of beds** - 24: 3x4, 2x6.
- **Booking** - Book on-line or telephone / e-mail.
- **Price per night** - £15 - £ 20 (seasonal) pp (incl. bedding).
- **Public Transport** - Two minutes' walk from Corpach Railway Station-the Mallaig Line. Three miles - 2 stops out from Fort William (trains from Glasgow and London).
- **Directions** - Take A82 north out of Fort William towards Inverness. After one mile take A830 west towards Mallaig and follow for 2 miles to village of Corpach. Turn left before shops, signposted 'Snowgoose Mountain Centre'. The hostel is 30 yds on left.

CONTACT: John or Tina
Tel: 01397 772467
enquiry@highland-mountain-guides.co.uk www.accommodation-fortwilliam.co.uk/
Snowgoose Mountain Centre, Station Road, Corpach, Fort William, PH33 7JH

GLENCOE
SCOTLAND INDEPENDENT HOSTEL

Glencoe Independent Hostel, centred around an old highland croft in the heart of Glencoe, offers great value accommodation for groups, families and individuals. It is set in secluded and peaceful woodland midway between Glencoe village and the Clachaig Inn with immediate access to world class cycling, walking, climbing and kayaking. The hostel is 20 minutes from Glencoe Ski Centre and the West Highland Way and 40 minutes from Nevis Range. The hostel has 4 rooms, a lounge with open fire, cooking and dining facilities and offers private family and couples rooms when available. The alpine bunkhouse sleeps 16 in 3 rooms, ideal for outdoor activity and school groups. Also available are 4 luxury caravans for 2 to 4 people, 2 luxury en suite cabins for 2 people, and a log cabin for 2 to 3 people. Free WiFi in reception, top class drying room, bike storage, and mountains all around. Go Glencoe guided walks available.

DETAILS

- **Open** - All year (phone in Nov and Dec), 9am - 9 pm.
- **Number of beds** - 65: hostel:26, bunkhouse:16, caravans: 4x2-4, cabins: 2x2, 1x3
- **Booking** - Booking advised all year, 30% non refundable deposit (min. £10).
- **Price per night** - From £12.50 to £22 per person.
- **Public Transport** - 1.5 miles from bus stop in Glencoe Village (crossroads). Citylink buses 914, 915 and 916 from Skye, Fort William, Glasgow. Bus 44 from Fort William and Kinlochleven. For West Highland Way take White Corries near Kingshouse Hotel to Glencoe Crossroads (20 mins) then 1.5 miles' walk.
- **Directions** - From A82 south, take right turn for Clachaig Inn, 1 mile after pub on left. From north, take left turn for Kinlochleven, then immediate right to Glencoe Village. 1 mile out of village on right.

CONTACT: Keith or Davina
Tel: 01855 811906
info@glencoehostel.co.uk www.glencoehostel.co.uk
Glencoe Independent Hostel, Glencoe, Argyll, PH49 4HX

Àite Cruinnichidh, 15 miles northeast of Fort William, occupies a unique sheltered spot adjacent to the Monessie Gorge where you can explore remote glens, mountain passes and lochs. There are numerous walks easily accessible from the hostel and seven magnificent canoeing rivers within 20 miles. The location is ideal for climbing (rock and ice), mountain biking, skiing or just relaxing. A warm, peaceful, friendly, country hostel in a converted barn, Àite Cruinnichidh sleeps 28 in eight rooms with all bedding supplied in simple accommodation. The hostel has a fully equipped kitchen/dining room, sitting room, excellent showers, sauna suite, seminar room and garden. There is a good selection of maps, board games, magazines, books and a small reading room. No TV and, although the hostel has WiFi, guests are encouraged to socialise and enjoy the natural environment that the hostel has to offer. Advice available on walking/cycling routes. Groups and individuals welcome. No wheelchair facilities but glad to accommodate people with disabilities.

BEST PRICE

DETAILS

■ **Open** - All year, all day.
■ **Number of beds** - 28 : 1x6, 4x4, 1x twin, 1x double, 1x family/double en suite.
■ **Booking** - Booking advised, 50% deposit.
■ **Price per night** - From £16 per person.
■ **Public Transport** - Roy Bridge station & bus stop (2 miles) has several connections to Fort William daily. Pick up from Roy Bridge with advanced notice
■ **Directions** - From Spean Bridge take A86 to Roy Bridge. Go though village and continue for 2 miles. Hostel is on right 100m after Glenspean Lodge Hotel.

CONTACT: Gavin or Nicola
Tel: 01397 712315
gavin@highland-hostel.co.uk www.highland-hostel.co.uk
1 Achluachrach, By Roy Bridge, Near Fort William, PH31 4AW

COORIE DOON
SCOTLAND SELF CATERING CABIN

This beautiful timber cabin offers high quality, 5 star accommodation in an area ideal for those who love the outdoors. Next to NCN Route 78 the cabin offers easy access to world class hiking, climbing, skiing, mountain biking, or simply enjoying the amazing view. Es is an accomplished mountaineer happy to offer advice on how best to enjoy the area. Set on the Caledonian Canal (route of the Great Glen Way) with stunning views to Ben Nevis, Loch Linnhe, Aonach Mor and the Mamores. Perfect for the GGW, the West Highland Way, Nevis Range and the Glencoe Mountain Resort. Two en suite bedrooms, each sleep three (double bed with a single bunk above). The open plan kitchen and dining/sitting room are well equipped for self catering and relaxing with WiFi, TV with DVD, iPod and CD player, plus reference books and maps. Outside, enjoy the mountain view from the deck or watch ships on the canal. Store canoes, skis & bikes in the secure bunkers and racks then come in to underfloor heating, a drying room and the luxury of a sauna after a day of strenuous exercise.

DETAILS

- **Open** - All year, check in 4pm-10pm, check out 10am.
- **Number of beds** - 6: 2x3 (each room as one double and a single bed)
- **Booking** - phone or email to book.
- **Price per night** - From £80- get in touch for accurate prices.
- **Public Transport** - Nearest trains at Banavie Stn. On bus routes no. 45 & 46.
- **Directions** - On the A82 take the A830 signed for Mallaig, After about 1 mile, turn right into Banavie, (B8004) then immediate left onto Old Banavie Road. Coorie Doon is the wooden cabin behind the willow tree on the uphill side of the road.

CONTACT: Es Tresidder
Tel: 07503775874
e.tresidder@gmail.com
Coorie Doon, Old Banavie Road, Banavie, Fort William, PH33 7PZ

Surrounded by the beauty of Deeside, Braemar Lodge Hotel and Bunkhouse is in a quiet setting only a two minute walk from the village itself. Braemar Lodge Hotel was formerly a Victorian shooting lodge and is set in extensive grounds two minutes from the centre of Braemar in the heart of Royal Deeside. The great value Bunkhouse provides comfortable accommodation for up to 12 people (expanding to 20 during 2017) within the hotel grounds,

The bunkhouse is equipped with two shower rooms, one of which is suitable for wheelchair access. The bunkhouse also has good drying and laundry facilities, excellent for damp clothes and ski boots. A generous fully equipped kitchen is available for all your self-catering needs. Guests are also welcome to use the hotel's excellent dining facilities if a rest from self-catering is required. All bed linen and towels are supplied for the duration of your stay.

DETAILS

- **Open** - All year, all day.
- **Number of beds** - 12: 3x4 (expanding to 20 in 2017)
- **Booking** - Book by phone or email
- **Price per night** - From £15 per person
- **Public Transport** - Aberdeen airport 59 miles. Railway stations at Perth (50 miles) and Aberdeen. Buses to Braemar from Aberdeen where the bus and rail station are side by side. Two minute walk to hotel from Braemar village bus stop.
- **Directions** - The hotel is situated on the A93 on the left if you are arriving from the south. Two minutes' walk from the village centre.

CONTACT: Reception
Tel: 01339 741627
mail@braemarlodge.co.uk www.braemarlodge.co.uk
6 Glenshee Rd, Braemar, Aberdeenshire, AB35 5YQ

ABERNETHY
BUNKHOUSE

Sharing a car park with the Speyside Way and just yards from the river, the converted Nethy Station offers all that a group of 10-26 could expect from a bunkhouse and you only pay for a maximum of 20 beds. It is well equipped, fully central heated and has two public areas. Most rooms have triple bunks and there is a 2 bunk room with unusual access: we call it Narnia, as you get there through a wardrobe! There is also 'The Shed'. Whether you self-cater or we cook for you as a group, you will have access to the kitchen at all times. We never ask people to share the building so you may sleep, walk, ski, board, hike, ride, fish, etc. at your own convenience. Stag and hen groups are welcome. The bunkhouse is only 200 yards from the centre of Nethy Bridge with its shop, butcher, pub and interpretive centre and half way between two winter sports areas. Dogs are welcome but please do not let them sleep on the beds!

DETAILS

■ **Open** - All year, anytime.
■ **Number of beds** - 26: 2x9,4x2
■ **Booking** - Essential (with deposit)
■ **Price per night** - £16.75 per person. After the minimum of 12 we only charge for those who stay. 10% discount midweek and 20% discount for stays of over 4 nights.
■ **Public Transport** - Take train or Citylink coach to Aviemore. Local buses are available from Aviemore to Nethy Bridge Post Office, phone 01479 811566.
■ **Directions** - GR 002 207. Hostel is adjacent to the Speyside Way. From the B970, with post office on your right, go over the bridge and turn left immediately. Go past the butcher turn second right.

CONTACT: Patricia or Richard
Tel: 01479 821 370
info@nethy.org www.nethy.org
Station Road, Nethy Bridge, PH25 3DN

Part of the award-winning Craggan Outdoors activity centre, Ardenbeg offers good value self-catering accommodation across rooms of four, five, six & eight bunks, along with two well appointed kitchen / dining / common room areas, four bathrooms and a large private garden with BBQ, picnic tables & a children's play area.

The property is situated on a quiet residential street in Grantown-on-Spey, the historic capital of Strathspey. As well as the wide range of outdoor activities on offer through Craggan Outdoors (see www.cragganoutdoors.co.uk), Ardenbeg is perfectly situated - 15 minutes from Aviemore, 45 minutes from Inverness, 2 hours from Aberdeen, 3 hours from the Central Belt - to enjoy all that the Cairngorms National Park & wider central Highlands have to offer.

DETAILS

- **Open** - Year round, access 24 hours.
- **Number of beds** - 23: 1x4, 1x5, 1x6, 1x8.
- **Booking** - In advance to avoid disappointment
- **Price per night** - From £16.50 to £24 per person per night, subject to number of people & duration of stay.
- **Public Transport** - Rail: Aviemore. Bus: stop on the High Street in Grantown. Air: Inverness
- **Directions** - Once in Grantown-on-Spey, find the Co-op on the High Street, & then take the road that runs beside the Co-op (keeping it on your right), & turn left after 100 yards into Grant Road. Ardenbeg is the fifth building on the right.

CONTACT: Keith & Jill Ballam
Tel: 01479 873283 / 01479 872824
info@cragganoutdoors.co.uk www.cragganoutdoors.co.uk
Grant Road, Grantown-on-Spey, Moray PH26 3LD

FINDHORN
VILLAGE HOSTEL

Located in the heart of the coastal village of Findhorn, on the Moray Coast, an Area of Outstanding Natural Beauty, Findhorn Village Hostel is just a stone's throw from a beautiful bay. A short walk from the hostel are the dunes and the Findhorn Foundation Eco Village. Extensive sandy beaches, great wildlife sites and the Speyside distilleries are within reach of the village. The Cairngorm mountains are under an hour's drive. The hostel provides newly renovated self-catering accommodation in a former village school which can be booked by groups or individuals. It has a well equipped kitchen and communal area, WiFi, TV, DVD, modern showers and central heating. Sleeping accommodation is in shared bunk-bed rooms, a two person room and an en suite family room. A new annex, available to smaller groups or families, has a small kitchenette and en suite shower room. The communal areas provide plenty of space for large groups but can be rearranged into a more intimate setting for individuals.

DETAILS

- **Open** - All year. Office hours 9am-1pm Mon to Fri.
- **Number of beds** - 34: 28 in hostel & 6 in Annex; 2x8; 1x2; 1x4/5
- **Booking** - Booking is essential via email or phone. Groups should send a deposit and pay in full one month prior to visit. Individuals should pay in full on booking.
- **Price per night** - £17pp. Groups £15pp with minimum booking of £120 and subject to £30 cleaning fee. Bed-linen £3.50. Continental breakfast for groups £4.50.
- **Public Transport** - Trains and intercity buses to Forres. Bus No 31 runs hourly (except Sundays) from Forres to Findhorn (until 18.15) and stops by the church.
- **Directions** - B9011 into Findhorn. At the end of the one-way system through the village take a left turn. Findhorn village centre is directly ahead.

CONTACT: Justina
Tel: 01309 692339 Mob: 07496 230266
findhornvillagecentre@gmail.com www.findhornvillagehostel.com
Church Place, Findhorn, Forres, Moray, IV36 3YR

THE SAIL LOFT
BUNKHOUSE

Overlooking the beach and across the Moray Firth this newly created bunkhouse has an absolutely stunning location. Converted from the near derelict Portsoy sail lofts, the Sail Loft Bunkhouse is a modern and well equipped facility providing self-catering accommodation for 25 persons in a mixture of double, twin and quadruple rooms.

The Banffshire Coast, also known as Scotland's Dolphin Coast, is a perfect base for exploring this glorious part of the world. With rugged natural beauty, an abundance of wildlife, historic castles, whisky trails and more, there is plenty on offer for all to explore and enjoy. Portsoy is also just 10 minutes' drive from the eastern end of the Moray Coast Trail at Cullen. The Sail Loft Bunkhouse is within easy walking distance of the historic harbour and town with its wide range of amenities. Don't miss the Traditional Boat Festival, which takes place in late June/early July each year.

DETAILS

- **Open** - From January 2017
- **Number of beds** - 25
- **Booking** - via phone.
- **Price per night** - From £25 per person.
- **Public Transport** - Stage coach bus from Aberdeen and Inverness.
- **Directions** - From A98 follow signs for the Sail Loft Bunkhouse and after passing the caravan park on the left carry straight on to the Bunkhouse, which is right in front of you.

CONTACT: Ian Tillett
Tel: 01261 842695
contact@portsoysailloft.org thesailloft.org.uk/
The Back Green, Portsoy, AB45 2RQ

Cullen Harbour Hostel's special location on the shores of the Moray Firth offers guests a relaxing break with the sound of the sea at night and coastal walks by day. Accommodation is spacious with wooden details, slate floors and sumptuous fabrics. The solid single beds have thick curtains around them. The kitchen has a wood burning Rayburn and comfortable seating. There is a power shower and a separate bathroom. The hostel has been awarded 4 stars by VisitScotland. Next to the hostel is a holiday cottage sleeping 4, this has a single room, an upstairs sitting room with single bed and a magnificent double bedroom with sea views. Cullen is at one end of the Speyside Way and on the National Cycle Route 1. Outdoor activity groups enjoy sea kayaking, surfing, rock climbing and wildlife watching. Dolphins are seen from the hostel. Children enjoy the sandy harbour and rock pools. Pubs and food are readily available.

DETAILS

■ **Open** - All year, all day. But please check in initially by 21.00. Telephone enquiries are welcome from 07.00 to 20.00.
■ **Number of beds** - 14 + 4: 2x6, 1x4 en-suite (family room) + 4 in holiday cottage.
■ **Booking** - Book by e-mail or phone. Group and peak season bookings pay in advance by bacs. Other bookings pay by cash on arrival.
■ **Price per night** - £20pp (£18 without bedding). Four-bed family room with en suite shower: £88 for four people, £72 for three and £52 for two. Cottage from £280/week.
■ **Public Transport** - Nearest station Keith (12 miles). Taxi from Keith is economical if there are a few people, or bring a bike!
■ **Directions** - The hostel is found immediately adjacent to the harbour, a 5 min walk downhill from Cullen village square.

CONTACT: Ruth or Howard
Tel: 01542 841997, Mob: 07432 591201(Ruth) 07912 079416(Howard)
ruth@cullenharbourholidays.com www.cullenharbourholidays.com
The Sailors Store, Portlong Rd, Cullen, AB56 4AG

RATTRAY HEAD
ECO-HOSTEL

Rattray Head Eco-Hostel is a former lighthouse shore station among huge dunes on an isolated 11 mile long sandy beach. Come and relax in this gorgeous most easterly part of mainland Scotland, and enjoy one of its driest, sunniest, midge-free areas.

The 1892 granite building has been renovated to form a modern, non-smoking, dog-friendly coastal retreat with self-catering kitchens, bunkrooms, and double and family bedrooms.

The North Sea Cycle Route (Sustrans 1) is 17 miles inland and passes through historic Aberdeenshire with stone circles, castle ruins and golf courses.

DETAILS

- **Open** - All year, phone in winter. Check in 4–8pm, check out 11am. No curfew.
- **Number of beds** - 24: 1x3, 4x4, 1x5
- **Booking** - Booking is available with first night as deposit.
- **Price per night** - Bunk £16pp. Triple £19pp. Double/Twin £24pp. Includes bedding and drinks.
- **Public Transport** - Airport, coach and train stations at Aberdeen (43 miles). Buses 60, 63 run frequently between Aberdeen and Peterhead. Bus 69 runs hourly between Peterhead and Fraserburgh. Taxi from Peterhead about £23.
- **Directions** - NK103577 Rattray is signed from the A90 Peterhead to Fraserburgh road. The hostel is at the end of the lane near the lighthouse, about 3 miles from the A90.

CONTACT: Rob and Val
Tel: 01346 532236
hostel@rattrayhead.net www.rattrayhead.net/hostel
Lighthouse Cottages, Rattray Head, Peterhead, Aberdeenshire, AB42 3HA

INVERNESS
STUDENT HOTEL

Set amongst some of Scotland's most fascinating attractions, the bustling town centre of Inverness soon gives way to lochs, hills, forests and glens. Close to Inverness Castle, the cosy and friendly Student Hotel enjoys panoramic views of the town and the mountains beyond. After a hard day's Nessie hunting, the hostel provides the perfect place to unwind, just yards from the city's varied night-life and a few minutes' walk from bus and train stations. Relax in the fabulous lounge with real log fire and drink as much free tea, coffee & hot chocolate as you like. Knowledgeable staff can give you tips on what to see and do in the area and free WiFi is available. Visit the beautiful ancient pine forest of Glen Affric, tranquil but deeply historic Culloden Battlefield, the 4,000 year old standing stones at Clava Cairns or stroll down the riverbank to the waterfront to try to glimpse the wild dolphins in the nearby Moray Firth. Famous Loch Ness lies just a few miles upstream and of course has its own special wild animal.

DETAILS

- **Open** - All year, all day, reception 7am - 10.30pm.
- **Number of beds** - 57.
- **Booking** - First night's payment required to confirm booking.
- **Price per night** - From £15 per night. ID required for check in.
- **Public Transport** - Inverness train station and bus station are a mere 10 minute walk from the hostel. Alternatively jump in a taxi for around £5.
- **Directions** - From train/bus station left onto Academy St, take right down Inglis St. then right onto High Street, turn left onto Castle St past the castle. Continue up Culduthel Road and hostel is on right. By road take B861 over the river then follow the road round into Castle Street/Cuthuthel Road the hostel is on the right

CONTACT: Receptionist
Tel: 01463 236 556
info@invernessstudenthotel.com www.invernessstudenthotel.com
8 Culduthel Road, Inverness, IV2 4AB

SLOCHD MHOR
LODGE

Slochd Mhor Lodge is perfectly situated in spectacular Strathspey in the Cairngorms National Park, halfway between the villages of Carrbridge and Tomatin. The Lodge is on an 'off road' section of the No 7 Sustrans cycle route, surrounded by hills and forests. This is perfect walking country and in winter there are nordic ski trails from the doorstep. Slochd Mhor Lodge offers a genuine welcome in warm cosy surroundings with full central heating. Fully equipped kitchen and a spacious dining area together with large lounge/lecture room with woodburner, TV, WiFi, books and games. Other facilities include a drying room and laundry facilities, some en suite rooms, bedroom, shower and toilet suitable for wheel-chair users, on site cycle shop/workshop, MT bike hire and nordic ski hire. Locked bike shed. Coffee and tea. Outside seating and BBQ area. Ample parking. VisitScotland 4 star graded. Silver Green Tourism Award. Cyclists and Walkers Welcome.

DETAILS

- **Open** - All year, new arrivals 5-9pm. Checked in gets key.
- **Number of beds** - 22: 1x10, 1x6, 2x5, 1x2. Maximum 22 people.
- **Booking** - Booking recommended
- **Price per night** - £21, £20 for 2+ nights. Family rooms sleep 5 from £21 each. 2-12 yrs £15, under 2s free. Prices include bedding and linen. Towels extra. Sole use rates available for Christmas, New Year, clubs, meetings, courses etc.
- **Public Transport** - Nearest bus and train station Carrbridge (4miles). City Link London/Edinburgh and Glasgow/Inverness stop at Aviemore (11 miles).
- **Directions** - Northbound on A9, after mileage board 'Inverness 23' travel 1.5 miles, take first left marked 'Slochd', then first right after ¼ mile into large car park.

CONTACT: Liz or Ian
Tel: +44 (0)1479 841666
Slochd666@aol.com www.slochd.co.uk
Slochd, Carrbridge, Inverness-shire, PH23 3AY

LOCH NESS
BACKPACKERS LODGE SCOTLAND

Your highland home away from home. Owners Patrick and Nikki and their team provide a warm welcome in all weathers, with free tea and coffee, a wood burning stove, a well stocked bar (30+ Scottish beers!), a large guest kitchen and lots of local information. The farmhouse dates back to the 18th century, nowadays, it retains its charm but has been modernized to ensure that you get a good night's sleep and a nice hot shower in the morning before you head out to explore the spectacular surroundings. Within easy walking distance of Loch Ness, Urquhart Castle, pubs, restaurants and supermarket. A perfect location for activity or relaxation surrounded by spectacular scenery. Horse riding, fishing, watersports and mountain biking can all be arranged locally. Free parking and free WiFi. Inverness is just 20 mins by car or bus. On the Great Glen Way. BBQs, outside seating, drying area and garden all provided. Breakfast, packed lunches and laundry service are available. Dogs welcome (but please call in advance). Bike storage available except in Jul/Aug.

DETAILS

- **Open** - All year round, all day every day.
- **Number of beds** - Dorm beds: 32, family rooms: 2 private doubles/twins: 3
- **Booking** - Check availability on website or by phone.
- **Price per night** - From £17 pp. Discounts apply to groups or long term stays
- **Public Transport** - Plane, bus or train to Inverness, then 20 minutes by bus to Drumnadrochit (ask to be dropped in Lewiston).
- **Directions** - Near the A82 Inverness to Fort William road. Look for brown signs saying "Loch Ness Backpackers Lodge" just near petrol station.

CONTACT: Patrick & Nikki Kipfmiller
Tel: 01456 450807
info@lochness-backpackers.com www.lochness-backpackers.com
Coiltie Farmhouse, East Lewiston, Drumnadrochit, Inverness, IV63 6UJ

THE LOCHSIDE
HOSTEL

Perched right on the banks of Loch Ness, the Lochside Hostel has amazing views up and down the loch and can give you direct access to the water's edge. Why not go for a dip in Scotlands largest water body? Take a walk to watch for wildlife? Or even hunt the elusive Nessie!? The Great Glen walking route passes the front door and the End to End cycle route is nearby. Drumnadrochit is just 12 miles away with boat cruises, the Loch Ness museum and Urquhart Castle. Recently reopened by MacBackpackers who also own three hostels in Edinburgh and an award winning tour company, the Lochside Hostel provides accommodation in twin or 3-8 bed dorms. There is a communal lounge and kitchen for self catering. As it is situated right on the A82, The Lochside Hostel is perfect as a base for exploring this part of the highlands or as a stop off on a Scottish tour. There are no shops locally so don't forget to bring enough provisions!

DETAILS

- **Open** - Check in from 2pm check out by 10am
- **Number of beds** - 40-50 to be confirmed
- **Booking** - book online, groups of 6 or more contact the hostel direct via email or phone.
- **Price per night** - From £17
- **Public Transport** - Train at Inverness, bus 119 from Inverness (40 mins) stops outside the hostel
- **Directions** - Directly on A82 half way between Fort Augustus and Drumnadrochit. Parking is available

CONTACT: Reception
Tel: 01320 351274
lochness@macbackpackers.com thelochsidehostel.com
Altsigh, Inverness. IV63 7YD

A multi-award winning hostel with a range of rooms to meet all needs and budgets in the bustling village of Fort Augustus on the banks of Loch Ness. The perfect base to explore the Loch Ness area and an ideal stop off on the Great Glen Way. Surrounded by stunning mountain scenery and set in wooded grounds this is the perfect budget accommodation option in the hub of the Highlands! A variety of room types include dorms, doubles, twins, and family rooms; 24 hour self-catering facilitates, excellent home-made cheap meal options, a rustic bar stocked with a great selection of local beers and malts, a beer garden, free WiFi, bike hire, ample car parking, an awesome team to look after you, plus a whole lot more. FINALIST "Tourism Everyone's Business" 2015 & "Best Holiday Accommodation" 2014, WINNER 'Best Self Catering Accommodation' 2012 Highlands & Islands Tourism Awards. WINNER 'Team of the Year' Hospitality Assured Business Excellence Awards 2012. Member of Europe's Famous Hostels, 4 Star VisitScotland.

DETAILS

- **Open** - Open all year. Check in from 4pm (earlier by arrangement).
- **Number of beds** - 75: 1x7, 6x6, 6x4, 4x2/3
- **Booking** - Booking recommended.
- **Price per night** - From £23pp in dorm beds. Doubles/twins from £29pp. Family rooms from £81.
- **Public Transport** - Bus stop for Fort William and Inverness only 200m away.
- **Directions** - From north, arrive at Fort Augustus, turn first right up Bunoich Brae. From south through village past petrol station & car park. Next left up Bunoich Brae.

CONTACT: Claire
Tel: 01320 366289
info@moragslodge.com www.moragslodge.com
Bunoich Brae, Fort Augustus, Inverness-shire, PH32 4DG

GREAT GLEN
HOSTEL

SCOTLAND

Nestled between mountains and lochs in the heart of the "Outdoor Capital of the UK", 20 miles north of Fort William and 10 miles south of Loch Ness, the Great Glen Hostel is an ideal location whether you're touring the Highlands, bagging Munros or paddling rivers and lochs, and it is only a few minutes' walk from the Great Glen Way.

The hostel provides comfortable accommodation in twin, family and dormitory rooms. Hostel facilities include a self-catering kitchen, drying room, laundry, bike and canoe storage, free internet access, hot showers and a hostel store.

The whole hostel is available for exclusive rental for groups throughout the year.

DETAILS

- **Open** - All year, all day. Please call first Nov-March.
- **Number of beds** - 49: 3 x 2, 1 x 3, 4 x 5, 2 x 6, 1 x 8
- **Booking** - Booking recommended. Please telephone in advance or book online
- **Price per night** - Dorm beds from £18. Twin rooms from £22 per person. Whole hostel available for exclusive hire from £350 per night.
- **Public Transport** - Citylink bus services between Glasgow and the Isle of Skye, and between Fort William and Inverness will stop nearby. Nearest railway station: Spean Bridge. Nearest airport: Inverness.
- **Directions** - We are located 11 miles north of Spean Bridge and 3 miles south of Invergarry on the A82 in a small settlement called South Laggan. Citylink buses stop 100m north of the hostel on the A82. If you are walking the Great Glen Way, stay on the Way until you see signs directing you to the hostel.

CONTACT: The Manager
Tel: 01809 501430
bookings@greatglenhostel.com www.greatglenhostel.com
South Laggan, Spean Bridge, Invernesshire, PH34 4EA

SADDLE MOUNTAIN
HOSTEL
SCOTLAND

Saddle Mountain Hostel is a four star hostel in the village of Invergarry, between Loch Ness and Fort William and at the junction with the road to the Isle of Skye. Surrounded by mountains, glens, lochs and forests, the amazing scenery and wildlife make Saddle Mountain Hostel a great place to explore the Scottish Highlands. Great for Munro bagging, walking, cycling, scenic tours, visiting castles, water sports, fishing, and wildlife watching. The hostel has lots of maps and guidebooks and the friendly owners are happy to help plan your day out. The hostel is spacious and comfortable, sleeping up to 24 people in 5 bedrooms with a mix of dorm and private rooms available. Ideal for your stay whether you are travelling on your own, with your family or friends or have booked the whole hostel for your group. Facilities include a large self-catering kitchen, separate dining room, relaxing visitors' lounge, free WiFi, drying room and bike storage. And to kickstart your morning you could try a genuine Italian coffee from the Espresso Hub!

DETAILS

- **Open** - All year except Nov. Closed on Tuesdays Dec-Easter. Check-in 4.30-10pm.
- **Number of beds** - 24: 2 x 6, 1 x 5 (1 dbl, 3 singles), 1 x 4, 1 x 3 (1 dbl, 1 single).
- **Booking** - Recommended. Dec-Easter please book at least a day in advance.
- **Price per night** - From £17pp. Whole hostel prices available on request.
- **Public Transport** - Citylink buses between Fort William & Inverness and Glasgow, Fort William & Skye stop in Invergarry. Trains at Spean Bridge. Airport at Inverness.
- **Directions** - The hostel is the third house along the road to Mandally, just off the A82 in Invergarry. Look for Mandally road sign just south of Invergarry on the A82.

CONTACT: Helen or Gregor
Tel: 01809 501412
info@saddlemountainhostel.co.uk www.saddlemountainhostel.co.uk
Mandally Road, Invergarry, PH35 4HP

Glenfinnan sleeping car provides unique, comfortable accommodation in an historic railway carriage adjacent to Glenfinnan Station. An ideal location for the mountains of Lochaber, Rough Bounds, Moidart and Ardgour. Glenfinnan makes a great starting point for bothy expeditions and is a useful stopping-off point on the route to Skye. Why not use it also for extended stays using road or rail for trips to fishing, golf, ferries, cruises, and beach locations?

The sleeping car has a fully equipped kitchen, showers, a drying room and total hydro-electric heating. The adjacent dining coach provides excellent meals to give you a break from self-catering.

Your overnight stay includes free admission to the railway museum housed in the station buildings.

DETAILS

- **Open** - All year, 24 hours.
- **Number of beds** - 10
- **Booking** - Booking preferred and advisable to avoid disappointment.
- **Price per night** - £15 pppn, £5 for hire of bedding and towels, £130 for exclusive use of whole coach.
- **Public Transport** - Bunkhouse is adjacent to Glenfinnan Railway Station on the West Highland Line (Glasgow-Fort William-Mallaig) and is 100m from a bus stop.
- **Directions** - On the A830, 15 miles from Fort William and 30 miles from Mallaig with ferry connections to the Small Isles and Skye.

CONTACT: John or Hege
Tel: 01397 722295
glenfinnan@btconnect.com www.glenfinnanstationmuseum.co.uk
Glenfinnan Station, Glenfinnan, nr Fort William, PH37 4LT

SHEENA'S
BACKPACKERS LODGE SCOTLAND

The Backpackers Lodge, the oldest original croft house in Mallaig, offers a homely base from which you can explore the Inner Hebrides, the famous white sands of Morar and the remote peninsula of Knoydart.

Mallaig is a working fishing village with all the excitement of the boats landing. You can see the seals playing in the harbour waiting for the boats, whale and dolphin watching trips are available from the harbour. The hostel provides excellent budget accommodation with two rooms each with six beds, full central heating and fully equipped kitchen/common room with free WiFi. Scottish Tourist Board three star. All hot water and heating provided by renewable energy.

On site is the Tea Garden Café (open from 9am to 6pm March to November and 9am to 6.30pm June, July and August) serving quality meals, snacks, speciality coffee and home baking. See website for pictures of the restaurant and the beautiful countryside around.

DETAILS

- **Open - :** All year, 9am-8pm
- **Number of beds -** 12: 2 x 6
- **Booking -** Telephone ahead for availability and bookings. No email booking.
- **Price per night -** £20 per person.
- **Public Transport -** Mallaig has a train station and services by Citylink coaches. For information on local buses phone 01967 431272.
- **Directions -** From railway station turn right, hostel is two buildings along.

CONTACT: Norman or Sheena
Tel: 01687 462764
backpackers@btinternet.com www.mallaigbackpackers.co.uk
Harbour View, Mallaig, Inverness-shire, PH41 4PU

GLEBE BARN

Situated on the extraordinary Isle of Eigg in a charmingly converted 19th century building, the Glebe Barn offers 4 Star, homely hostel accommodation within 1 mile of the well stocked island shop and cafe/restaurant. The hostel boasts outstanding sea views, a well equipped kitchen, cosy log fire and wide range of books and games for all ages. Sleeping up to 22 in a combination of twin, triple, family and dormitory rooms, Glebe Barn is perfect for individuals, families or large groups. If you fancy more privacy an adjoining 2 person mezzanine apartment is also available. What better place than Eigg to relax or energise? A haven for nature and wildlife lovers, photographers or outdoor enthusiasts, with stunning beaches and coastal landscapes, traditional music sessions and exquisite local produce and cuisine, a magical Hebridean holiday.

DETAILS

- **Open** - Groups all year round; individuals from April to October. Open 24 hours.
- **Number of beds** - 22: 1x2, 2x3, 1x6, 1x8.
- **Booking** - Booking essential prior to boarding ferry. Deposit required.
- **Price per night** - £20 (1-2 nights), £18 (3+ nights). Twin room £45 (1-2 nights), £40 (3+ nights), £36 (6+nights). Triple room £60 (1-2 nights), £54 (3+ nights), £48 (6+ nights). Exclusive use : £330 (1-2 nights), £297 (3-5 nights), £248 (6+ nights).
- **Public Transport** - Passenger ferry (1 sailing per day) from Mallaig with Caledonian MacBrayne or Arisaig (summer only). Check Caledonian Macbrayne or Arisaig Marine ferry timetables before booking beds. Eigg taxi contact 01687 482404.
- **Directions** - 1 mile from ferry pier. Take the shore road that forks right from the ferry pier. Pass a white cottage close to the road & continue uphill away from the bay. Take the track, signed Glebe Barn, on the right before reaching the church.

CONTACT: Tamsin or Stuart
Tel: 01687 315099
mccarthy@glebebarn.co.uk www.glebebarn.co.uk
Isle of Eigg, Inner Hebrides, PH42 4RL

Kintail Lodge stands at the foot of the Five Sisters of Kintail, right on the shores of Loch Duich. It is an ideal base for touring Skye and the Western Highlands or for bagging some of the 30 Munros in the area. In the grounds of the hotel there are two budget accommodation units which are especially popular with walkers, climbers and fishermen. The Wee Bunk House has a cosy room with bunks to sleep 6 people and a snack kitchen containing fridge, hot rings, kettle, microwave and basic cooking utensils. There is a shower room with a toilet and the building is wheelchair friendly. The Trekkers' Lodge sleeps 6 people in two twin rooms and two single rooms, each with their own washbasin. There are 2 shower rooms with toilets and a snack kitchen equipped as in the Wee Bunkhouse. After a long day in the hills you can unwind in the relaxed atmosphere of the traditional Kintail Bar, where good food is served and beer is plentiful, or enjoy the lochside garden and patio. Packed lunches available.

DETAILS

- **Open** - All year with winter restrictions. All day (restricted winter hours).
- **Number of beds** - Trekkers' Lodge 6: 2x2, 2x1, Wee Bunkhouse 6: 1x6.
- **Booking** - Book by phone or email with credit card details.
- **Price per night** - £17.00pp, 3+ nights £16.50pp. Sole use of Trekkers' Lodge £95, Sole use of Wee Bunkhouse £90. Duvet and towel £6.50. Full Scottish breakfast in the hotel £15.00. Continental breakfast in hotel £10.00.
- **Public Transport** - See Citylink website. Inverness to Skye or Glasgow to Skye.
- **Directions** - Kintail Lodge is situated on the A87 between Invergarry and the Isle of Skye Bridge.

CONTACT: Reception
Tel: 01599 511275
reception@kintaillodgehotel.co.uk www.kintaillodgehotel.co.uk
Kintail Lodge Hotel, Glenshiel, Kyle of Lochalsh, Ross-shire, IV40 8HL

SKYE
BACKPACKERS

Skye Backpackers sits in the picturesque fishing village of Kyleakin, skirted by mountains and sea. It's a small, cosy hostel with an open fire in the lounge and a lovely backyard garden. Whether you are coming to Skye to tackle the mighty mountains, meet the legendary faeries or simply want somewhere relaxed and comfortable to chill out, Skye Backpackers has everything you will need to ensure that you make the most of your time on this magical island.

The hostel has dorm, double and twin rooms and all beds come complete with sheets, duvets and 2 comfy pillows. There is also a fully equipped self-catering kitchen, a sunny dining area, as much free tea, coffee & hot chocolate as you can drink and free WiFi. Friendly & knowledgeable staff know all of the best places to visit and are on hand for you to ask them to help you plan your Skye adventure.

DETAILS

- **Open** - All year, all day. Reception 7am-12noon and 5pm-10pm (times may vary).
- **Number of beds** - 39
- **Booking** - Booking in advance not always essential, first night's payment required.
- **Price per night** - From £12 per night. ID required for check in.
- **Public Transport** - Trains at Kyle of Lochalsh, only a short bus ride (approx 10 mins) from the hostel. The bus drops opposite the hostel.
- **Directions** - From Kyle of Lochalsh go over the Skye Bridge then take first exit at roundabout, which takes you into Kyleakin. The hostel is on the right hand side after the Kings Arms Hotel. Park in the car park opposite hostel or in the grounds.

CONTACT: Receptionist
Tel: 01599 534510
info@skyebackpackers.com www.skyebackpackers.com
Benmhor, Kyleakin, Isle of Skye, IV41 8PH

SKYE BASECAMP

SCOTLAND

Skye Basecamp offers small private rooms and shared rooms for individuals accommodating up to 30 visitors. The facilities are aimed at lovers of the great outdoors with staff and guests creating a fantastic atmosphere.

Hot showers, comfy beds and a good drying room are the basics but you'll find a whole lot of other reasons to hang out at Basecamp. Broadford is right on the main A87 trunk road only 10 minutes' driving from the Skye Bridge. The Basecamp is right in the centre of town with shops, 24-hour fuel, restaurants and pubs all just a short stroll away. This is very much a rural setting however and Basecamp has an uninterrupted view out across Broadford Bay to the mainland mountains. A 2 minute walk leads to the beach where otters and other wildlife are commonly seen.

DETAILS

- **Open** - All Year, all day, check in 3-8pm
- **Number of beds** - 30
- **Booking** - Book online
- **Price per night** - From £20pp (dorm), £30pp (premium rooms) discounts for groups/sole use.
- **Public Transport** - Train to Kyle of Lochalsh or Mallaig with local buses to Skye, Direct coaches from Inverness and Glasgoe
- **Directions** - On A87 in Broadford turn left at junction with red sign for Creelers Restaurant. Follow this road round to the right. Skye Basecamp is on the corner beside the red phone & postboxes. Park immediately opposite. There is limited parking so please double park in our space rather than upsetting local residents.

CONTACT: Catriona Lates
Tel: 01471 820 044
bookings@skyebasecamp.co.uk www.skyebasecamp.co.uk/
Lime Park Broadford Isle of Skye IV49 9AE

Raasay is considered a real 'hidden gem' for backpackers and budget travellers. Although off the beaten track it is close to the ferry to the Isle of Skye which has a bus service to the rest of Scotland. There really isn't an easier way to step into a small authentic Hebridean island community before continuing your Isle of Skye itinerary. Private and shared hostel style rooms have the price tag of hostel whilst having access to the same facilities as the rest of the house. If you are happy climbing a couple of flights of stairs and a TV isn't top of your list of requirements then these simplistic rooms might be the perfect option for you. Bed linen is supplied and towel hire and toiletries can be purchased. There is a good value bar menu available as well as the restaurant meals.
Raasay House is an outdoor activity centre, so why not have a go at sea or loch kayaking, coasteering, climbing, sailing, abseiling or much more. Or maybe you just want to explore this idyllic, wildlife rich, island quietly on foot or by bike. Raasay House has hybrid and electric bikes for hire.

DETAILS

- **Open** - All Year, 24 hour reception.
- **Number of beds** - 28: 1x2, 1x3, 1x4, 1x5, 1x6, 1x8
- **Booking** - Book online via the website
- **Price per night** - From £15 to £22 pp in dorm (not including breakfast)
- **Public Transport** - Citylink coaches to Sconser ferry terminal. Train to Kyle of Lochalsh then Citylink to the ferry. Pick up from the ferry can be arranged.
- **Directions** - Ferry from Sconser on Isle of Skye. Follow road from ferry terminal, take first left then next right. Raasay House is on the left (7 min walk, 1 min drive)

CONTACT: Reception
Tel: 01478 660300
info@raasay-house.co.uk www.raasay-house.co.uk
Raasay House, Isle of Raasay, IV40 8PB

Nº5
DRINISHADER

Nº5 Drinishader is located on the Isle of Harris, Outer Hebrides, 5 miles from Tarbert and 8 miles from the famous white sandy beaches. Situated above Drinishader harbour, overlooking the beautiful East Loch Tarbert, the hostel and self-catering units provide a variety of accommodation for individuals, families and groups as well as activities. The hostel has a cosy lounge with open fire, a well-equipped kitchen, shower, WC and comfortable beds. Pick-up services from Tarbert can be arranged for a small cost if there are no bus services. Among the activities guests enjoy are coastal/hill walking, cycling, kayaking, boat trips, sightseeing and bird/wildlife watching. Breakfast and packed lunches are available. Croft camping will be available from 2017. For full information on activities please visit the website.

DETAILS

■ **Open** - All year, 0700-2300.
■ **Number of beds** - 20
■ **Booking** - Online booking available via website. Advisable to book in advance. Deposit required.
■ **Price per night** - From £20 per person. Reductions for families, groups and longer stay.
■ **Public Transport** - Caledonian MacBrayne ferries (01876 500337) from Ullapool to Stornoway or from Uig (Skye) to Tarbert. Drinishader is a 10 min bus journey from Tarbert (01851 705050). Bus stop at hostel. There are 3 - 5 buses each day.
■ **Directions** - From Tarbert follow the A859 south. After 3.5km turn left along the Golden Road. The hostel is located just above the small harbour in Drinishader.

CONTACT: Roddy or Alyson
Tel: 01859 511255
info@number5.biz www.number5.biz
5 Drinishader, Isle of Harris, HS3 3DX

GEARRANNAN
VILLAGE HOSTEL   SCOTLAND

Part of the Gearrannan Black House Village, The Gearrannan Hostel was 'Taigh Dhonnchaidh' (Duncan's House) with its solid drystone walls and thatched roof. It has been newly refurbished inside to sleep 13 including a 3 bed family room.
The hostel (available to individuals) has a well equipped kitchen and cosy warmth from radiators heated with renewable energy. The bedrooms have cosy bunk-beds, and all linen is provided. There are two modern shower rooms.
The bunkhouse (group only), Taigh Làta (John MacLeod's house) sleeps 14 in bunks, with heating, solid fuel stove, a kitchenette and hot showers. The perfect base for visitors to enjoy the many and varied local attractions from surfing at the local stunning beaches to country walks, archaeology, cycling, wildlife and more. Further accommodation available in Blackhouse holiday cottages. It is advisable to buy your provisions before arrival as there are no shops nearby.

DETAILS

■ **Open** - All year.
■ **Number of beds** - Hostel: 13: 1x10 1x3. Bunkhouse: 14: 2x6 1x2. Black houses: 1x2, 2x3-5
■ **Booking** - Advisable to be certain of availability, walk-ins accepted if space is available. Book via website, phone or email.
■ **Price per night** - From £15.00 per person. Family room £47.00.
■ **Public Transport** - Ferry service between Ullapool and Stornoway, or Uig (Isle of Skye) and Tarbert. Gearrannan is on bus route W2.
■ **Directions** - Gearrannan is about 25 miles west of Stornoway, and about 45 miles north west of Tarbert. Follow signs for Càrlabhagh (Carloway) on the A858.

CONTACT: Mairi
Tel: 01851 643416
info@gearrannan.com www.gearrannan.com
5a Gearrannan Carloway Isle of Lewis HS2 9AL, Scotland

HEB HOSTEL

The Heb Hostel is a family-run backpackers' hostel in the heart of Stornoway on the enchanting Isle of Lewis. It is an ideal stop/stay for travellers visiting the Hebrides. Surfers, cyclists, walkers, families and groups are all welcome.

Clean, comfortable, friendly and relaxed, Heb Hostel aims to provide you with a quality stay at budget prices.

There are many facilities, including a common room with TV, peat fire, local guides and information.

DETAILS

- **Open** - All year, all day. New arrivals phone for access code if warden not around.
- **Number of beds** - 26: 1x8, 2x7,1x4 (family dorm).
- **Booking** - Booking is not essential but may be advisable at busier times. Deposits are only required for groups. Payment is due on arrival by cash or cheque.
- **Price per night** - £18 per person per night. Family dorm £72 for a family, £80 for adults only
- **Public Transport** - By plane: from Glasgow, Edinburgh or Inverness (Flybe), Aberdeen (Eastern Airways), Inverness & Benbecula (Highland Airways). By ferry (Caledonian McBrayne) Ullapool to Stornoway (Lewis), Uig (Skye) to Tarbert (Harris) or Berneray (Uists) to Leverburgh (Harris)
- **Directions** - From bus station: exit front door, cross South Beach St and walk up Kenneth St. Pass 1st intersection and we are 2nd on the right. From ferry terminal come out main exit, turn left, follow pedestrian walk-way to the bus station. From airport take bus to Stornoway bus station.

CONTACT: Christine Macintosh
Tel: 01851 709889
christine@hebhostel.com www.hebhostel.com
25 Kenneth St, Stornoway, Isle of Lewis, HS1 2DR

SANACHAN
BUNKHOUSE
SCOTLAND

Sanachan Bunkhouse, in Kishorn is the perfect base for walking, climbing, kayaking, cycling and sailing. Just a few minutes will get you into all the fantastic mountains, crags, lochs and beaches Wester Ross has to offer.

After your fun filled day, the group can come back to a warm fire, comfy bunks, a hot shower and simple living. There is parking for six cars and beds for fifteen people split between two rooms (bring a sleeping bag).

The bunkhouse is self-catered, with a fully equipped kitchen. There is a lounge/dining room with enough tables for the whole group to sit around and eat and our large garden can be used for activities, with a fire pit and BBQ available in the summer. After all that activity you can use our drying room and washing machine to get ready for doing something different tomorrow.

Great prices and student discount available.

DETAILS

- **Open** - March to December
- **Number of beds** - 15: 1x7, 1x8
- **Booking** - Via email.
- **Price per night** - £16.50 pp. Discounted Student rate of £15.00 pp. Groups less than 6 minimum payment of £90.00 per night.
- **Public Transport** - Train at Strathcarron. Bus from Strathcarron and Inverness.
- **Directions** - On the A896 4.5 miles after Lochcarron.

CONTACT: Sean and Sophie
Tel: 01520 733 484
bookings@ourscottishadventure.com www.ourscottishadventure.com/
Sanachan House, Kishorn Strathcarron Ross-shire IV54 8XA

GERRY'S HOSTEL

Gerry's Hostel is situated in an excellent mountaineering and wilderness area on the most scenic railway in Britain. It is on the Cape Wrath Trails, The T.G.O Challenge Route and is 0.5 miles from the Coulin Pass at Craig. Gerry's Hostel sleeps 20, 10 in a large dormitory with comfortable beds, the rest in 5 or 6 bed family rooms. The hostel has a comfortable common room with log fire and library, old records and WiFi it has everything you need! Meals and draught ale are available 15 minutes drive away. Come and go as you please use as a centre to explore this stunningly beautiful area or as a stop off point on your way through. The perfect base for a wide variety of activities including walking, climbing, fishing, cycling, golfing and wildlife watching. See: pine martens, buzzards, red deer, waterfalls and pinewoods from the doorstep.

DETAILS

■ **Open** - All year, check in anytime after 2pm.
■ **Number of beds** - 20: 1x10 2x5 or 6
■ **Booking** - Via the website, e-mail, phone or text.
■ **Price per night** - £17per person main dorm, family room from £18 per person, twins and doubles available for £25 per person
■ **Public Transport** - Achnashellach station is 4km west of the hostel. Nearest Citylink coaches drop off at Inverness. Local bus between Inverness and Lochcarron garage Wednesday and Saturday 3pm.
■ **Directions** - GR037 493. 95 miles north of Forth William, 50 miles west of Inverness on A890. 10 miles west of Achnasheen and 10 miles east of Lochcarron. 4 kilometres east of Achnashellach train station.

CONTACT: Simon Howkins
Tel: 01520 766232 Mob: 07894 984294
s.howkins@gmail.com www.gerryshostel.com/
Craig Achnashellach, Strathcarron, Wester Ross, IV54 8YU

LEDGOWAN LODGE
HOTEL & BUNKHOUSE SCOTLAND

Ledgowan Lodge is a traditional country house hotel with cosy log fires, original features and friendly bar open to residents and non-residents. The bunkhouse is adjacent to the hotel and bunkhouse guests have full use of the hotel's facilities.

Ledgowan Lodge is perfectly situated for the hill walker, climber or anyone wanting low cost basic overnight accommodation. It is within easy driving distance of the Torridon and Fannich Mountain ranges and Fionn Bheinn Mountain is on the doorstep. The bunkhouse sleeps ten adults in five separate rooms, each with a set of bunk beds, hand basin, chest of drawers and thermostatically controlled heating. There is a bathroom with shower and a toilet. There are cooking facilities and a refrigerator for self-catering, but it is recommended that guests socialise within the hotel where the welcome provides a restaurant, bar meals, real fires and lively conversation. There is ample car parking in the grounds and an excellent drying room within the hotel. Camping available.

DETAILS

- **Open** - All year, all day.
- **Number of beds** - 10: 5 x 2
- **Booking** - Book by phone or email.
- **Price per night** - £17.50pp. £35 for sole use of 2 bed bunkroom. Camper vans and tents £6pp
- **Public Transport** - Achnasheen station is one mile from the hotel/ bunkhouse.
- **Directions** - On the A890, 1 mile south of Achnasheen

CONTACT: Reception
Tel: 01445 720252
info@ledgowanlodge.co.uk www.ledgowanlodge.co.uk
Ledgowan Lodge Hotel, Achnasheen, Ross-shire, Scottish Highlands, IV22 2EJ

KINLOCHEWE
BUNKHOUSE

Walkers, climbers and mountain bikers enjoying the Torridon Mountains and wilderness areas will be delighted to find the Kinlochewe Hotel with its warm, welcoming bar and bunkhouse accommodation. There are over 20 Munros within 20 miles of Kinlochewe and the hotel provides a great base from which to explore them. It is also on the amazing North Coast 500 road route. The hotel bar is open all the year round, and serves excellent home-made food, a selection of real ales and over 100 malt whiskies. The bunkhouse is ideal for outdoor enthusiasts with a well-equipped self-catering kitchen, an efficient drying room, toilets and hot showers. There is one dormitory with 12 bunks (this makes it unsuitable for children). Each bunk has an individual locker and a pillow with pillowcase is provided (bring sleeping bags, towels and a padlock)

DETAILS

- **Open** - All year, 8am - midnight.
- **Number of beds** - 12.
- **Booking** - Essential for groups. Advisable for individuals.
- **Price per night** - 17.50 per person. Special offer: reduction for group bookings with sole occupancy for 2 nights or more.
- **Public Transport** - Nearest train station is in Achnasheen (10 miles away). In summer trains run four times a day (twice a day on Sundays) from Inverness and the lunchtime train can be met by the local Dial-a-Bus which comes to Kinlochewe. Phone 01520 722205 for further details. On Tuesdays, Thursdays and Fridays the 5pm Westerbus from Inverness to Gairloch stops outside the bunkhouse at 6.45pm.
- **Directions** - Kinlochewe is situated at the junction of the A832 Garve to Gairloch road and the A896 north from Torridon.

CONTACT: Andrew and Gail Staddon
Tel: 01445 760253
bookings@kinlochewehotel.co.uk www.kinlochewehotel.co.uk
Kinlochewe by Achnasheen, Wester Ross, IV22 2PA

Sail Mhor Croft is a small rural hostel which is situated at Dundonnell on the shores of Little Loch Broom. The mountain range of An Teallach, which has the reputation of being one of the finest ridge walks in Great Britain, is right on the doorstep and the area is a haven for walkers of all experience. Whether you wish to climb the summits, walk along the loch side, visit a beautiful sandy beach or just soak up the tranquillity of the area, you know the scenery cannot be beaten anywhere in the country. We are also on the NC500 route.

The hostel offers accommodation for up to 16 persons in three dorms which are fitted with anti-midge screens during the summer. Bedding is provided (just need personal towel). It is advisable to ring in advance in order to book yourself a bed.

DETAILS

- **Open** - All year except from mid Dec until mid Feb. Flexible opening hours.
- **Number of beds** - 16: 2 x 4: 1 x 8
- **Booking** - Always phone in advance. Groups should book as soon as possible.
- **Price per night** - £17.50 per person self-catering only. £215.00 per night sole occupancy.
- **Public Transport** - Nearest train station is Inverness (60 miles). Nearest City Link bus drop off is Braemore Junction (15 miles). Westerbus passes the hostel 3 times a week; Mon, Wed and Sat. It also provides a service between Gairloch and Ullapool on Thursday afternoon.
- **Directions** - GR 064 893 (sheet 19) 1.5 miles west of Dundonnell Hotel on A832.

CONTACT: Dave or Lynda
Tel: 01854 633224
dave.lynda@sailmhor.co.uk www.sailmhor.co.uk
Camusnagaul, Dundonnell, Ross-shire, IV23 2QT

BADRALLACH
BOTHY AND CAMPSITE

On the tranquil shores of Little Loch Broom overlooking An Teallach, one of Scotland's finest mountain ranges, Badrallach Bothy and Campsite, with its welcoming traditional buildings, offers a fine base for walking and climbing in the hills of Wester Ross, Caithness and Sutherland. You can fish in the rivers, hill lochs and sea, or simply watch the flora and fauna including many orchids, golden eagles, otters, porpoises, pine martens, deer and wild goats. Guests often sit around the peat stove in the gas light (there is now electric here too) and discuss life over a dram or two. Hot showers, spotless accommodation (STB graded 4 star excellent), an unbelievable price, and the total peace makes the Bothy and camp site one that visitors return to year after year. There is also a 4 star cottage and you can hire bikes, kayaks and boats. The EarthMind Fellowship, our social enterprise, runs nature-oriented workshops at Badrallach exploring both our inner nature and the nature all around. Includes natural medicine, wilderness therapy and creativity such as music, art and writing.

DETAILS

- **Open** - Open all year. Access all day.
- **Number of beds** - 12+ (alpine style platforms) 20 at a squeeze. Mats required.
- **Booking** - Recommended.
- **Price per night** - £8pp, £2 per vehicle. £100 sole use.
- **Public Transport** - Westerbus (01445 712255) Mon/Wed/Sat between Inverness and Gairloch drops at Dundonnell, 7 miles from hostel. Pick-up can be arranged.
- **Directions** - GR 065 915 Located on the shore of Little Loch Broom 7 miles along a single track road off the A832, one mile east of the Dundonnell Hotel.

CONTACT: Owen and Christy Okie
Tel: 01854 613240
mail@badrallach.com www.badrallach.com
Croft No 9, Badrallach, Dundonnell, Ross-shire, IV23 2QP

THE CEILIDH PLACE
BUNKHOUSE

The Ceilidh Place is a small complex, consisting of a music venue/performance space, restaurant, hotel, bar, bookshop, coffee room, gallery and bunkhouse. There are regular ceilidhs and concerts (sometimes jazzy/classical) at the Ceilidh Place with visits from folk musicians and small touring theatre companies occuring regularly. The bunkhouse (group only) does not have self-catering facilities but the coffee shop is open from 8.30am to late evening, 7 days a week. It serves hot food, soups, salads, great coffee and cakes and is a super place to relax, read and write cards or memoirs. Rooms for individuals are also available in the hotel where there is a social living room area and balcony. The village of Ullapool is a small exciting port and fishing town, with ferries from the Outer Hebrides. The Ceilidh Place is in the centre of Ullapool. It is also next to the campsite. The bunkhouse is much favoured by hill walkers and families as an ideal base for touring.

DETAILS

- **Open** - All year.
- **Number of beds** - Bunkhouse: 32,
- **Booking** - Booking is advisable in summer.
- **Price per night** - Get in touch for prices.
- **Public Transport** - Nearest train station Garve (33 miles). Citylink coaches from Inverness stop at Ullapool pier a short walk from the bunkhouse. Phone (0990 505050) for details. Also leaving from the pier are ferries to Stornoway on the Isle of Lewis.
- **Directions** - Turn right after the pier and first left. Check in at Ceilidh Place reception.

CONTACT: Effie
Tel: (01854) 612103
stay@theceilidhplace.com www.theceilidhplace.com
14 West Argyle Street, Ullapool, IV26 2TY

Situated at the heart of the dramatic Assynt mountains, Inchnadamph Lodge has been tastefully converted to provide luxury hostel accommodation at a budget price. Twin, family and dormitory (4-8 people) rooms are available and a continental-style breakfast is included. There is a large self-catering kitchen, a games room, a lounge and a dining room (both with real fires). Bar meals are usually available at the Inchnadamph Hotel just across the river. Based at the foot of Ben More Assynt, and overlooking Loch Assynt, visitors are free to explore one of the wildest areas in the Highlands. Mountains can be climbed from the door, there are caves and other exciting geological features in the Traligill river valley and a wide diversity of birds, plants, animals can be found. Nearby lochs are popular for trout fly fishing. Details and photos are on the website where you can also book online.

DETAILS

■ **Open** - Mid March to Mid October. 24 hours.

■ **Number of beds** - 30: 8x2, 6x2, (dormitory). 14 (twin/double).

■ **Booking** - Strongly advised. No vacancies May & June 2017. From Oct-March booking is required as the hostel may be closed.

■ **Price per night** - £20 (dormitory), £28-£32 (twin room) including continental breakfast and linen. Group discounts.

■ **Public Transport** - Transport is available to the door from Inverness 6 days a week, by coach to Ullapool and minibus to Inchnadamph. Times vary - please call for details.

■ **Directions** - Inchnadamph is 25 miles north of Ullapool on the Lochinver/Durness road. The lodge is the big white building across the river from the hotel.

CONTACT: Chris
Tel: 01571 822218
info@inch-lodge.co.uk www.inch-lodge.co.uk
Inchnadamph, Assynt, Nr Lochinver, Sutherland, IV27 4HL

BLACK ROCK
BUNKHOUSE

Situated in beautiful Glenglass and sheltered by Ben Wyvis, this comfortable bunkhouse is named after the breathtaking Black Rock Gorge. It is an ideal base for touring the Highlands and seeing wildlife, including seals in the Cromarty Firth and dolphins at Cromarty. The bunkhouse is at the eastern end of a hikers' route across Scotland and on the Lands End to John O'Groats route for walkers and cyclists. The Highland Games are held throughout the area. The village has a general shop, Post Office, bus service and an inn (serving good bar meals and breakfasts) 250m away. Available to groups or individuals, accommodation is in four rooms of four. Sheets and duvets are provided free of charge. There is a self-catering kitchen and dining area with TV. Showers and launderette facilities are available on-site. There is also a camping ground. All areas of the bunkhouse are easily accessible by wheelchair and suitable for the disabled.

DETAILS

- **Open** - April 1st to October 31st, 24hr access. New arrivals 12noon - 9pm.
- **Number of beds** - 16 : 4 x 4,
- **Booking** - Not always essential. Deposit of 1 night's fee to secure booking.
- **Price per night** - £15 per person. 10% off for groups of 8+.
- **Public Transport** - Nearest train station Dingwall (6 miles). Nearest Citylink drop off Inverness (15 miles). There are local buses hourly.
- **Directions** - Follow A9 north from Inverness, 2 miles north of Cromarty Firth bridge take left turn for Evanton. Follow camping signs.

CONTACT: Lillian
Tel: 01349 830917
janemacpherson@btconnect.com www.blackrockscotland.com/backpackers-bunkhouse
Evanton, Dingwall, Ross-shire, IV16 9UN

BUNKHOUSE
@ INVERSHIN HOTEL SCOTLAND

A small hotel in the north Highlands run by a young family. The bunkhouse is situated within the hotel and consists of 4 rooms which share a shower room and toilet. Guests can use the large, comfortable, reception area and the cosy wee bar where the fire is always lit, and enjoy an evening meal and a real cask ale. Situated on the main route north if wanting to avoid the A9, and ideally placed to reach the far north, as well as both east and west coasts. Cyclists, walkers, bikers, fishers, munro baggers, families, groups, and lone travellers are all welcome. Breakfast: tea/coffee, cereal, toast, homemade jam/marmalade,(£5) or fully cooked (£10), is served in the conservatory with views overlooking the Kyle of Sutherland. Bed linen is included but not towels. There are no self-catering facilities available, however breakfast and a small selection of home cooked meals in the evening are available. Discount for parties of 6 or more, please enquire when booking. Some spots at the back of the hotel for campers. Free WiFi within the hotel public areas.

DETAILS

- **Open** - April - end October. Check in from 4pm.
- **Number of beds** - 10: 2x twin, 2x triple (bunkbeds)
- **Booking** - Please call for any booking enquiries or questions.
- **Price per night** - £20pp. Breakfast: £5 or £10. Discount for groups 6 or more.
- **Public Transport** - Train daily to Inverness from Invershin station (30 secs' walk from hotel). The local bus to Tain stops outside the hotel. Connecting buses to Inverness from Tain. Approx 1 hour 20 minutes' drive from Inverness Airport.
- **Directions** - On the A836 from Bonar Bridge to Lairg beside the railway bridge.

CONTACT: Angus or Cheryl
Tel: 01549 421 202
enquiries@invershin.com www.invershin.com
Invershin Hotel, Lairg, Sutherland, IV27 4ET

Stay on a first class train in Rogart in the heart of the Highlands, halfway between Inverness and John O'Groats. Two railway carriages have been tastefully converted, with many original features. One sleeps 9, and one is subdivided to sleep 4 and 2. There are two beds per room, and a kitchen, dining room, sitting room, showers and toilets. The carriages are heated and non-smoking. All bedding is included. There is also a cosy showman's wagon which sleeps 2 or a family of 3.

Four trains per day in each direction serve this small crofting community which has a shop, post office and pub with restaurant. Glenmorangie and Clynelish distilleries, Dunrobin Castle and Helmsdale's Heritage Centre are easy to reach by train or car. See the silver salmon leap at Lairg and the seabirds and seals in Loch Fleet. Or just enjoy the peace of Rogart. The climate is good and the midges are less prevalent than in the west! Families welcome. Free use of bikes

DETAILS
- **Open** - April to September inclusive, 24 hours.
- **Number of beds** - 18 (1x9), (1x4+1x2), (1x3)
- **Booking** - Booking is advisable
- **Price per night** - From £19 per person, 12yrs and under £15 per person. (£1 discount if you arrive by cycle or train).
- **Public Transport** - Wick to Inverness trains stop at the door.
- **Directions** - We are at the railway station, 4 miles from the A9 trunk road, 54 miles north of Inverness.

CONTACT: Kate
Tel: 01408 641343   Mobile/Text: 07833 641226
kate@sleeperzzz.com www.sleeperzzz.com
Rogart Station, Pittentrail, Sutherland, Highlands, IV28 3XA

Helmsdale Hostel is still closed pending refurbishments. It will be reopening sometime in 2017. Watch this website for updates. Set in the scenic coastal village of Helmsdale (halfway between Inverness and John O'Groats), the hostel offers spacious en suite accommodation including fully equipped kitchen and comfortable lounge area with log burning stove plus a large garden area. On the main Land's End to John O'Groats route, the hostel is popular with 'end to enders' and walkers exploring the Far North Marilyn hills such as Morven and Scaraben. An ideal stop when travelling to and from Orkney and great location for beach walks, archaeology, geology, mountain biking, horse riding, fishing, bird and wildlife watching. Dogs welcome on request (private rooms only). Groups welcome, discount for sole use during the months of April and October.

DETAILS

■ **Open** - Closed for refurbishment. Re-opening in 2017.
■ **Number of beds** - 24: 2x8, 2x4
■ **Booking** - Advance booking not essential - book on line, by email or phone.
■ **Price per night** - Adults from £19. Children from £12. En suite rooms from £50. During April & October sole use of the hostel is available for groups for £350 per night with a minimum of 3 nights booking.
■ **Public Transport** - Helmsdale is served by the City Link bus service and is on the railway line from Inverness to Thurso.
■ **Directions** - The hostel is situated on the corner of the A9 and Old Caithness Road. From bus: walk up the slope for 100 metres. The hostel is after the old church on your left. (200 metres). From train: Cross over the old bridge, turn right along Dunrobin Street, then left up Stafford Street. Hostel is 200m up the slope on the left.

CONTACT: Irene
Tel: 07971 516287 or 07778 377078
info@helmsdalehostel.co.uk www.helmsdalehostel.co.uk
Helmsdale Hostel, Stafford Street, Helmsdale, Sutherland, KW8 6JR

CORNMILL
BUNKHOUSE

Cornmill Bunkhouse is situated on a traditional croft which has been in the family for many generations. The croft runs ewes, spring-calving cows, and grows winter feed and woodland. The mill was built in the early 1800s and was active until around 1926. It has been converted into 4 star affordable and comfortable accommodation for individuals or groups. The bunkhouse can sleep up to 14 people. It has a large self-catering kitchen and open-plan sitting room on the first floor, in which the old grinding wheel now serves as a coffee table. There is level access to the first floor at the rear of the building, with an easy going stair down to the ground floor, which has two bunk rooms, a disabled access toilet/wetroom and a toilet with a shower. The first bunk room sleeps 8. The second sleeps 6 and has a patio door looking onto the workings of the old mill with its large wooden cog driving wheels. Activities can be organised for groups including Laser Tagging, Shooting and Clippage. Hen and stag parties welcome. Come and enjoy this historic setting. 4 star tourist board graded.

DETAILS

- **Open** - All year, advanced notice required 1st Oct - 1st April. All day.
- **Number of beds** - 14: 1x8,1x6
- **Booking** - Please enquire for availability by phone or email.
- **Price per night** - £15 per person. Discounts available for group bookings.
- **Public Transport** - Forsinard railway station is only 10 miles away. The line runs from Inverness to Wick, stopping at Forsinard three times a day.
- **Directions** - The Cornmill Bunkhouse is located on the A897, 6 miles from Melvich, 20 miles to Thurso, 42 miles to John O'Groats and 34 miles to Helmsdale.

CONTACT: Sandy Murray
Tel: 01641 571219   Mob: 07808 197350
sandy.murray2@btinternet.com www.achumore.co.uk
Cornmill Bunkhouse, Achumore, Strathhalladale, Sutherland, KW13 6YT

KYLE OF TONGUE
HOSTEL & HOLIDAY PARK SCOTLAND

Kyle of Tongue Hostel is a stone lodge, magnificently situated on the romantic shores of the Kyle of Tongue on the north coast of Scotland. It has supreme panoramic views of Castle Varich, Ben Hope and the queen of Scottish mountains - Ben Loyal.

The hostel is relaxed and welcoming with irresistible home baking on offer. Beautifully furnished, like a boutique hotel, but with all the friendliness of a hostel. There are comfortable private bedrooms, roomy shared dormitories and relaxing communal areas. Relax in the lounge, the well equipped dining area or the spacious self-catering kitchen. There is a drying room and bike shed for your outdoor gear and an on-site well stocked mini shop. Camping also available. The atmosphere of this remote area is quite special. To truly leave the hustle and bustle of life behind, you must escape to the very edge of Scotland.

DETAILS

- **Open** - Open all year, check in from 4pm.
- **Number of beds** - 36
- **Booking** - Book via e-mail or telephone.
- **Price per night** - Dormitory beds from £17, Private rooms from £39.
- **Public Transport** - Train station - 37 miles. Public bus routes through Tongue, Ferry terminal (Scrabster) - 45 miles
- **Directions** - Situated on the A838 road in the village of Tongue, in the north of Scotland within the Scottish Highlands

CONTACT: Richard Mackay
Tel: 01847 611789
kothostelandhp@btinternet.com www.tonguehostelandholidaypark.co.uk
Kyle of Tongue Hostel & Holiday Park, Tongue, By Lairg, Sutherland, Scotland, IV27 4XH

BB'S BUNKHOUSE
EAST MEY

Opening in spring 2017, BB's is the most northerly hostel on the mainland. Located in the village of East Mey on the highly praised NC500. The perfect place to switch off and relax in glorious surroundings. The eco bunkhouse has bespoke pods equipped with light, socket, privacy curtain, bedding and storage. 3 shower rooms (one for disabled guests) and towels are available. Highland hospitality extends to a complimentary breakfast, including locally sourced produce and home baking. A selection of frozen, home cooked, vegetarian meals are available and wholesome evening meals can be provided for large groups. The comfortable communal area has a well-appointed kitchen and open plan dining/lounge area all centred around a wood burner. The garden has views of Orkney. A perfect base for walking, cycling, surfing, fishing and stargazing with Caithness's best kept secrets right on the doorstep. The Castle of Mey is a short walk away and Gill's Bay ferry terminal a few minutes' drive.

DETAILS

- **Open** - All year, all day from spring 2017
- **Number of beds** - 10,1x6,2x2 (1 double, 1 twin)
- **Booking** - Join our mailing list to get updates
- **Price per night** - £25 including breakfast and bedding, discounts available for groups and families
- **Public Transport** - Stagecoach no.80 bus leaves every 2 hours from Thurso Station to John O'Groats, alight at the stop is before Gill's Ferry.
- **Directions** - Take the A836 out of Mey towards John O'Groats after 1.5 miles look out for the bunkhouse sign and turn left, 500m later you will see the bunkhouse.

CONTACT: Bronagh Braidwood (BB)
Tel: 01955 611499
bronagh.braidwood@yahoo.com www.bbsbunkhouse.com
St Johns, East Mey, Caithness KW14 8XL

SANDRA'S
HOSTEL

Thurso is the northern-most town on the UK mainland. Caithness has a rich history which can be traced back to its Viking roots. The cliffs are spectacular and every narrow rock ledge is alive with guillemots, kittiwakes, fulmars and posing puffins. The wildlife off shore is equally fascinating where seals and porpoises haunt the surf. A great way to experience both the coast and the wildlife is to take one of the boat trips around the coast.

The Hostel has been upgraded and is a Visit Scotland 4 Star hostel with all rooms en suite and some with TVs. Using their own backpacking experience the owners have developed a level of comfort and service which ranks it amongst the top places to stay for families, individuals and couples wanting privacy in the twin / double rooms. A breakfast of cereal etc. is included. Surfing, pony trekking, fishing, quad biking and coastal walks are all available in the area.

DETAILS

- **Open** - All year
- **Number of beds** - 26: 3 x 4, 1 x 5, 3 x 2 (or 3) beds
- **Booking** - Advisable, deposit please for groups.
- **Price per night** - Dorm £18pp. Double/twin £42. Family room £72 (4 people), £80 (5 people). Breakfast is included in the price.
- **Public Transport** - Train station 10 minutes' walk. Bus stop 2 minutes' walk.
- **Directions** - From train station follow Princes Street downhill to Sandras. Buses stop on St George Street. Walk uphill (2 mins) 1st right, 1st left and 1st right again to Princes Street. By car or bike follow A9 to Olrig St, take junction opposite bank onto bottom end of Princes Street.

CONTACT: George or James
Tel: (01847) 894575
info@sandras-backpackers.co.uk www.sandras-backpackers.co.uk
24-26 Princes Street, Thurso, Caithness, KW14 7BQ

ORCADES
HOSTEL

Welcome to Orcades Hostel in Kirkwall. A warm and friendly welcome awaits you at this modern, comfortable 4 star hostel which makes an excellent base for exploring the beautiful Orkney isles.

This hostel is run by a family who have carefully considered the guest's comfort and created a homely feel.

Accommodation is in doubles, twins, 4 and 6 bedded rooms (mixed or single sex). All of the bedrooms have en suite toilet/shower rooms, TVs and all bedding is provided. There is a stylish fully equipped kitchen, including oils and spices for cooking. The lounge has a DVD player, XBOX 360, lots of board games, books and free internet access.
There is WiFi throughout the building.

DETAILS

- **Open** - All year. Check in after 2pm. Check out by 10am on day of departure.
- **Number of beds** - 34: doubles, twin, 4 and 6 bed
- **Booking** - Book by email or phone. Credit or debit card details must be given to secure bookings.
- **Price per night** - £20 pp in a shared room, £25 pp in a double or twin room (£50 for the room), £40 for single occupancy of a double/twin room. Winter rates available.
- **Public Transport** - Kirkwall is the centre for buses on mainland Orkney and the harbour is the hub for ferries to the Northern Isles.
- **Directions** - Take Pickaquoy Rd from roundabout at the west side of the waterfront. Proceed for 300m, turn left onto Muddisdale Rd and hostel is after 500m.

CONTACT: Erik or Sandra
Tel: 01856 873745
orcadeshostel@hotmail.co.uk www.orcadeshostel.com
Muddisdale Road, Kirkwall, KW15 1RS

HAMNAVOE
HOSTEL

On the Stromness waterfront, a short distance from the ferry terminal, Hamnavoe Hostel makes an ideal base for your visit to Orkney. It has single, twin, twin en suite and family rooms. The rooms have easy access to the shower, bathroom and toilet on each floor. All bedrooms are fitted with hand basins, pine bunk beds and have stunning views out across Hamnavoe. The light and airy kitchen is well appointed with two cookers, microwave, double fridge, fridge freezer and a large dining table allowing you to enjoy your meals whilst taking in the fantastic views of the Stromness harbour and marina. The lounge has comfortable seating, freeview TV, DVD's and a stock of books. The laundry room has a coin operated washing machine and tumble drier. The hostel has WiFi internet connection throughout. Entry to the hostel is by a coded door lock and individual rooms have keys. Free long stay car park is available in front of the hostel. Come and visit the nearby islands of Graemsay and Hoy, check out the World Heritage Sites or just relax in the tranquillity of island life.

DETAILS

- **Open** - All year, all day. No curfew, check in from 2pm and check out by 10am. Reconfirm your booking by 7pm on the scheduled date of arrival.
- **Number of beds** - 13: 1x4, 1x1, 4x2.
- **Booking** - Book with deposit of first night, re-confirm by 7pm on the arrival day.
- **Price per night** - From £21pp. Private rooms £23pp
- **Public Transport** - Orkney Ferries run to Stromness ferry terminal. There is a regular bus service to and from the town of Stronmness from the terminal.
- **Directions** - On the waterfront a short walk from Stromness ferry terminal.

CONTACT: Mr George Argo
Tel: 01856 851202
info@hamnavoehostel.co.uk www.hamnavoehostel.co.uk
10a North End Road, Stromness, Orkney, KW16 3AG

BROWN'S
HOSTEL AND HOUSES SCOTLAND

Brown's Hostel and Houses make ideal bases for your stay in Orkney, situated close to all amenities and just 3-5 minutes' walk from the bus and ferry terminal. Stromness is a small friendly town full of character. It has a museum, art centre, scuba diving, free fishing, golf, festivals etc. The hostel is within walking/cycling distance of the historical sites at Maeshowe, Standing Stones, Ring of Brodgar, Skara Brae etc.

Self-catering accommodation is offered nightly or weekly. Facilities include fully equipped kitchens and sitting rooms and accommodation is in single, double, twin, triple and family rooms from smaller to the very comfortable en suite bedrooms, all with bed linen and towels provided. All properties have computer/internet access and WiFi. There is a shed for cycle storage and free car parking up the lane.

DETAILS

- **Open** - All year, all day. No curfew, keys provided.
- **Number of beds** - 28: 3x1; 4x2; 3x3; 2x4
- **Booking** - Booking advisable especially if wanting private rooms.
- **Price per night** - From £20.
- **Public Transport** - Train or bus to Thurso, bus 2 miles to Scrabster then boat to Stromness. Alternatively from Gill's Bay to St Margarets Hope by boat or John O'Groats by boat to Burwick then bus to Stromness via Kirkwall.
- **Directions** - Brown's accommodation is just three minutes' walk along the street from the Stromness ferry terminal and bus stop.

CONTACT: Sylvia Brown
Tel: 01856 850661
info@brownsorkney.co.uk www.brownsorkney.co.uk
45/47 Victoria Street, Stromness, Orkney, KW16 3BS

OBSERVATORY
HOSTEL

The North Ronaldsay Bird Observatory is situated at the south west corner of the island with outstanding views and an adjacent shell sand beach. Seals and the unique seaweed-eating sheep are abundant along the coast which skirts the 34 acres of croft managed by the observatory. The observatory sees spectacular bird migration through the island in spring and autumn. It offers a special attraction for those interested in wildlife, but welcomes all visitors. The Observatory Hostel consists of three dormitories and a self-catering kitchen in a converted barn and byre of the croft. The Byre sleeps four in two bunks and has en suite washing, shower and toilet facilities, great for family use. The Barn also sleeps four and shares facilities with the Bøl which has a single bunk sleeping two. Adjacent is the Observatory Guest House (3 star) which has a lounge bar and meals which are available to hostellers. Camping and grocery shop on-site.

DETAILS

- **Open** - All year, open all day, no curfews.
- **Number of beds** - 10: 2x4, 1x2. Guest house: en-suite rooms.
- **Booking** - Advance booking essential.
- **Price per night** - Hostel £17.50-£18.50. Half board in hostel from £37. Guest house private rooms £55 - £72.50 half board.
- **Public Transport** - Loganair flights from Kirkwall (Orkney) leave daily. Ferry from Kirkwall on Fridays and between May-Sept also on Tuesdays (subject to tides and weather). Small boats may be chartered. Orkney can be reached by vehicle ferries from Aberdeen, Thurso (Scrabster) and Gill's Bay, and a passenger summer service from John O'Groats.
- **Directions** - Situated at the south west corner of the island

CONTACT: Duty Warden
Tel: 01857 633200
bookings@nrbo.prestel.co.uk www.nrbo.co.uk
NRBO, North Ronaldsay, Orkney Islands, KW17 2BE

SHETLAND
CAMPING BÖD NETWORK SCOTLAND

The Shetland Camping Böd Network offers low cost accommodation in nine historic buildings with fantastic scenery - giving the opportunity to tour these beautiful islands, staying in böds en route. Due to the böd's historic nature, no two buildings are the same and facilities vary. The smallest böd sleeps four and the largest sixteen. Electricity, hot water and showers are available in six of the nine buildings and solid fuel stoves and mains water in all. Each böd has a story to tell, for example Voe Sail Loft was once a knitwear workshop, where the jumpers for Sir Edmund Hillary's expedition to reach the peak of Mount Everest in 1953 were produced. Seven out of nine have local meals available within two miles and seven out of nine have (variable) facilities for less able people. Under 16s must be accompanied by an adult. No pets allowed. Explore Shetland on a budget - bed down in a böd. For further info look at the Camping Bod website.

DETAILS

■ **Open** - 1st March – 31st October. Böds are unmanned. Contact custodian up to 9pm on day of entry.
■ **Number of beds** - 4 to 16 (depending on böd).
■ **Booking** - Booking is not essential however, as böds are unmanned it is best to book in advance to ensure the custodian is available before arrival.
■ **Price per night** - £10 to £12. Group discounts are also available.
■ **Public Transport** - Information on public transport within Shetland: www.shetland.gov.uk/transport/. Information on cycle and car hire: http://visit.shetland.org/car-and-bike-hire
■ **Directions** - Ferry from Aberdeen to Shetland (NorthLink). Flights to Shetland from Orkney, Inverness, Aberdeen, Edinburgh and Glasgow (Flybe).

CONTACT: Reception
Tel: 01595 694688
info@shetlandamenity.org   www.camping-bods.co.uk
For info: Shetland Amenity Trust, Garthspool, Lerwick, Shetland, ZE1 0NY

Find us on
Facebook

www.lakelandcampingbarns.co.uk

Dry camping in prime locations around the English Lake District. Camping barns offer the opportunity to stay in restored farm buildings at affordable prices. Experience Cumbria's stunning lakes and lofty peaks literally from your doorstep. All the barns are unique and offer differing facilities. Visit our website to take our virtual tours.

We look forward to welcoming you and your families and friends in 2017.

Barn	Facilities	Page
St John's-in-the-Vale Camping Barn		242
Bents Camping Barn		
Catbells Camping Barn		252
Swallow Barn Camping Barn		257
Murt Barn Camping Barn		
Cragg Barn Camping Barn		
Dinah Hoggus Camping Barn		
Fell End Camping Barn		
Hudscales Camping Barn		
Wythmoor Farm Camping Barn		205
Blakebeck Camping Barn		250

SYMBOLS

 Breakfast bookable in advance

 Shop (miles)

 Pub (miles)

 Shower

 Pets by arrangement

 Electric lighting

 Toilets not in main building

 Hot water

 Campfire

 Power points

 Disabled facilities

 Wood-burning stove

 BBQ area

 Cooking facilities

 Heating

you feel home with our friendly and helpful staff.
People of all ages welcome. No membership required.

BOOK ONLINE: WWW.SWISSHOSTELS.COM

7031	Laax-Cons, Backpacker Deluxe Hotel Capricorn, info@caprilounge.ch	0041 81 921 21 20
3550	Langnau i.E., Emme Lodge, info@emmelodge.ch	0041 34 402 45 26
1007	Lausanne, GuestHouse & Backpacker, info@lausanne-guesthouse.ch	0041 21 601 80 00
3822	Lauterbrunnen, Valley Hostel, info@valleyhostel.ch	0041 33 855 20 08
6005	Luzern, Backpacker's Lucerne, info@backpackerslucerne.ch	0041 41 360 04 20
6010	Luzern, Bellpark Hostel, info@bellparkhostel.ch	0041 41 310 25 15
1260	Nyon, Nyon Hostel, info@nyonhostel.ch	0041 22 888 12 60
4310	Rheinfelden, Hostel Tabakhuesli, welcome@hostel-tabakhuesli.ch	0041 61 813 32 16
6430	Schwyz, hirschen backpacker-hotel & pub, info@hirschen-schwyz.ch	0041 41 811 12 76
7500	St.Moritz, Hostel by Randolins, welcome@randolins-hostel.ch	0041 81 830 83 83
1800	Vevey, Vevey Hotel & Guesthouse, reservation@veveyhotel.com	0041 21 922 35 32
8400	Winterthur, Depot 195, info@depot195.ch	0041 52 203 13 63
8001	Zürich, City Backpacker - Hotel Biber, sleep@city-backpacker.ch	0041 44 251 90 15
8004	Zürich, Langstars – Hostel & Café-Bar, info@langstars.com	0041 43 317 96 55
3770	Zweisimmen, Vista Resort Hostel, info@hostelvista.ch	0041 33 729 80 80

Photos: Jungfrau Region & maennlichen.ch

Wake up Ready...
...to Explore

Great Hostels for an Irish adventure

Book online at
www.hostels-ireland.com

The network of
Irish Tourist Board
Approved Hostels
all over Ireland

INDEPENDENT HOLIDAY
HOSTELS
OF IRELAND

BEST PRICE GUARANTEE

Look out for this logo!

It can be found on many hostel websites.
It means you've already found the
cheapest way to book.

No need to look any further. Guaranteed!

Find all hostels offering the Best Price Guarantee here:
www.bestprice-hostels.com

BENEFITS
FOR IHUK MEMBERS

Members are listed on our website, in this guidebook and on the Long Distance Walker's website.

We actively promote members' accommodation on Twitter, Facebook, YouTube, Pinterest and Instagram.

Our group booking service promotes members' accommodation to group leaders and the IHUK stand tours the UK's leading consumer shows.

Active message boards host conversations between members and we keep them in touch with industry news.

We provide IHUK branded signs, mugs and literature to our members and to tourist information centres.

Official **(IH)** Member

Independent Hostels UK
The largest network of hostels, bunkhouses & group accommodation in England, Scotland and Wales

Independent Hostels UK is the largest network of bunkhouses and hostels in the UK.

The network's website is viewed by 200,000 individuals each year. 10,000 guidebooks are distributed at events and by bookshops, tourist information centres, hostels and bunkhouses

To join IHUK visit:-
www.independenthostels.co.uk/advertise-your-hostel
or phone 01629 580427

GREEN TOURISM

The IHUK office and some hostels and bunkhouses are members of the Green Tourism Business Scheme. We are audited by GTBS assessors to ensure we are using the most environmentally friendly practices. Green Tourism is the largest sustainable certification body of its kind. Look out for the Green Tourism symbols on the hostel pages to see who has achieved GTBS grades.

The IHUK office has been awarded GOLD.

INDEX

INDEX

INDEX